The Street] Lew

CU00661960

L.S. Davey

revised and expanded by Kim Clark

Copyright © L.S.Davey and Kim Clark 2010
No part of this publication may be reproduced without permission.

New, revised and enlarged edition
First published in 1961
Second edition 1970
Third edition 1981

Title page: The *Halifax* undergoing repairs at Higham's Wharf, South Street

Published for the Friends of Lewes Society by Pomegranate Press,
Dolphin House, 51 St Nicholas Lane, Lewes, Sussex BN7 2JZ
pomegranatepress@aol.com
www.pomegranate-press.co.uk

ISBN: 978-1-907242-05-2

British Library Cataloguing-in-Publication Data.
A catalogue record for this book is available from the British Library

Printed and bound by Henry Ling Ltd, Dorchester DT1 1HD

Contents

Introduction to the first edition

The study of the street names of an old town is a fascinating yet strangely neglected task, for there are but few towns in England where an attempt has been made to fill this blank in their historical records.

Wherever dwellings have clustered together, the intersecting roads and byways have acquired names; perhaps from a former local trade or craft; or from the gentry once living there; or from an old hostelry that existed nearby; or from the particular geography of the locality.

In the past, before the introduction of street signs, these names survived only so long as was dictated by custom and common usage. It was not until 1812 that the town authorities resolved that the streets of Lewes should be distinguished and that the houses should be marked 'with a number conspicuously placed thereon'.

In searching the ancient history of Lewes for the task on hand, it became apparent that whilst some names have remained unaltered through the centuries, others have been changed and, indeed, some have sunk into oblivion.

Where, for instance, was Eldestold Street which existed in the old parish of St. Andrew in 1316? Or Kirke Street and Romans Street in 1498? Lodders Lane (beggars lane), Pilcher Street (where the makers of pilches, or fur cloaks, traded) and Shereue Street (sheriff's street) – each found in early records? Where was the lane in Southover 'called Lortepole over against the fountain of the same name'? Where, too, was the regal sounding Plantagenet Street?

Such names as Quadrant Row, Marlborough Place, Wintons' Lane, Swing Pump Alley, Tiger Bay, Tobystown, Russell Place and Botany Bay, were familiar to Lewes folk of a century ago but are now probably meaningless. Modern re-development schemes have erased more names from the street directory and, no doubt, from our memory too.

I have endeavoured, therefore, through the medium of the works of earlier writers and from old records, to collect and blend the stories of some of our local street names into brief cameos of the past, and whilst I lay no claim to originality, I hope to have achieved a result which will meet with approval and be read with interest.

I acknowledge my indebtedness to Mr N.E.S. Norris, Mr W.K. Rector and the late Mr S. Godman for their interest and valued assistance when the seeds of the first edition were germinating.

L.S. Davey

Introduction to the revised edition

The first edition of this book was prepared from a collection of articles by Leslie Davey which appeared originally as a series in the *Sussex Express and County Herald*. They attracted so much interest and appreciation that the Friends of Lewes, with the cooperation of the author, arranged for their publication in 1961 to make them available to a wider public and to ensure their becoming a worthy addition to the town's historical records.

The second edition in 1970 was sponsored by Lewes Borough Council and, in addition to appropriate revisions of the original text, it included an appendix of some additional street names which had been the subject of enquiry. A third edition with eight extra names appeared in 1981.

Almost thirty years have passed since the last edition, and Lewes has changed considerably, although most of the new building has been on a relatively small scale. Whether this will change in the next few years remains to be seen.

The former Stag Inn in North Street.

Leslie Davey died in 2006, aged 96, and when in 2009 the Friends of Lewes decided to produce an updated and expanded version of *The Street Names Of Lewes*, the task of editing and researching the new edition fell to me. The first edition contained 56 names, the second 72 and the third 80. This edition has 166 entries.

I have rearranged the book so that there are now eight sections, each representing a different part of the town. As far as possible L.S. Davey's work remains unaltered, except for essential factual updating. In a few cases I have made a new entry out of material that he included in his text: in order to differentiate between the original entries and the new, mine are prefixed by an asterisk (*).

I am extremely grateful to the following. John Davey has given enormous support and has also made available his father's papers and photographic collection. Many of the new illustrations come from his collection. The help and advice of Colin and Judith Brent was invaluable, and I endlessly referred to his *Georgian Lewes* and *Pre-Georgian Lewes*: I am afraid that I plagiarised them shamelessly. John Bleach solved my difficulty with St Swithun's Lane and Christopher Whittick gave great help at the Records Office. I had interesting talks with Arland Kingston, archivist to the Nevill Estate Company. Graham Mayhew was also helpful, and David Holland and Frances Tufnell provided information on Sheepfair and The Gallops. Finally, Carol Hemsley helped solve the mystery of Toronto Terrace.

On the technical side David Hutchins scanned the original text of the book for me, while David Arscott of Pomegranate Press sorted out all the production difficulties and provided the cover photograph. Liaison with Lewes District Council was facilitated by Steve Brigden of Lewes Town Council, and this resulted in any fees being waived. Helen Dugard of Lewes District Council provided the street name database and other information, and I am grateful to Claire Onslow of the District Council and Barry Clark of Arca Cartographics for permission to include the modern map of Lewes. Robert Cheesman proofread the book for me and made many useful suggestions. My husband Terry gave great encouragement and sorted out the many problems with the computer.

Finally I should like to thank the Friends of Lewes for sponsoring this new edition and Lewes Town Council for their most generous financial assistance.

Kim Clark

1
The Old Town and St Anne's

*Lewes is one of the best-preserved small towns in England and there has recently been great concern that unsympathetic large-scale modern development relatively close to the town centre will irrevocably change its character. When I first started to revise Leslie Davey's much loved book, I thought I could write it almost as a history of the development of a county town, starting with the walled medieval town, then the Tudor period, the Georgian New Town, the Victorian and Edwardian terraces and, finally, the modern 20th century estates.

It did not work for a book of this size, because throughout the centuries there has always been continuous rebuilding and infilling within the historic core of the town. So many of the street names remind us of this change and of the fact that Lewes was not just a country market town but also an industrial centre with heavy, polluting foundries allied to a busy port, with wharfs and yards all along South Street and Cliffe.

Cows being driven down St Anne's Hill on their way to Lewes market.

7

This first chapter, 'The Old Town', therefore includes all the New Town, most of which was built within the walls of the ancient borough, as well as the streets beyond Westgate, extending as far as Spital Road. Cliffe and Southover have their own chapters since the boundaries there are easier to define, as are the modern estates.

ABINGER PLACE

Until the early years of last century and before White Hill and Offham Road were constructed (1821), this was the parish road leading down to the church of St. John-sub-Castro, and it was known in those days as Church Street or Church Lane. The change of name is linked with the political history of the town and recalls the time when the old prescriptive borough exercised its ancient privilege, which dated back to 1295, of electing two members of parliament. The third Reform Act of 1885 swept the town out of existence as a parliamentary borough and merged it in a county electoral division.

James Scarlett of Abinger House, Surrey, who was later created a baron and became the first Lord Abinger, stood as an Independent candidate at the election in 1812. The customary show of hands at the hustings outside the newly-erected County Hall was in his favour, but his opponent, George Shiffner, demanded a poll and successfully reversed the decision. Lord Abinger again sought election in 1816 but lost by nine votes to Sir John Shelley. Lord Abinger undoubtedly held sway over some of the privileged electorate and in those days, before the introduction of the secret ballot, success often came to the candidate with the longest purse!

On the west side of the street, marked by an inscribed stone, was Gallows Bank, where the hangman carried out the severe penalties of earlier times. The old telephone exchange, now converted into flats known as Abinger House, was the site of a school which, some 150 years ago, was run by John Dudeney, the self-taught Sussex shepherd who became a schoolmaster. Earlier still, the site enclosed the manor pound and the parish stocks.

ALBION STREET

Albion, the poet's name for England, was chosen by the patriotic developers of this street in 1821, when a roadway was cut from School Hill to Poplar Row, now known as East Street. Until this time the whole site had been occupied by a large Tudor dwelling standing in extensive grounds. It was known as the Turk's Head Inn in 1678 and, later, it was the residence of Dr. Thomas Frewen, a pioneer of inoculation against smallpox. In the late 18th century it became a school academy under a Swiss named Raymond.

The Christmas fat stock show was held regularly in this street until 1879 when it was removed to a site near the Pells. The old market in the High Street covered an area from St. Andrew's Lane to St. Nicholas Lane – cattle on the north side, sheep and pigs on the south, farm implements opposite the Crown Inn and horse auctions outside the Star Inn (now the Town Hall).

ANTIOCH STREET

This shortest street in Lewes is all that remains of a highway which is said to have once linked with St. James Street in Southover, leading directly to the Great Gateway of the Priory. In 1559 the whole street was apparently destroyed by fire and the Town Book records 'divers sums of money disbursed for men to watch when the great fire was in Westout'. In 1595 'every trace of its buildings having disappeared,' the land was enclosed.

John Rowe, historian and antiquarian, writing about 1622, stated that 'Antioch Street is now enclosed,' but as late as 1861 (before Grange Road was constructed) the line of the old street was 'easily traced in a southerly direction through a large field in front of Southover Grange'. When the paddock opposite Southover Grange was levelled in 1957 to form a new playing field for the adjacent school, a well and some medieval pottery were found, and traces of the old road were revealed when the embankment on the south side of Grange Road was cut away.

It has been suggested that the name was originated by Crusaders returning after the capture of Antioch in 1099, or it may conceivably have been the location of a community of Jewish immigrants who, in Norman and Plantagenet times, were permitted to settle within isolated limits, usually outside the town walls, under sufferance of heavy taxation on their money-lending activities.

*BATH PLACE

This short cul de sac of pretty cobbled houses stood at the entrance to the Phoenix Iron Works. It was the site of the former public baths, which primarily served the men working at the foundry.

BROOMANS LANE

This is probably one of the most ancient of Lewes street names. It first appears in early 14th century records when John Rygate of Lewes, a member of a brotherhood of archers known as the Gild of St. Sebastian (the patron saint of bowmen), bequeathed to the brotherhood a house in Broomeman Street. About the year 1600, the lane was described as 'Broomemanstreet, lying on the west side of the almshouses on Schoole Hill and bending down towards the friars wall'. Over the centuries the name has contracted to Broomans, but there is good reason to believe that the lane was originally the ancient and long-lost Plantagenet Street which is said to have once existed in Lewes.

Hameline, the brother to Henry II, the first of the Plantagenet line of English kings, became by marriage in 1164 the fifth Lord of Lewes. In those days, when heraldry was in its infancy, his family had taken as their emblem a sprig of broom (the *planta genista*, from which their surname derives), so that the association of the names Plantagenet and Broomeman may not be mere coincidence.

The reference to the almshouses is of interest. The ancient house for the reception of paupers in the former parish of All Saints' formerly stood at the corner of this lane on the site now occupied by 31 High Street. The property having become dilapidated, the Vestry Meeting in 1758 decided to sell it and to build new almshouses in St. Nicholas Lane. The old almshouses appear, however, to have survived until well into the 19th century, when they were replaced by shop premises and occupied by a chemist named Winton about 1825. This gave rise to the lane being called at that time Winton's Lane. Subsequently it was locally known as Herd's Lane, when a chemist of that name succeeded Winton.

*BROOK STREET

Developed about 1820, all the houses were demolished in 1962. The street takes its name from the Town Brook which was formerly at the north end of the road. It was also known as the Horse Pond at Pells End.

BULL LANE

The old gabled house with its curious carved satyrs at the top of the lane, which is now known as Bull House, was in medieval times an inn called the Bull, which stood conveniently just inside the West Gate and was frequented by travellers who used this entrance to the town. The house, which retains 15th and 16th century features, was restored by John Every in 1922, and is now owned by the Sussex Archaeological Society.

Sir Henry Goring, brother of George Goring who built Pelham House, bought the old inn in 1583. He built on the south side of it a large town house, the shell of which was extensively altered and converted in 1698 into the present Westgate Chapel. The Bull, it seems, had long since ceased to be used as a hostelry, although the name has survived the centuries. The house became a lasting memorial by sheltering under its roof Thomas Paine, when he came to Lewes in 1768, and lodged with the owner, Samuel Ollive, a tobacconist. The story of Thomas Paine is told in history. It is an illuminating thought, however, that some of the seeds which germinated in the American War of Independence were sown by this 'free thinker' in this corner of Lewes before he went to America to help to establish the United States. The lower part of Bull Lane was renamed as Paine's Twitten (*qv*) in 1949.

CHURCH TWITTEN

This is the story of a street which suffered the double indignity of becoming a lane and then being reduced to a twitten (a word which is found almost exclusively in south-east England and comes from the German 'zwischen', meaning 'between'). Its first name was Pinwell Street, and it led originally from School Hill down to the ancient Pinwell which once belonged to the Greyfriars who gave Friars Walk its name.

Few people who now pass by the drinking fountain in the wall of All Saints' churchyard know of its interesting history. It was originally a spring well on the opposite side of the road at the corner of the Greyfriars property. The approach to the well becoming unsafe, it was sealed in 1838 and replaced by a pump at the expense of John Hoper, a local solicitor. In 1874 the constables of the borough removed the pump and enclosed the ground and erected the drinking fountain against the churchyard wall, the water supply being taken from the public main. The fountain was restored in 1888 but in the 1930s it fell into disuse, the water supply was cut off and it became derelict. Some years ago the Friends of Lewes restored the exterior to its 19th century appearance. Centuries ago, the simple folk believed the well to be the home of fairies who could be placated to keep off evil spells and enchantments if a pin were cast into the water.

The 14th century record of bequests to Lewes Priory includes the gift by Anges-de-Pinwell of a house in Pinwell Street. In the early 18th century the name was changed to Church Lane because at that time its route was diverted to lead down by the west side of the former All Saints' Church. The building has been 'secularised' and is now used as the All Saints' Community Centre.

When extensive building development took place at Malling, bringing another Church Lane into prominence, the town council resolved to avoid confusion and, in 1954, the old lane was re-named Church Twitten. To complete the record of the street which lost its name, it should be recalled that in 1937 the lane running behind Friars Walk and Lansdown Place, on the south side, once familiarly known as The Beach, was officially named Pinwell Road (*qv*).

*EAST STREET

In the 16th century the population of Lewes was about 2000, virtually all living within the town walls. The population remained fairly static for centuries and it was not until the 1780s that the town began to grow beyond its medieval boundaries. After that the increase was rapid, censuses recording 5200 inhabitants in 1801, 8900 in 1831 and 9500 in 1841. After that the increase was much slower and the population was still below 12000 in 1901.

To accommodate the growing numbers there was a building boom, encouraged by low interest rates in the 1780s, and the nucleus of the New Town emerged. The quiet lane known as Poplar Row was renamed East Street. About the same time East Street in Cliffe was conveniently renamed Chapel Hill. The present East Street and its neighbour North Street were built in the 1790s. These houses were built on a light wood frame and clad in red mathematical tiles so that to a casual eye they appeared, as they still do today, to be built of solid brick.

The terrace of mathematically tiled houses in East Street has survived to this day, although the inn built at the corner of East Street and North Street, the Stag, was destroyed by a bomb in the war. The same raid destroyed virtually all the houses at the top of North Street. Although damaged in the blast, they would have been repairable but unfortunately

The sign of the Stag stands proud after the bombing of North Street.

the bomb fractured the gas main and caused a fire in which almost all of the terrace was destroyed. In the 1960s Lewes Borough Council finished off what Hitler failed to achieve. The council blithely bulldozed what was left of the Georgian houses in North Street, including two old pubs, the Blacksmith's Arms and the Kings Arms. All were demolished to make way for a sheltered housing development.

West Street originally extended as far as White Hill, but when the houses nearer to the new turnpike road to Offham were built in 1821 they were given the name Mount Pleasant (*qv*) and West Street became a very short road between Market Street and Fisher Street. There never was a South Street in the town centre. The only South Street (*qv*) is in the Cliffe.

EASTGATE STREET

At the crossroads at the bottom of School Hill in medieval times stood the East Gate in the town wall. No record concerning this gate has survived, except that it is known that the church of Holy Trinity adjoined it on the site of the premises at the bottom of School Hill.

The roads running to the north and to the south (Eastgate Street and Friars Walk) were originally open spaces within the wall, which were a customary feature of medieval fortifications. Until about 1800 Friars Walk had been known as Eastgate Lane, and Eastgate Street was then a nameless road which led into open fields and to the Greenwall, a narrow shaded walk which ran along the top of an embankment which had formed the north-eastern defence of the town. Those open fields became the North Street and Waterloo Place areas, which sprang up with the spate of building development in the early part of the 19th century.

The course of the Town Ditch bisected Eastgate Street at a point near East Street (formerly known as Poplar Row). In the days long before a piped drainage system, this open sewer drained from the higher part of the town, and disgorged into the river by way of Eastgate Wharf. The Ditch was maintained by the town authorities, who invoked by-laws for 'keeping the town sweete and free from annoyances'. Repeatedly the Constables' accounts record payments for 'drawing and casting ye Town Ditch and carrying away the loades of soyle'.

Early in the 19th century a public weighing machine was in general use adjacent to the Volunteer Inn, and the name of Weigh Scale Corner persisted long after the machine had disappeared.

*EASTGATE WHARF
Until the 1960s large boats still came to Eastgate Wharf to unload timber for the timber yard that still exists on the bank of the river. Cottages led down to the wharf, but all were demolished when the supermarket was built in 1978.

FISHER STREET
The Duke of Norfolk's estate accounts for the year 1498, which are preserved in the national archives, include an item for the 'half-rent of a shop in Fisshestrete' in Lewes, and the description 'Fisher Street' occurs in deeds as early as 1383.

The Old Fire Engine House and Record Room in Fisher Street.

The name could have derived fromWilliam Fyssher, whose property in Lewes was taxed by Edward III in 1340 to provide funds for the waging of the Hundred Years' War. Although without any apparent material evidence, it has been suggested that the name indicates the market of the fisherfolk, known as Juggs, who brought their fish by pack donkeys from Brighthelmstone by way of Kingston Hill, the route being to this day still known as Juggs Road.

During the 19th century the street was also known as Star Lane as it gave access to the coach yard and stabling of the old Star Inn (now the Town Hall). Here, until the building of the Town Hall in 1893, was the Old Fire Engine House and Record Room of the borough. It had been erected in 1817 by Amon Wilds, a Lewes builder of repute who was responsible for much of the development of the Kemp Town district of Brighton. The inscribed tablet on the staircase of the adjacent council offices is a relic from the old building as, also, is the town coat of arms which is now set in the north gable.

The junction with High Street was once recognised as Star Corner. Before the cattle market was removed from the streets in 1879, this spot was the rendezvous of casual labour for hire, who stood around rendering the pavements so impassable by their language and expectoration that the corner was cynically dubbed 'Spithead'.

FRIARS WALK

Corrupted from Friars Wall, this road follows the boundary of the Friary of St. Mary which was founded in the 13th century by friars of the Franciscan Order, known as Greyfriars.

The monastery was situated outside the town walls and it occupied an area now absorbed by the magistrates' court and the former Fitzroy library. After its dissolution by Henry VIII, it was replaced by a Tudor mansion, called The Friars, and it was here that William IV and Queen Adelaide were entertained when they visited Lewes in 1830. The house was unfortunately demolished when the first railway came to Lewes in 1846 and the surviving traces of the Greyfriars were swept away. The original station house (a terminus in those days) stood until 1968 next to

16

no. 1 Friars Walk, which used to be the Railway Inn. The name Greyfriars is now used for a sheltered housing development in nearby Court Road.

About 1622 the highway was described as 'Eastgate Lane, leading out of the High Street by the friars wall to All Saint's Church'. Writing in 1846, Gideon Mantell recalled that in the days of his boyhood there was not a dwelling on the east side of the road: 'A venerable wall, built of the ruins of the ancient monastery, then formed the eastern boundary. A high bank, which served as a footpath, abutted against the wall where plants, ferns and mosses grew abundantly. Old houses on the west side were interspersed between gardens, rows of poplars and other trees, so that the aspect of the "walk" in those days harmonised well with its antique appellation.'

The Friars in 1784, from a painting by
James Lambert in the Burrell
Collection, British Museum.

*FULLER'S PASSAGE

This short cul de sac off School Hill is nearly opposite the fine house 213 High Street, now occupied by the solicitors, Adams and Remers. A house on this site was occupied by Thomas Trayton in Elizabethan times and his family remained there for centuries. In 1768 his descendant John Trayton Fuller inherited the house. A distant relative of the more famous John ('Mad Jack') Fuller of Brightling, he was once the MP for Tregony and a supporter of the Whig First Lord of the Treasury (prime minister), the Duke of Newcastle (Thomas Pelham-Holles), who had houses at Lewes and Halland.

Lewes in the mid 18th century was a hot bed of intrigue, and Fuller soon fell out with the duke and stood against his chosen candidates in the election of 1761. He performed ignominiously, but the duke, anxious to reinforce his position, showered favours on the local gentry and awarded lucrative armament contracts to his kinsmen, the Fullers of Brightling, who were gun founders.

The Fuller clan were, and still are, extremely numerous in Lewes, and the archives record many less illustrious Fullers who lived and traded in the High Street, some extremely close to where Fullers Passage is situated. Fullers Passage may therefore owe its name to a very distant relative of the Trayton Fullers. However, some extensive wine cellars still survive behind Steamer Trading and these are rumoured to have been connected to the large houses opposite by a passage, now blocked. For commemoration of a 20th century Fuller who gave great service to Lewes, see Fuller Road, Landport.

*GREEN LANE

This lane running from Stewards Inn Lane to Elm Grove was originally part of St Swithun's Lane (*qv*). William Green had a garden there in the late 18th century and St Swithun's Lane is now only an opening from the High Street to Stewards Inn Lane. William Green gave part of his garden to widen the adjoining St Martin's Lane.

*GREEN WALL

Green Wall was part of the town wall and skirted the Ouse wetland until it reached the Eastgate. Until 1778 the footway along it was shaded by a 'fine row of elms'. By the mid 19th century the water meadows had been replaced by the belching chimneys of the Phoenix Ironworks. Prior to that, in 1716, Richard Puxty ran a flourishing tannery at 'Greenwall near St John's Church'. His son Nicholas Puxty was succeeded by William Hammond until John Chatfield bought the yard in 1781, running it until the 1820s, when his son Thomas sold much of the site for housing. These houses were demolished in the 1960s and the site, between Spring Gardens and Brook Street, is now used as a car park.

IRELAND'S LANE

About 1630, John Rowe wrote: 'Irelands-lane, or Buckettwin, where the bounderstone of the Burrough lyeth over against the East end of the Chancell of the Church of St. Mary Westout.'

Of the meaning of Buckettwin, it seems that he and subsequent historians were totally ignorant. No explanation of 'Ireland' has previously been attempted, but the name appears to derive from John Ireland, who owned and probably lived in a house at the corner of the lane at the beginning of the 17th century. His name appears in a town deed dated 1619.

The lane originally led down to a bridleway and footpath leading over the Paddock and Wallands towards Offham, and the right of way was preserved when Bradford Road (1905) and Gundreda Road (1923) were constructed.

The boundary stone mentioned by Rowe is now set in the churchyard wall opposite Ireland's Lane. At the ancient ceremony of beating the bounds, before the old borough limits were extended upon incorporation in 1881, it was traditional to 'bump' the beaters on this stone and then regale them with bread and cheese and beer at the inn nearby called The Dog. The name was changed about 1790 to the Pelham Arms.

KEERE STREET

The earliest reference to this street name appears in an ancient deed dated 1272, where it is referred to as 'the path called Kerestrete'. The name may have originated from the Saxon word 'cerre' which means 'winding or sloping', but a more likely explanation is that it derives from the old British word 'caer', which was applied to fortified places and which, in this case, would mean the street in the fosse or ditch of the town wall, the remains of which rear up behind the houses on the east side.

An interesting theory suggests that the word 'kere' or 'keer' is a phonetic corruption of 'Cahors' – a name which appears at the time of the Norman Conquest and which was commonly descriptive of merchant foreigners who immigrated to this country in the wake of the Norman invasion and, later, as refugees from political strife and oppression. They were permitted by the boroughs to settle in isolated communities usually situated outside the town walls, where they abstained from agricultural work or crafts and confined their activities to money lending, purchasing tolerance and protection by submitting to heavy taxation by the realm. There is, however, no local evidence to support this suggestion.

The name has been frequently corrupted in the past. It is found as Care Street and also as Scare Hill. The latter had its special significance in 1774 when the scribe writing in the Town Book recorded 'paid 21s. for watching the small pox on Scare Hill'. The street still retains many of its old blue cobblestones with which most of the streets in Lewes were once paved. In those days they were fondly known as 'petrified kidneys'.

Tradition has associated this street with George IV who, when Prince of Wales, is said to have driven a coach and four down the steep hill on his way from Lewes Races to be entertained by the Newton's of Southover Grange.

A charitable bequest of Thomas Matthew in 1688 to the poor of the parish of St. Michael provided the old almshouses which were situated here until 1960. In that year, having become outmoded and beyond restoration at reasonable cost, they were sold by public auction by the trustees of the charity. Income from the invested proceeds of the sale was applied for the benefit of the old and needy in the Town.

LANCASTER STREET

Before the introduction in 1870 of a State system, elementary education, where it existed, was dependent upon private enterprise or charity. At the beginning of the 19th century, Joseph Lancaster, son of a Chelsea pensioner and a keen educationalist, opened a private school in Southwark to teach under a system of instruction that he had devised. His method, known as the monitorial system, gained great popularity, and many other schools on similar lines were established. Lancaster toured and lectured widely and he was associated with the founding of the British and Foreign School Society in 1808.

The old British School in Lancaster Street.

21

In a district of Lewes that was being developed at that time, a British School was established in 1809, originally for 200 children, who received their instruction on the system introduced by Lancaster, and the new street in which the school stood took its name from him. Educational advances in the latter half of the 19th century led to the eventual dissolution of the old British School. Its buildings have disappeared and the site is now occupied by modern cottages. The original school house was known as the Rotunda and was octagonal in design, scholars sitting in a circle with the teacher in the middle, using a sand square as a 'blackboard'.

The row of houses known as The Fosse was built (1902) on the supposed site of the fosse or ditch of the ancient encampment, possibly of Roman origin, which is now the churchyard of St. John-sub-Castro.

*LANSDOWNE PLACE

Lansdowne Place was built in 1827. It appears to have been named after the Marquis of Lansdowne, who, as the Earl of Shelburne, was a Whig politician who became first lord of the treasury (the equivalent of the prime minister today) in July 1782. There seems to be no direct connection with Lewes other than the town's reputation as a hotbed of Whiggish intrigue (*see* Fuller's Passage).

MARKET STREET

Many years ago, a stranger seeking the Grenadier Inn would have been directed beyond the Black Lion and down Aylwards Corner. From Tudor times until 1790, Market Street appears to have been known as Aylwards (or Aylards) Comer, the name applying particularly to the junction with School Hill. It was probably so called after John Aylard, a Lewesian who died in 1544.

When Joseph Spittle became landlord of the Black Lion in 1790, he changed its name to the Crown, and the street seems to have been promptly rechristened Crown Lane. But the name did not continue very long. The old Provision Market House, which had stood since 1564 (rebuilt 1648) in the High Street opposite Castlegate, having become an obstruction to traffic, was pulled down and a new market was erected in 1792 on the site adjoining the Crown Inn.

In the tower of this new market was hung the ancient bell Gabriel, which had been removed in 1761 from the remains of the church of St. Nicholas (on the site of the war memorial). Thereafter, the street came to be known as Market Street. The old Grenadier Inn has long since disappeared, although the building, later occupied by Farncombe's printing works, remains, now used as shops and offices.

MOUNT PLEASANT

The construction of a new turnpike road to Offham from White Hill in 1821 coincided with considerable building activity in that part of the town, and the houses of Mount Pleasant are contemporary with this period. Before the development, West Street originally extended beyond its present limit to White Hill, but at the request of the residents the new name Mount Pleasant was approved, being chosen because of the situation of the houses around the base of Brack Mount, one of the twin mounts of the castle. At the same time cottages which were previously known as Russell's Row and The Round were re-christened Mount Place.

The Mount in those days seems to have been particularly attractive. The proprietor of the Lewes Arms Inn advertised his tea gardens on the Mount: 'Its sides are clothed with ornamental trees and flowers, among which are built a variety of summer houses where parties can enjoy themselves in rural retirement . . . and where several amusing games are provided for the visitors.'

Commercial Square, into which Mount Pleasant runs, got its name in the middle of last century when, at a local meeting, it was jocularly stated that the commerce of the town was centred in that area, there being a butcher, baker, grocer, dairyman, blacksmith, painter, plumber, silversmith, stonemason, carpenter and two inns. One morning somebody nailed up the sign 'Commercial Square', and so it has remained ever since.

Until mid-2010 the police station occupied the site of the old Mechanics' Institute, which, in its turn, occupied the site of the old

23

Lewes Theatre, which had a chequered existence from 1789 to about 1830. The area adjacent to the old theatre was once an undesirable neighbourhood, for it was referred to as Botany Bay by the local people. Poetic justice was served when the arm of the law erected its headquarters in the place named after the penal settlement in Australia to which convicts were once transported

NEW ROAD

In the early years of the 19th century William Balcombe Langridge of St. Anne's decided to develop the land he had acquired from the Lords of the Borough, which was situated on the Castle Banks and fell steeply from the Castle Wall down towards the Paddock. He constructed a road along the line of the bridleway, which formerly hugged the side of the escarpment and led from Westgate Street to St. John's and Landport. Building operations were commenced, and the first cottages in Langridge's new road were called County Row.

But development was impeded by a protracted argument which arose between Langridge and the Town Commissioners concerning the responsibility for making the road safe by building a retaining wall on the Paddock Road side. Ineffectual litigation was followed by compromise in 1831, when Langridge accepted the Commissioners' offer of £30 and agreed to build and maintain the wall. 'Mr. Langridge's new road' was for so long a subject of argument and a topic of local talk that the description persisted in preference to the original name of County Row, and it has so remained ever since.

The inscription set in the wall of no. 18 is of interest. The house was called Provident Cottage by the first owner, Mr. J. L. Slarks, who built it in 1870 with the first loan advanced by the old Lewes Building Society, founded in that year.

*PADDOCK LANE

This was once a bridleway leading from Mr Shelley's stables to the Offham turnpike road. In the early 20th century the Paddock Estate was developing the area and applied to Lewes Borough Council to divert the path. It was refused permission. Hangman's Acre was sited here, as was

24

the Ropery (also called Rope Walk) where rope was made. The Paddock Estate Company gifted some of the land for recreational use.

*PAINE'S TWITTEN

Paine's Twitten runs from Bull Lane almost to Southover Road. It is a recent name. In 1949 the lower section of Bull Lane was renamed Paine's Twitten at the request of residents. Thomas Paine, author of *Rights of Man*, arrived in Lewes in 1768 to work as an excise officer. He lodged at Bull House, then a grocer's shop owned by Samuel Olive. After Olive's death he married his daughter Elizabeth and ran the shop until April 1774, when he separated from his wife and shortly afterwards emigrated to America.

*PHOENIX PLACE

This name commemorates the Phoenix Ironworks which occupied the site between 1861 and 1969. Founded by John Every in 1835, it originally occupied a site in Railway Lane before moving to North Street in 1861. Look down on the pavements of, among others, East Street and Lansdowne Place, and you will still see the decorated covers of the coal holes that gave access to the cellars below. All these were made by John Every, although confusingly there were actually three generations of John Everys.

The iron foundries of Lewes have a history going back to about 1700. The iron was mined in the Weald and brought by barge to be smelted in Lewes. John Every had a large collection of Elizabethan firebacks. He presented them to the Sussex Archeological Society and they can still be seen in Anne of Cleve's house today.

PIPE PASSAGE

This narrow passage leads northwards from the site of the West Gate in the High Street in the direction of (and in parts actually along) the old town wall. In medieval times it was the sentry walk within the parapet of the fortifications. The remains of a pipe-maker's kiln can still be seen on the waste ground at the rear of the Freemasons' Hall. The site was excavated in 1956 and several hundred broken clay pipes were found, yielding much information on the early 19th century pipe-making of Lewes. George Holman (a former mayor of Lewes, who died in 1932) recalls in his *Reminiscences* that as a boy he used to watch an old man named Tucknott making 'churchwardens' (a type of pipe) in this kiln.

In 1800, the need for a public corn mill was expressed. It was at first intended that the windmill should be erected on the Brack Mount, but as the Duke of Norfolk refused permission the site was chosen in Pipe Passage on a plot of land then known as Smith's Croft. The cost of the mill (£600) was met by private subscription.

For some years the mill was used by the subscribers, but 'not being found to answer the intended purpose', it was sold to William Smart, a Lewes miller, who continued to use it until 1819. In this year, it was taken down and the lower part converted into the dwelling house, which exists to this day. Smart continued in business as a miller, operating from a new mill erected at the foot of Race Hill. The remains of this windmill can still be seen, converted into a house

*PINWELL ROAD

The present Pinwell Road runs behind Lansdowne Place, but the now vanished Pinwell Street lay on the opposite side of the road. It was first recorded in 1280 (*see* Church Twitten).

The Pinwell was a powerful source of fresh water for the townsfolk, and the spring appears to have been supplemented by water channelled from the wetland into a Town Ditch. In 1244 the Franciscans vaulted over the ditch and included it in their new monastery precinct

Although Leslie Davey indicates that this was the original name of Church Twitten, it seems in fact to have had a separate existence. In 1702 it is recorded that Pinwell Street ran from Church Lane to the Pinwell, until it was blocked by a Dr Tabor who owned the land on either side.

POPE'S PASSAGE

One of the many byways named after former townsfolk leads off the High Street between the former Rainbow tavern, now Lincolns, and the adjoining shop. It is known as Pope's Passage. This narrow right of way, which once gave access to stabling and terraced gardens, winds between the houses and leads into Castle Ditch Lane, the site of the dry moat surrounding the castle.

About 1900, George Holman wrote that the passage was formerly called Pope's Entry, and that it took its name from a chemist named Pope, in business a century earlier. No mention of this name, however, is found in the early directories of 1790 and 1812, nor indeed in subsequent surveys. The surname Pope is rare in Lewes records, but it does appear in 1683 and, being linked with the adjacent Newcastle House, may suggest a connection with this passage. Benjamin Court, a successful ironmonger of the Cliffe, purchased Newcastle House (subsequently rebuilt as the old County Hall extension) in 1711. At that time he already owned the adjoining property, and his interest therein may have derived from his first wife, Mary Pope of Lewes, whom he married in 1683.

Incidentally, Newcastle House did not get its name until 1734 when Benjamin Court was persuaded to lease it to the Duke of Newcastle, a celebrated member of the Pelham family, for the establishment of a political club and coffee house.

RAILWAY LANE

This lane, which leads southward from the old river bridge, acquired its present name about 1900, but its existence goes back many centuries. When there was a thriving river traffic it was a busy thoroughfare, giving access to wharves, warehouses, granaries and shipbuilding yards.

From Stuart times until the 18th century, the lane appears to have been known as Puddlewharfe (or Puddledock), and it was here that a prominent Lewes merchant, Ambrose Galloway, who suffered persecution and imprisonment from 1662 to 1685 for his Quaker beliefs, had his dwelling and storehouses 'at the bridge foot'. An early map indicates the lane as 'the road to the brooks', giving a right-of-way to the west bank of the river.

Towards the end of the 18th century, Sir Henry Blackman, wine merchant, had his house on the site of the present Riverside Centre. Before the Riverside was built there was a taxi garage there which was previously Albion Russell's boot and shoe manufactory. Incidentally, Sir Henry, who was high constable of Lewes in 1795, is the only titled person ever to have held the position of chief citizen of the borough.

The shipbuilding yard of Messrs. Rickman and Godlee was down this lane, and it was here that ships were built and launched in the early decades of last century. There is a well-known engraving of the launching of the *Lewes Castle* on March 2, 1839 – an occasion which, from contemporary accounts, was accompanied by much ceremony and witnessed by large crowds.

John Every erected his iron foundry in this lane in the early 1830s, but sold the ground to the railway company in 1861 and moved to a new and larger site at the bottom of North Street, for years known as the Phoenix Ironworks and now an industrial estate complex.

At the close of last century, the Etna Ironworks of C.A. Wells occupied the site of the old Tabernacle Sunday schools (now offices), and the lane at that time was often referred to as Etna Wharf or Wells' Lane. It was also familiarly called Vipers Lane after The Viper – the name given to the once well-known riverside granary. It was badly damaged by fire in 1918, prior to which it was readily identified by its large weather-vane in the form of a snake. The building has now been restored for residential purposes and the original 'viper' once again dominates the skyline.

ROTTEN ROW

This thoroughfare takes its name from a row of old almshouses which fell into decay and have long since disappeared. The following description of the properties was recorded by John Rowe about 1622: 'In anno 1586, Richard Rykehurst, of St. Peter's parish Westout, by his will gave four houses (lying on the back side of St. Peter's Church), now called

Rotten Row, to certain townsmen in trust, with the intent that three houses should harbour three poor people and the fourth house be let out for rent therewith to repair the other three tenements.'

The word 'rotten' in its early form was 'ratoun' or 'ratton', and it was commonly used as a derogatory expression to describe a rat-infested place, which condition was undoubtedly the fate of the row of dilapidated cottages. *Richard Coates has collected a number of quotations from the late 16th and early 17th century in which the expression 'Rotten Row' appears. Several of these play on the image of bad teeth, whilst others appear to refer to a place of ill repute. He therefore believes that the name can be interpreted in a wider way than simply a rat infested place.

The site of St. Peter's Church is now occupied by 110 High Street opposite the Grammar School. Its parish was merged in the 16th century with the present parish of St. Anne. There is no evidence to support the suggestion that the name was originally Routine Row – the route used on saints' days by the monks in procession from the Priory.

Some years ago a sign board was displayed at the entrance from High Street, revealing the doubtful but unconscious humour of 'Rotten Row – to the Cemetery'. The name also formerly applied to the road that continued to Southover High Street. When this area was first developed it was severally known as St. Pancras, Spring Gardens or Tobystown – the latter because of a common lodging-house once situated there which was a nightly rendezvous for many a toby, as the 'gentlemen of no fixed abode' used to be called.

ST. ANDREW'S LANE

When Henry VIII ordered the destruction of Lewes Priory in 1537, the church of St. Andrew lost its patron. After struggling along for a few years the church was eventually closed down and its parish merged with that of St. Michael in 1545. A record has been preserved of those who pulled down the church and divided the spoils. Mr. Fissenden secured the high altar; Robert Morley took all the brass work; Mr. Shelly carted away the stone; and Mr. Mall the timber. The parish clerk took the christening sheet and a cross – in fact, the churchwarden found it so difficult to keep a tally that he put everyone 'upon his conscience' to pay their dues, and his list included 'our parson'!

The actual site of St. Andrew's Church is not definitely known, but during drainage excavations in the courtyard of Pelham House in 1890 foundations were exposed which were thought to be the remains of the church. Pelham House, of course, was built in 1579 – some 35 years after St. Andrew's Church had been pulled down. St. Andrew's Lane has been known as Pelham Lane and also as Campions Lane, both being the names of families that once lived at the 'big house'.

ST. MARTIN'S LANE

In the year 1337 John, Bishop of Chichester, issued a decree for the amalgamation of certain impoverished churches in Lewes, and the parish of St. Martin was absorbed into the parish of St. Andrew. Two centuries later, in 1545, St. Andrew was united with St. Michael.

The church of St. Martin stood near the lane which bears its name. The dedication is of interest, for William de Warenne, who built the castle, was descended from an ancient and noble Normandy family who bore the name of St. Martin. It has been suggested that the medieval stone vault which still exists beneath 72 High Street may have formed part of the vanished church.

Fifteenth century and later records quote an alternative name for the lane – Snellings Lane –preserving the name of the family of Snellyng, the fishers, of whom the earliest mention appears to be in 1296.

In 1564, a market house was built in the High Street opposite this lane and in front of Castlegate. The cost was met by a legacy of £10 by Alice Holter, the widow of a high constable of the town, and £10 provided by the Fellowship of Twelve. It was rebuilt in 1648 and removed in 1792, when the present market was erected in what is now known as Market Street.

The proximity of the old market house to St. Martin's Lane, alias Snelling Lane, caused it to be known by yet another name – Market Lane. Despite the removal of the market, this name persisted, in company with the present name, until about 1840.

*ST PETER'S PLACE

The church of St Peter Westout was first recorded in 1121 but almost certainly existed before that date. Following the destruction of the priory by Thomas Cromwell in 1538, the parish of St Peter Westout was united with that of St Mary Westout (now St Anne's) in 1539.

St Peter's Place was built in 1868 and the date is recorded on a plaque featuring the Nevill family coat of arms. The 4th Earl of Abergavenny (later 1st Marquis), William Nevill, was a prominent Tory politician and he was anxious to create as many potential Tory voters as possible. Accordingly he demolished a large house he owned on St Anne's Hill and built a terrace of houses with a rent of £12 a year. The level of rent was important – occupiers of homes who paid less were not eligible to vote and he carefully chose tenants who could be relied on to vote the right way. In any case, they had little choice. The ballots were not secret in those days. St Peter's Place came to be known as Tory Terrace and the name stuck for many years. Sadly for him, the earl's machinations were in vain. Secret ballots were introduced in 1872, before the next election, and the rent threshold abolished.

ST. NICHOLAS LANE

The plague known as the Black Death, which decimated the population of England in the 14th century, left its scar upon Lewes. The social upheavals of those times resulted in the impoverished parish of St. Nicholas being united with All Saints', and the little church of St. Nicholas, which stood at the top of School Hill opposite this lane, was left to decay. Its tower, however, survived, and became known as the Broken Church.

In the bell loft was hung the great town bell Gabriel which 'was new cast in 1555', and which used to ring the curfew. The Town Book records that in 1690 Thomas Barratt, a Lewes clockmaker, was paid 'four pounds yearly for ringing ye bell at four in the morninge and eight at night'.

In 1761, the remains of the broken church were pulled down and the site thrown into the High Street, but the venerable stones were not far removed. They were used to fill in the town well which was in the middle of the roadway opposite the Crown Inn, and which had become an obstruction to traffic. The bell Gabriel was 'grounded' for 30 years until 1792, when it was re-hung in the present Market Tower, built in that year.

In November, 1934, workmen laying a water main in the road opposite 39 and 40 High Street, uncovered skeletons which were probably the remains of burials at the old church.

The lane has also been known as Dolphin Lane, after the inn of that name which existed there until 1958. The inn used to be a popular resort for drovers and cattlemen until 1879, when the market, which until then had been held in the High Street, was removed to the outskirts of the town.

*ST SWITHUN'S LANE (AND TERRACE)
The earliest mention of St Swithun's Lane, now only a very short connection from the High Street to Stewards Inn Lane, is in 1624 when it was recorded as St Swithun's Lane, alias Stewards Inn Lane. In 1799 William Figg, the map maker, marked St Swithun's Lane as continuing down the line of what is now known as Green Lane (*qv*). The fine Georgian House at 82 High Street on the corner of St Swithun's Lane, now occupied by Lloyds Bank, used to be known as St Swithun's House.

St Swithun was a 9th century Bishop of Winchester, but dedications to the saint are uncommon. Indeed there is only one church, at East Grinstead, dedicated to him in all of Sussex, Surrey and Kent. However in the late 15th century there was a 'light' or illumination dedicated to St Swithun in nearby St Michael's church. It is probable that this actually meant there was a statue, or possibly painting, of the saint that was illuminated. It is conjectured that this statue could originally have been in a chapel attached to the Stewards Inn.

William Green had a garden in the late 18th century near the lane now called after him. In 1881, the Reverend Thomas Molineux sold 82 High Street, St Swithun's House, along with its stables and gardens. In

1906 the property was sold again and shortly afterwards the new owner sold gardens on the 'south side of Stewards Inn Lane' to William Marchant, a Brighton builder. He developed the site and built the present St Swithun's Terrace.

SCHOOL HILL

There is a popular fallacy that this name arose from the several private schools which at one time were situated here. From 1790 to 1812, Mary Adams kept a 'Boarding School for Ladies' at No. 208, and opposite, on the site of Temple House, a school used to be run by Miss Lund prior to 1790. A Swiss Protestant named Raymond ran the ancient School Hill Academy (formerly the Turk's Head Inn) which was demolished in 1821 to make room for Albion Street.

But the name of the hill is of much earlier origin, the first known record being in a rent roll of 1498 which brings into account 'a plot of land lying in the parish of All Saints at Scholehill'. The name appears in 1624 in the Town Book, and Paul Dunvan, writing in 1795, suggests it is a corruption of Cole, or Cool Hill, 'which will not appear improbable to those who have experienced the constant draught of air which prevails along this street at every season'. It is, however, probably derived from the Old English word 'scoh' (shoe). In the 13th century, Shoe Lane in the City of London appeared as 'Scholane', and in its local application 'Scholehill' would mean a hill shaped like a shoe, a feature which was more pronounced before the high 'instep' was cut away about a hundred years ago.

The hill leads down to the site of the East Gate in the medieval town wall, all trace of which is now lost. Adjoining the gate was the church of the Holy Trinity, whose parish was merged with All Saints' in the 14th century. The premises at the corner of Eastgate Street were once known as Church House, and there are traces of foundations below which may belong to the old church.

The surface of School Hill was paved with cobblestones until 1826, when the Town Commissioners, aided by the frontagers, took up the boulders and 'McAdamised the road' by rolling in broken flints.

SPITAL ROAD

The long arm of coincidence has reached over nine centuries to give a reminder that this road, which leads towards the Victoria Hospital, takes its contracted name from another hospital which was built and endowed about 1085 by the founder of Lewes Priory. *On an isolated site outside the Borough, now occupied by a day care centre, the first Earl de Warenne built the hospitium of St. Nicholas for lepers. It was linked with the Priory and later came to dispense relief and hospitality to pilgrims and travellers until 1537, when the Priory and its possessions were surrendered to Henry VIII

The remains of the building were converted into cottages which were used for a time by the parish as paupers' homes. It is recorded that in 1795, on the death of a former inmate, the first to enter was eligible to fill the vacancy. As soon as the corpse was brought out a waiting crowd fought desperately for the privilege. The cottages were demolished in 1933 to provide space for school extensions.

Astley House and its racing stables have been replaced by garage premises used by the Police – horsepower has replaced the horse – and the memory of the equestrian skill and daring of the Astley family, whose circus toured the district in the early part of the last century, has been dimmed.

STATION STREET

Until 1857, the street was known as St. Mary's Lane (once popularly corrupted into Simmery Lane), being named after the church of St. Mary-in-Foro (in the market) which stood on the site of the old premises at High Street corner. Its parish was merged with St. John-sub-Castro in 1538 and the church was converted into a parsonage, passing later to a more secular use. The cellar and structure of the present building still retain traces of the old church.

In 1857, a new passenger railway station was built on the present site, replacing the original station in Friars Walk. In its honour the approach road from the town centre was renamed Station Street. There was strong opposition to changing the old style of St. Mary's Lane and it became the scene of the 'battle of the boards'. The old and new name-plates were substituted almost daily by the opposing parties. Eventually the 'progressives' won, although for a long time both name-plates were exhibited one above the other at the top of the street.

The remains of the church of St Mary-in-Foro by James Lambert, 1783.

STEWARD'S INN LANE

A disastrous fire in 1592 must have destroyed much of the material evidence which would have helped to explain the origin of this name. The meagre fire-fighting equipment of those far-off days is included in an annual inventory of 'divers things belonginge unto the towne,' which is preserved in the Town Book. In 1592 two 'grete hookes of iron' fixed on long poles (for tearing down burning thatch) and twelve 'lether buckettes and mattockes' were recorded intact, but eight shovels were written off as 'lost in the fyre at Stewardes Inn'.

In early deeds dating from 1309 there are references to 'the house of Earl Warenne called La Perynne', which can be identified as being situated here and which may have been the steward's residence. The name of Steward's Inn is now only applied to the lane which runs parallel with the High Street, but until the 17th century it also included the connecting lane now known as St. Swithun's. This was probably the entrance to the inn or precinct of the offices of the steward of the lords of the castle.

The office of steward no doubt lost its importance in 1347 when the castle ceased to be the lord's residence on the death of the last of the de Warennes. The account of the income from the Duke of Norfolk's share of the barony of Lewes for the year 1498 reveals a state of disuse as 'the Styward's Inn charged at 7d. raised nothing therefrom in this year', although the 'pigeonhouse in the Stywardsynne' brought in a rent of 3s. 4d. The fire of 1592 must have removed surviving traces of the Stewards domain and it probably existed in name only by 1620, when orders were given to dismantle much of the castle and its precincts to provide building material at 4d. a load.

*STYLES FIELD

When the new Lewes Library was finally built in 2003 it occupied ground once called Styles Field which more recently was the former kitchen garden of Lewes House. Richard Styles was a cooper who was recorded as living near Eastgate corner in 1662.

WALWERS LANE

The vennels of School Hill, those high-walled, narrow lanes connecting it with the old town wall fortifications, are of medieval origin. Walwers has been so-called through the centuries, perpetuating the memory of William le Walewere who was one of the members of parliament for Lewes in 1319 and 1323–4, and who once lived there. His name appears as a taxpayer in a subsidy roll of 1296, as also does Matilda Walwer, a widow, who was probably his mother. The other M.P. for Lewes in 1323–4 was Robert the Spicer (the grocer) whose house, there is little doubt, stood on the site of the present town hall.

Other local names have sometimes usurped the real one of Walwers. It was known as Carters Lane in the 17th century, undoubtedly honouring a worthy burgess of that period. In Victorian times it was called Birdcage Lane, as a result of the ornithological pursuits of John Maxfield Smith (high constable in 1879) who lived at School Hill House in the latter part of the last century. His collection of 175 showcases of birds was preserved for many years in the former borough museum in Albion Street and was later moved to the Booth Museum in Brighton.

*L.S Davey claimed that the name 'Walewere' meant 'builder of walls'. Research by Richard Coates has questioned this assertion. He believes that in fact the most likely explanation is that the name comes from Middle English 'wallower' and is either an uncomplimentary comparison with pigs or could be 'something rounded'. In either case it appears that Mr le Walwere was not a popular man in 14th century Lewes.

*WATERGATE LANE
The present Watergate Lane leads down to the site of the old Water Gate in the town wall. The Watergate was situated on the other side of Mill Pond, an extensive spread of water formed by the Winterbourne stream. A rental for the year 1498 includes a record of 'land lying to the east of the bridge of Watergate'.

*WATERLOO PLACE
Waterloo Place and its neighbour, Wellington Street, were built shortly after the battle in 1815. A tavern, the Waterloo Inn, stood at the corner of Wellington Street. Several other small streets, including Norfolk Street and Bouverie Street, ran between them. All, except one side of Waterloo Place, were demolished in the 1960s to make way for a council housing development. The name Wellington Street survived in the new development (*see* East Street).

*WELLHOUSE PLACE
St Anne was much venerated as a patron of healing wells. A well on or near this site was recorded in 1240. The Cluniacs owned a strip of land, later known as Wellcroft, opposite the church of St Mary Westout, where in 1533 they repaired a water supply. In 1990 a mid-Gothic corbel of a

smiling woman and three blocks of late Norman stone with a hole pierced through their centre were found on the site of the former Wellcroft, and it has been suggested that these could have been part of a well-head and conduit. The importance of this well may have been responsible for the change of dedication of St Mary Westout. In 1537 it was spoken as 'saint Anne's' even though its patron was the Virgin Mary.

By 1639 complaints were made that what is now Western Road was in decay 'for want of taking in the water' from adjacent land. It was another two hundred years before this was remedied. The advent of a piped water supply to Lewes in 1833, and the building of a reservoir at the corner of what is now St. Anne's Crescent (on the site of the old town pest house), stirred up building activity in the area. Apart from a few small wells, the only water supply previously available in the area was from the public pump house at the rear of the Pelham Arms Inn. When a row of houses was built there in 1963 they were appropriately called Wellhouse Place.

WESTGATE STREET
The 14th century West Gate in the town wall, from which this street takes its name, was set across the High Street opposite the Freemasons' Hall. Owing to its ruinous state it was pulled down about 1777, but fragments of its bastions still remain within the framework of the

The sign of the White Lion high on the wall in Westgate Street.

present buildings on each side of the road. In Tudor times, the street was known as Cutlers Bars, descriptive of the cutlers trade that was once centred there. By the 17th century it had become Westgate Lane and, later, it was called White Lion Lane,* after the 18th century ale house that stood below the wall. The curious 18th century inn sign, a white lion fashioned out of sheet copper by a Lewes metal worker named Larwill, was preserved when the pub was demolished in 1939 under a slum clearance scheme. In 1954, the Friends of Lewes refurbished and re-placed the sign near its original site. At the time of writing, in 2010, it is again looking bedraggled and has lost its tail, but the Society hopes to restore the lion later this year.

*This inn was not the first White Lion Inn in Lewes. There was a much older White Lion Inn in the High Street that can be traced back to 1526, when the landlord, John-a-Wood was concerned in Star Chamber proceedings with Thomas Scrase, the landlord of the Vine, now Shelleys Hotel. The white lion is heraldic in origin and was in fact the armorial bearing of Simon de Montfort.

WESTERN ROAD

Ireland's Lane was formerly the western limit of the old borough boundary. The roadway beyond used to be an open highway passing over grasslands known as The Hides and leading to The Spital, where the road forked to London on the right and Brighthelmstone on the left. The road itself was nameless in those days. Its christening was a gradual process linked with the development of the area. It was not until 1833 that the availability of a piped water supply made the area attractive. A further event in 1854 speeded up development. In that year the new civil prison was completed, and another water reservoir was built on the Race Hill to supply it. The prison, incidentally, cost £56,000, and 5,300 tons of flints were used in its construction.

The recently closed Meridian pub was formerly known as the Rifleman. The original building was contemporary with the prison, and is said to have been originally a canteen for the workmen employed on the building. It was substantially rebuilt in the 1960s and was then known as the Pewter Pot.

*In 1883, after the St. Anne's area had been incorporated into the borough, the limits of Western Road (from Ireland's Lane to Brighton Road) were formally defined by the corporation. The borough council were divided over the name to be given to the extended road. A faction preferred 'St Anne's Road', but after a debate 'Western Road' prevailed. Those in favour of this rather pedestrian name were no doubt influenced by the fact that the terrace of houses just beyond St. Anne's Church, built in 1848, had been called Western Road and felt confusion would arise. To add variety, groups of cottages along the road were called Christie's Cottages (after the Reverend William Christie of Glyndebourne) and George's Cottages.

WHITE HILL
The full name was originally White Chalk Hill, descriptive of the steep narrow lane which formerly crossed the Paddock valley. Offham Road, as we know it today, did not exist prior to 1821, and the lane was very little used on account of horse-drawn vehicles being unable to negotiate the precipitous gradient. All London coach traffic at that time entered and left the town by way of Nevill Road. Writing in 1821, Horsfield says: 'The trustees of the Offham turnpike (which leads into the town by Spital Barn) obtained authority from Parliament to take this branch of road (White Hill) under their control and to make it adequate to traffic. This was effected by lowering the hill on either side and filling up the valley with the materials, whereby a causeway is now formed. By this plan the distance from Offham is shortened half a mile.'

The London railway subsequently burrowed a tunnel under the causeway. The road improvements resulted in building development in the neighbourhood, and in September 1838 a report of the ceremony of laying the first stone of the Elephant and Castle Inn, at the Offham entrance to the town, was given prominence in the local paper.

2
Cliffe

*The pedestrian precinct just west of the old river bridge is the final part of Lewes High Street. Cliffe High Street starts on the other side of the river. Early origins of Cliffe are uncertain. Any settlement there was grouped with Lewes in the Domesday Book, but by 1300 there was certainly a causeway leading from the river bridge to Cliffe Corner where a church stood, probably since the 12th century.

The first recorded vicar was John of Arundel in 1320, but the dedication to St Thomas the Martyr was almost certainly well before this. The street pattern was easily recognisable from an early date. West Street (now Cliffe High Street), East Street (now Chapel Hill), North Street (now Malling Street) and South Street all met just in front of the church at Cliffe Corner. Because the growth of Cliffe has always been constrained by the river, downs and wetland, virtually all the other roads are cul de sacs, often recalling the rich commercial history of the area.

Cliffe Bridge showing the Bear Inn (right).

*BEAR YARD

For almost three centuries until it burned down in 1918 the Bear Inn stood at the side of Cliffe Bridge, on the site now occupied by Argos. It was an important inn, much used for meetings and the centre of local affairs when Cliffe had a separate administration prior to its incorporation into the borough of Lewes in 1881. The inn used to be the centre of the Lewes wool trade. Sheep farmers and merchants would sit on opposite sides of tables making offer and counter offer until more sophisticated public auctions were introduced. The present John Harvey tavern occupies a building once used as the stables of the Bear.

CHAPEL HILL

There is little doubt that this road, cut into the rock chalk of Cliffe Hill, follows the line of an early hill track, or borstal, leading down from the hilltop encampments of the early Britons.

The original name given to this road was East Street, but the present name derives from the chapel for Independent Nonconformists which was erected by voluntary subscriptions in 1775 under the patronage of the Countess of Huntingdon, a zealous promoter of Calvinistic Methodism. The Old Hill Chapel (as it was called) was situated near the bottom of the hill and from it sprang others – the Baptist in 1785, Jireh in 1805, Wesleyan in 1807 and the Tabernacle in 1816. The old chapel fell into disuse about 1868 and the building was sold in 1879, the proceeds being divided between the Jireh Chapel and the Tabernacle. The site is now occupied by some cottage properties.

Over a century ago, Baldy's Garden, with its embowered alcoves and grottos, adorned the hillside. Its site is now enclosed within the Cuilfail Estate, but it was once a popular rendezvous. A wayside wall seat remains to mark the location.

Hereabouts, also, was the old Cricketers' Inn, recalling many stories of the games played on the brow of Cliffe Hill in the days when the sport was in its infancy. An early broadsheet printed by John Baxter gives notice that 'the return game of cricket will be played on Cliff Hill between the Gentlemen of Newhaven and Bishopston and the Gentlemen of the Cliff on Monday, September 4th. 1815'.

CLIFFE HIGH STREET

The old bridge over the Ouse stands where, since the dawn of recorded history, the site of the river crossing has been situated. What is now the narrow High Street was originally a causeway constructed over the marshland, from the East Gate in the Town Wall (at the bottom of School Hill) to the old hill track now known as Chapel Hill, linking Lewes with Pevensey and other habitations to the east. Relics of this original roadway were revealed ten feet below the surface when the bridge was widened in 1932.

Since all traffic through the centuries had to converge at this point to cross the river, the extreme narrowness of the approach road was always a thorn in the side of authority. Prior to 1830, according to a contemporary, 'the upper stories of many houses overhung the narrow street so far that opposite neighbours might shake hands almost from their windows'.

When the trustees of the Malling Turnpike roads declared their intention, about 1825, to seek legislative sanction to construct a new entrance to the town, with a bridge across the river at Malling, the traders of the Cliffe considered that their commercial interests would be materially affected. They were so alarmed that they obtained statutory powers which, when implemented, resulted in most of the properties on the south side of the street being pulled down and set back 'some feet'.

Had the trustees of Malling Turnpikes been allowed to proceed with their scheme the problems of traffic congestion in this street, which plagued the town for many years until the construction of the Phoenix Causeway and new river bridge in 1969, might never have arisen.

Before the Cliffe was incorporated in the former Borough of Lewes, this street was known as West Street. (Malling Street was then North Street.) The whole area is steeped in historical associations, but it was, unfortunately, frequently flooded in the old days when the river overflowed. An old diary reads: 'On the 12 of September 1671 the water was so hi in the Clif that men waded up to their middle by the bridg.' Sadly a similar scene occurred on October 11th, 2000.

CUILFAIL

The early development of this estate on Cliffe Hill was undertaken by a well-known local solicitor, Isaac Vinall, about 1900. He named it after the village of Cuilfail, just south of Oban in N.W. Scotland, where he used to spend his holidays. One of the first houses he built on this estate was called 'Melfort' – after the Pass of Melfort in the same district.

ENGLISH'S PASSAGE

Hidden away between 10 and 11 Cliffe High Street is a narrow passage leading to a row of cottages which bear the name of a once well-known Lewes family named English. They traded as cutlers, having their shops at 11 Cliffe High Street and 48 High Street. The family appears to have been established in Lewes at least as early as 1768, and they continued in business until the middle of last century. An interesting example of their work – a table knife with a Delft pottery handle – is preserved at the Anne of Cleves museum. It is most unlikely that this knife is the sole survival of their work. No doubt more of this locally made cutlery is still in the possession of old Lewes families. The English family took an active part in local affairs and one of them, William, was a high constable of Lewes in 1820. Their shop in the Cliffe was the recognised agency for public lottery tickets until 1820, when parliament clamped down on this form of gaming.

The passage once gave access to the river at a point once known as Eel Wharf, and it was here that the last of the eel catchers, a man named Baker, made his living by 'bobbing and spearing'. It is said that many a wager used to be won by enterprising 'locals' who knew that this passage to the river bank was a much shorter way to South Malling Church than the normal route by way of Malling Street and Spences Lane.

*FARNCOMBE ROAD

This new road recalls the Farncombe family, who were printers in Lewes. In 1854 Joseph Farncombe founded the *East Sussex News*, a rival to the *Sussex Express* which they later took over. Joseph Farncombe was mayor of Lewes between 1885 and 1888.

*FOUNDRY LANE

In 1549 it was estimated that there were 53 furnaces and forges operating in the weald of Sussex, an industry that had continued since Roman times. These furnaces produced guns, many of which were shipped to Lewes and Newhaven and exported. There were probably no furnaces in Lewes itself until the 17th century. In 1685, four pattern woods, moulds used for casting iron artefacts, were stolen from Benjamin Court at Cliffe. Mr Court prospered however, and in 1724 was paid £8 7s 9d to entertain the judges who were presiding at the assizes. In 1707 Mr Court had opened a showroom at Newcastle House and his 'magazine of ironmongery' was much admired. The fine sundial that can be seen on Dial House in the Cliffe Precinct is his work. In 1784, Nathaniel Polhill of the Cliffe set up an iron foundry in the lane which, in due course, came to be known as Foundry Lane (*see* Morris Road).

Foundry Lane, once known as Puddle Street, seems to have been used as a meeting place for the Quakers, although it is unlikely that they were there from 1673 until 1784, as Leslie Davey wrote. The Rickman family were Quakers and owned land in Foundry Lane. The Baptists originally met in Friars Walk, but by 1784 the Quakers had built their meeting house there and the Baptists bought land from Thomas Rickman for a meeting house in Foundry Lane. They remained there until 1819, when their chapel was built in Eastgate Street. It is not clear if the Baptists built an entirely new chapel or whether they took over a building used by the Quakers. The old place of worship in Foundry Lane was pulled down when the gas works were established in 1822.

*HILLMAN CLOSE

The Hillman family were originally chalk quarriers and bargemen working on the wharfs that lined the river. By 1800 they owned several chalk pits at Malling and Southerham. By the mid 19th century they had expanded their interests to include brewing, opening the Southdown Brewery in Thomas Street in 1838. The fine building can still be seen today.

Edward Hillman founded the firm of solicitors that still has premises on School Hill. He was mayor of Lewes between 1892 and 1894, and he opened the new Lewes Town Hall, converted from the old Star Inn, on 9th November 1893. His son, George Edward Hillman, was also a town councillor at the time.

*JENNER'S WAY
Called after Anthony Jenner, who ran Harvey's Brewery for many years. His son Miles is now joint managing director of the company.

*MORRIS ROAD
In 1823 Ebenezer Morris acquired the foundry that had been set up by Nathanial Polhill in Foundry Lane. His son enlarged the foundry in 1835 to compete more effectively with the recently completed Phoenix Ironworks (*see* Phoenix Place). The firm continued to trade until the close of the 19th century. Their iron and brass foundry in the lane was linked with their general ironmongery business at 41–42 Cliffe High

The Morris Foundry.

Street. The extensive area of land behind these premises was developed in 1891, and the new road with its terrace houses was appropriately called Morris Road.

*THE NURSERIES

This development, which in 2010 was not yet complete, occupies ground used for about 50 years by Clayhill Nurseries. Before that time it would have been pasture land.

*RUSBRIDGE LANE

Rusbridge is not a name that occurs often in Lewes records, but Stephen Rusbridge was the parish road surveyor in 1796. Appropriately for a road surveyor, he carried on business as a pattern and clog maker in South Street. In 1836 Frances Rusbridge, a spinster of Cliffe, was granted an 81-year lease on a newly erected messuage (house) in South Street, Cliffe. Later, in 1851, Benoni Rusbridge Frank, a linen draper, agreed to enter into partnership with Ebenezer Vinall at 53, Cliffe High Street. The business is also recorded as having taken on James Pullinger as an apprentice in 1849. Much later, in 1933, Lewes Borough Council bought land in Rusbridge's yard near Cliffe Corner on which to build public conveniences. They are now converted into the Nutty Wizard café.

SOAP FACTORY LANE

This was one of the lanes which was entirely 'obliterated' by the major road improvements comprising the Phoenix Causeway and new river bridge in 1969. The derivation of this street name is very obvious, but the detail of its story is tantalisingly obscure. Before 1800, this lane appears to have been a nameless thoroughfare giving access to the barge wharves and sawmills that formerly existed there. About 1810 Thomas Evershed came from Billingshurst and converted an old sawmill into a factory for the manufacture of soap. Other members of the Evershed family opened similar factories at Arundel and Seaford. The latter appears to have been the most successful venture, and from it the modem firm bearing that name can trace its beginning.

In Lewes, Thomas Evershed's industry resulted in a lawsuit at the assizes in August 1816, when one of his neighbours, Thomas Hooper, gave evidence of the 'nuisance caused by the offensive smells from the soap manufactory which was begun 5 to 6 years ago'. Evershed's billheads advertised that he was producing 'curd, mottled and yellow soap'. When he died (in 1843) his son, William, carried on the business with the assistance of partners, who probably bolstered up the undertaking with capital investment.

At one time the firm was known as Johnston, Farnes, Elliot, Evershed and Lambe, and in 1855 it had become William Evershed and Son. When the factory eventually closed down, it seems that the business was absorbed by the successful Seaford firm, which by that time had moved to the Brighton area

SOUTH STREET

Of the four main roads in the Cliffe, South Street is the only one that has retained its original name. The North Street of former times has become Malling Street, East Street is now Chapel Hill and West Street was altered some 150 years ago to Cliffe High Street.

South Street was once quite a hive of local industry, especially when the river was the main means of transport. The extensive timber yards are now lost, save in name only. Much of the timber used to be unloaded from boats at Newhaven and floated up the river on the incoming tides.

During the last century part of the old river cut, now filled in, was known as Higham's Wharf, where shipwrights repaired and refitted seagoing vessels. The shipbuilding yards were on the opposite bank of the river.

In 1793, Edward Egles established a cotton manufactory in South Street; Stephen Rusbridge traded there as a patten and clog maker; George Wille, founder member of the Tabernacle, carried on his successful business as a builder; and Hillman's Pit was busy with its output of chalk and lime. Abraham Curtis and his son had yarn spinning and rope making works adjoining the former parish poorhouse which was behind the Thatched House inn (demolished in 1969).

The winter of 1836 was very severe, and on December 27 a mass of snow avalanched from Cliffe Hill, destroying some cottages known as Boulder Row and killing eight people. The site of the fall is now occupied by an inn called The Snowdrop.

At no. 20, demolished in the 1930s, Elizabeth Verrall opened in 1826 the Delap Hall Seminary for Young Ladies. It was named after Dr. Delap, who lived there for many years and died in 1812. He was rector of Kingston and a friend of the celebrated Dr. Johnson. In 1867 the premises became the Lewes Girls' Home, 'to receive friendless children to prepare them for domestic service'. The Old Ship Inn was on the site now occupied by no. 49, while no. 101 was the Anchor Inn.

*TIMBERYARD LANE
The River Ouse was an important commercial waterway, and the last wharf did not close until the mid-20th century (*see* Eastgate Wharf). Timber from the weald was hauled or floated to the wharves in Lewes and then loaded onto barges for shipment to other parts of the country.

A traffic policeman on duty at Cliffe Corner.

There was an import trade too. Baltic timber was brought directly to Newhaven and Lewes and sold on by the merchants to buyers further within the county. By the 17th century there were at least two timberyards between South Street and the Ouse. William Rice had a spacious yard off South Street in 1763 as well as others at Landport and Offham, but sadly became bankrupt in 1783. He was succeeded by William Gaston. By 1837 Charles Wille was boasting of a 'large connection' of suppliers within a 20- or 30-mile radius of Lewes. Shortly afterwards the growing railway network began to disrupt the waterborne traffic. Nevertheless, the Lewes wharfs continued to operate, transporting timber, coal, corn, seed and lime between Lewes and Newhaven. As late as 1870 the wharf merchants were still Lewes's largest employers.

*WHEATSHEAF GARDENS
This cul de sac stands behind the site of the Wheatsheaf Inn which stood in Malling Street for a century or more. After a brief name-change to the Cleopatra, Lewes's first nightclub, it closed completely in 1976. The sign on the wall can still just be made out.

3
Southover

*Southover, like Cliffe, was administratively separate from the borough of Lewes until 1881. The Cluniacs built their Priory at Southover in the 11th century and by the 13th century a densely packed settlement had grown up between the Winterbourne and the Cockshut streams to serve the Cluniac precinct that housed about a hundred monks.

It is believed that the first church at Southover was a Saxon wooden church, probably dedicated to St Pancras. A stone church was built on the same site by the de Warennes soon after the conquest and this was later used as the infirmary chapel. By the mid 12th century work had begun on a massive church, 420 feet long with two towers over 140 feet high. This was to stand until 1538 when it was demolished by Thomas Cromwell. The present parish church of St John the Baptist replaced the hospitium of the priory around 1264, possibly because St James hospital

Anne of Cleves House in Southover High Street.

just opposite had been enlarged. The tower of the church collapsed in 1698, and the church was largely rebuilt in the 18th century.

BELL LANE
This may be a corruption of Pell Lane, 'pell' being an old Sussex word meaning a pond or stream. The change of the initial letter P to B is not unusual in the evolution of the spoken Sussex word. Bell Lanes are quite common in Sussex and they usually lead down to water, which in this case is the Winterbourne. Before a bridge was built, travellers had to ford the stream which used to flood across the roadway. The word 'pell' has survived in the stretch of ornamental water, near St. John's Church, which is known as the Pells and which was originally a series of ponds.

   * An alternative explanation for the name is that it was called after the inn that stands on the corner of Southover High Street and Bell Lane. This was known as the Bell Inn but was changed to the Swan when another inn of that name, further down Southover High Street, closed in the 1780's. A later Bell Inn stood in Eastport Lane and closed in 1974

*CLUNY STREET
This modern estate was built in the grounds of Southover Manor, formerly an exclusive girls school but once occupied by the Verrall family (*see* Verrall's Walk). The remains of the Cluniac Priory of St Pancras are nearby, and the priory lands extended over what is now the estate.

COCKSHUT ROAD
Shakespeare in his play Richard III tells of 'cockshut time'. The word has an ancient and interesting origin, being found in documents as early as the 13th century and signifying a droveway through the woodland for catching woodcocks by means of nets. In Sussex and on the coastal plains the word indicated a place where flights of duck or geese could be ensnared.

   The marshlands between Lewes and Newhaven once abounded with wild fowl which were caught by nets or spring traps before the days of the sporting gun. A 'cockshut' could be the subject of tenure and could be granted to a tenant for a rental. By inference, the word 'cockshut' became an expression meaning twilight or the close of day because the netting of woodcocks and trapping of wildfowl habitually took place when the birds were setting to roost for the night. It was in this context that Shakespeare used the word.

Cockshut Road runs along the bank of the Cockshut stream. It is significant that Cockshut Road follows the western boundary wall of St. Pancras Priory and leads down to the site of the monks' great cruciform dovecote, said to have been capable of holding over 3,000 birds, which were an essential feature of the Priory's larder. It was pulled down about 1800 and its location is now 'lost' on the courts of the Southdown Tennis Club.

*Cockshut could also conceivably mean a flow of water to a mill. The stream was navigable, and it is recorded that in 1533-4 boats used the stream when ditches leading to a 'mine' and lime kiln were cleared.

CRANEDOWN
The part of the South Downs which runs from Kingston Hill to form the ridgeway leading down to Southover was anciently known as Cranedown – a name which was lost for centuries among musty deeds until it was used in 1963 to christen the estate development on the Kingston Road.

*DORSET ROAD
Richard Sackville had been granted Lords Place in Southover by Elizabeth I. He was wealthy and his son, Thomas Sackville, Baron Buckhurst added to his holdings by purchasing the estates of Old Malling, Malling Deanery and Southover Manor. Sackville lived at Buckhurst Park and was at the time Lord of the manor of Southover. Created Lord Treasurer in 1599, he was promoted by James 1 and became Earl of Dorset in 1604. He enlarged Lords Place and turned it into a fine mansion.

He may not have spent much time at Lewes because at the same time he was building a handsome new mansion at Buckhurst. The third earl was a spendthrift, and Lords Place was essentially abandoned by the family. It was still intact in 1688 but was eventually demolished, although part of the wall was allowed to remain. Some of the stone was incorporated into Fairhall, a fine house in Southover High Street. Buckhurst Park fared better. The house is still lived in and the present owner is William Sackville, 10th Earl De La Warr.

EASTPORT LANE

The old borough of Southover originally had its own administration separate from Lewes, from which it was divided by the once tidal waterway now reduced to the Winterbourne Stream. In those far-off days there used to be 'ports' (entrances) giving access across the watercourse to Southover from Lewes – the East Port and the West Port. At both points there formerly existed a watermill, and a deed of 1609 identifies the mill at the West Port as adjoining the bridge known as Pankridge (Pancras). The present St. Pancras Road and Rotten Row follow the ancient route.

The 'estporte of Sothover' is mentioned in a deed of 1316 and there is an early reference to the East mill in a register preserved from Lewes Priory. The mill is also mentioned in the will of Agnes Morley, who endowed Lewes Grammar School and who died in 1512. Its site can be reasonably identified at the east end of Eastport Lane, where the Winterbourne Stream formerly spread itself over an area later occupied by the cattle market to form a pond which was traditionally called the Mill Pond. This description of the locality still persisted in living memory.

Among early references to Eastport Lane is to be found the record of John Francis, who was hanged in 1577 for rape. His house and chattels in this lane were seized by the lord of the manor. No. 23 was once an inn called the Welcome Stranger. Adjoining it, and now a dwelling, is the old chapel of the General Baptists, with its inscribed stone over the door recording 'the first stone laid May ye 14, 1741'. The grammar school which Agnes Morley endowed in 1512 originally stood at the north-east corner of this lane. The school was transferred to premises on St. Anne's Hill in 1714 and re-built in 1851.

*GARDEN STREET

This street was formerly known as 'Gardeners Street' because there were once market gardens nearby. They covered the site of the former cattle market (*see* Tanners Brook) and adjoining Dorset Road.

HAM LANE

The Roman road from London to Lewes has been traced to Malling Down, where it linked up with a network of local roads which negotiated the low ground which at that time was intersected by a tidal estuary. One of these roads led from Caburn and the east to the ford at Southerham, and then along Ham Lane and the ridgeway on which Southover is built and over the Kingston hills. When the Saxons invaded Britain after the Romans had left they made use of the existing road system, setting up their homesteads on the fertile margin of river marshes. Their habitations are still identifiable by their characteristic place name termination of 'ham' (Southerham, Stoneham). The area now roughly enclosed by the Priory School and its playing fields was known on early maps as 'The Ham'.

Ham Lane originally stretched from the river to a point near Priory Crescent. In the early part of the 19th century Priory Street came into being and curtailed its length, and when housing development by the railway company took place in 1932 the lane was renamed Mountfield Road, leaving the original name only with a branch lane (familiarly known as Cuckoo Corner) leading down to the sewage works. The local expression of 'going down the Ham and round Cuckoo corner' is now lost.

Evidence of antiquity was revealed when the former county grammar school for boys, now the Southover campus of South Downs College, was erected in 1930. Some 200 fragments of pottery of La Tene III and Romano-British periods, and a Roman coin of the third century AD, were dug out of the foundations. A medieval pilgrim's flask was also found and deposited in the Barbican museum.

*JUGGS ROAD

This old track across Kingston Hill was used by the fishwives to bring their wares to market in Lewes. Jugg was a nickname commonly given to the fishermen of Brighton and it was along this steep road, formerly known as Juggs borstal, that the wives came to Lewes to sell their husbands' catch (*see* Fisher Street). Juggs Lane was also known as Mill Lane on account of the three windmills that stood on Kingston Ridge. In 2010 a new windmill, which will incorporate a subterranean house, is being built on the site of the old Ashcombe Smock Mill.

*LOVE LANE

There are Love Lanes in various parts of England and the name is often given to a secluded lane on the outskirts of town. Love Lane in Lewes is no exception, leading as it does off Juggs Road towards Haredean and Hope in the Valley. The belt of trees that the lane runs through was threatened by development, and in 1984 the Friends of Lewes bought the land to preserve it for future generations. It was gifted to Lewes Town Council in 2004.

*MORLEY CLOSE

A grammar school was founded in Southover in 1512 using money left by Agnes Morley, a rich childless widow. She left an annuity of £20 per year to pay the wages of the schoolmaster who was also a priest, and he had to pray regularly in Southover church for Agnes's soul. The school survived the suppression of Lewes Priory, and Agnes's original endowment of £20 per annum was increased considerably in 1709 by a further bequest from Mrs Mary Jenkins. This allowed new school premises on St Anne's Hill to be purchased in 1714. Lewes Old Grammar School still uses the site. The Morley family lived at Glynde from the 15th century and the present Glynde Place was built by William Morley in 1570. His descendant Lord Hampden still lives there today.

ST. JAMES STREET

This unpretentious byway reflects but little of its former glory, and there remains nothing to indicate that it was once a route leading to the great gateway of the Priory of St. Pancras. The street must have witnessed many grand occasions during those centuries when the priory flourished. The ancient gateway, from which emerged, after the Battle of Lewes in 1264, the treaty which laid the foundations of our present parliamentary system, survived until about 1830. It was then moved and rebuilt to allow the entrance to New Crescent (as Priory Crescent was first called) to be widened.

In the 14th century the hospitium at the Priory Gate appears to have been converted into the present parish church, and a new hospitium for pilgrims and travellers was built by the monks close by and dedicated to St. James. Its hall has disappeared, but the remains of its little chapel have been incorporated into the fabric of a house, just by the school entrance opposite Southover Grange.

There is a tradition that the street was once linked up across the valley with Antioch Street, but its long existence as a bulbous cul-de-sac inspired a parochial wag some 250 years ago to give it the name 'Pudding Bag Lane'. *Davey wrote that the lane was still known by that name, but unfortunately I think that this colloquialism is now lost.

*ST PANCRAS ROAD

The Cluniac Priory was dedicated to St Pancras sometime in the 1070s. It has been suggested that this building was not the first church on the

The ruins of Lewes Priory.

site and that a Saxon wooden building was first dedicated to the saint. Saint Pancras was a boy martyr who was killed about the year 204 when only sixteen years old. He lived in the reign of the Roman emperor Diocletian, who persecuted the Christians. The Roman Catholic church in Irelands Lane has been dedicated to the saint.

SOUTHOVER ROAD
Until the railway station was built in 1857 and a new road constructed to link Station Street with Priory Street, the way to Southover led along the line of the old town wall. The road then had no special name, and it was not until 1885 that it became known as Southover Road. Where it passes the Grange Gardens the road was formerly overshadowed by a row of majestic elms on one side and by walnut and ash trees on the other side.

It was a leafy, shaded walk, and during the 19th century it acquired the name of 'the Mabbotts' – apparently from the Mabbott family who occupied Southover Grange from 1837 to 1860. Near the railway tunnel at the east end of Elm Grove (the lane which runs parallel to the road), there used to be a cluster of tenements known as South Parade and an old tavern called The Grapevine. All have long since been demolished, although a house has recently been built on the site of The Grapevine and has been named after it.

The activities of a doubtful character who lived in Keere Street about 1890 are closely linked with the Mabbotts. He was known as 'Spring Heel Jack'. Wearing boots fitted with strong springs, he took delight in frightening passers-by out of their wits by jumping out on them at night from behind the trees and bushes. He appears to have confined his antics to frightening folk, but such was his notoriety that the locality used to be boycotted after dark.

*TANNERS BROOK
This street was built on the site of the former Lewes Market, which closed in the 1990s. The tannery at Southover was one of several in the town. A tannery replaced a cornmill on the site before 1658. It was run by Thomas Fuller in about 1750 and his son Joseph continued there until

1832 (*see* Green Wall). Lewes Market opened on the site in 1882, having previously operated in the High Street and, for a short time, in the Pells area (*see* page 62).

*VERRALL'S WALK

The Verrall family were a prominent Lewes family for several centuries, being brewers in Southover from the 17th to the 19th century. Thomas Verrall was a high constable of Lewes in 1686, followed by Richard in 1717 and 1735, Henry in 1753, William in 1754, Edward in 1758, Henry in 1766, the quaintly named Araunah (a bookseller) in 1788 and 1799 and Plumer in 1832 and 1837.

John Verrall (1697–1784) lived in Old Brewery house, and had two sons John II and William, both brewers. John II (1725–1808) bought Anne of Cleves house and its brewery, eventually leaving it to his nephew Harry (1763–1849), son of William. Harry rebuilt the brewery at the Old Brewery House.

William's other son, William II (1759–1837) acquired the brewery at Fairhall as well as a great many inns in Lewes and the surrounding countryside. His son, William III (1798–1890) moved up in the social scale in 1840 by buying Southover Manor and the Priory lands. Verrall's Walk is part of the estate built on land belonging to the Manor.

Making up Prince Edwards Road, 1909.

The former paper mill at the Pells, around 1870.

4
Wallands and the Pells

*A Saxon settlement was established at Lewes sometime in the 9th century, and the name Wallands may possibly denote a place where surviving British serfs lived outside the town. Wallands Combe lay just outside the walls and almost certainly became a deer park attached to the castle.

By the 18th century it was owned by the Shelley family. When Miss Cordelia Shelley, the last of her family to live at the house now known as Shelleys Hotel, died in 1854, her property passed to her nephews, members of the D'Albiac family. The parkland beyond Shelley's Paddock, which formed part of the estate, became the subject of building speculation. Plans were prepared setting out proposed roads, many of which were to be named after contestants at the Battle of Lewes in 1264. With admirable impartiality the streets were named after participants on both sides of the battle.

Development started soon afterwards, but building proceeded slowly and some roads were not completed until the 20th century. Not all the planned roads were actually built. Early plans show Leicester Road alongside Guy Road and Prince Richard's Road. The most recent homes in the area, Wallands Park Rise, were completed only in 2007.

The name 'pell' is derived from the old English 'pol', meaning pool and until recently was still used in Sussex dialect speech for a deep spot in a shallow stretch of water. The stretch of ornamental water near St John-sub-Castro Church known as the Pells was originally a series of ponds which fed a paper mill owned by George Molineux. It was made into a pleasure park in the 19th century when the surrounding land was developed.

The land was leased by the Earl of Abergavenny to the borough of Lewes on 2nd of March 1860. In 1897, when a water carnival was held there, it was described as 'a beautiful piece of ornamental water, fringed by trees.'

In 1879 the cattle market was removed from the High Street to a site on Woodcock Field, near the Pells, which was part of the old St. John's Farm which had belonged to the D'Albiac estate. This site was found to be unsuitable, and in 1882 the market was moved to a site near the Grange Gardens. The market finally closed in the 1990s and housing was built on the site (*see* Tanners Brook). The original site was sold to speculative builders, and development on the St John's Farm Estate commenced in 1883.

*ABERGAVENNY ROAD

The Nevill family once owned much of the land on which modern Lewes is built. The Marquis of Abergavenny, the head of the Nevill family, still lives at Eridge Castle, the seat of the family since the 15th century (*see* Eridge Green). In 1960 Lewes Borough Council built the blocks of flats served by Abergavenny Road. One block was called Abergavenny Close, commemorating the land ownership of the Nevill family, and another Shelley Close after the Shelley family who owned the land until 1854.

Before the flats were built the site was occupied by the former Lewes Workhouse erected in 1868 and still remembered with a shudder by some of the very old inhabitants of Lewes. In the early 20th century the 'Inebriates Reformatory' was housed in part of the buildings. (Some may feel it could still have a role today.) The workhouse closed in 1930 and the building was then used for municipal housing until its demolition.

*THE AVENUE

Originally D'Albiac Avenue, the name was altered at the request of residents in 1908. Formerly parkland, known as The Wallands and owned by the Shelleys of Lewes, the land had been inherited by the D'Albiac family through George D'Albiac, who married into the Shelley family in 1806. George D'Albiac lived at Isfield. He was selected as prospective Liberal candidate for Lewes, but left to take up an army appointment overseas before an election took place. Before leaving he presented the Bundle of Sticks Society (as the Liberals of Lewes were then known) with a fine George IV silver tankard, which now forms part of the Town plate.

*BRADFORD ROAD

The first houses in Bradford Road were built in 1905. Unusually for a Wallands street, it was not named after a participant in the battle of Lewes and for a long time I had no idea where this name came from. Fortunately John Davey found some notes left by his father that said that the road was called after the Bradford family who lived in The Shelleys around 1900. I then found details of the family in the 1891 census. At that time Selina F. Bradford was living in the Shelleys with her five teenage children. She was described as 'wife' but there was no mention of her husband.

Checking further back I found that in 1881 the family were living in Marylebone, London, in 1881 and that the father was called Robert. A Robert Bradford was buried in St Anne's churchyard in 1895, so he may have been ill at the time of the 1891 census. The family seem to have no connection with Lewes, although in Falmer churchyard there are a number of fine 17th century table tombstones of a family called Bradford. The 19th century Bradford family does not seem to have taken an active part in Lewes life, and they left the town soon after 1900.

CHRISTIE ROAD

In 1958 the Town Council chose this name to honour John Christie, who founded the Glyndebourne Festival Opera House in 1934. He was admitted as an honorary freeman of the borough on November 3, 1954, and he died on July 4, 1962. Glyndebourne Opera is now run by his grandson Augustus (Gus).

John Christie was the grandson of William Langham Christie of Glyndebourne, who was member of parliament for Lewes from 1874 to 1885. When the former borough received its charter of incorporation in 1881, he presented the mayor's badge and chain of office and the large ceremonial silver gilt mace.

CLARE ROAD

This road was named after Gilbert de Clare, Earl of Gloucester, a comrade of Simon de Montfort who successfully commanded the centre section of de Montfort's army at the Battle of Lewes.

DE MONTFORT ROAD

Simon de Montfort, Earl of Leicester, was the chosen leader of the barons who fought and defeated their king, Henry III, at Lewes. The treaty known as the Mise of Lewes, which was drawn up after the battle, sowed the seeds of parliamentary government by representation, from which has sprung our House of Commons.

Building in De Montfort Road was rather piecemeal. St. Mary's Terrace was built in 1864, Summervale Terrace in 1888 and Shelley Terrace in 1906. The old workhouse (demolished and replaced in 1960 by municipal flats) was erected in 1868, and the old St. Anne's School (now home of a playgroup) in 1872.

The De Montfort municipal workhouse before 1910. Flats were built on the site after it was pulled down in 1960.

*DE WARRENNE ROAD

William de Warenne was a distant cousin of William the Conqueror and was at his side at the battle of Hastings. (The road name inserts an extra 'r' for some reason.) He remained loyal to the conqueror's son, William Rufus, at a time when many other barons had declared allegiance to his brother, Duke Robert of Normandy. He was rewarded for his loyalty to both monarchs by being granted large tracts of land and was responsible for the building of both Lewes Castle and Lewes Priory. It has been estimated that in present day terms his wealth exceeded £57 billion.

He died in 1088 and was buried in Lewes Priory alongside his wife Gundrada. The tomb was disturbed by the building of the railway in 1845 and their bodies re-interred in Southover Church. The family's loyalty to the English crown continued.

A later de Warenne, John, the 7th earl, was one of 'the most constant and resolute of all King Henry's men' at the battle of Lewes. On his death in 1304 he was so greatly esteemed by King Edward I that the king ordered prayers to be said for him and promised a remission of 3000 days from purgatory to those who should relieve his soul by prayer. Like his forebears he was buried in Southover Priory.

ELEANOR CLOSE

Off the road named after her husband, King Henry III, is the close bearing the name of his queen, Eleanor of Provence, a French princess whom he married in 1236. Because of her preference for, and favours to, the country of her birth, she was extremely unpopular with her subjects and on one occasion was roughly handled by a crowd of Londoners.

Eleanor was in France before the battle of Lewes in 1264 trying in vain to raise an army of mercenaries to support the king's cause. Her son, Prince Edward, had the opportunity of avenging his mother's honour when the battle started. He attacked and slaughtered the left flank of the barons' army, which consisted mainly of untrained London volunteers.

*FERRERS ROAD

Robert de Ferrers, Earl of Derby was one of Simon de Montfort's barons.

*FITZJOHN'S ROAD

Called after Lord John Fitzjohn, one of the supporters of Simon de Montfort

*GUNDREDA ROAD

Although the road is spelt with an 'e', it was actually called after Gundrada, who was the wife of William de Warenne. Sometimes described as the daughter of William the Conqueror, she was in fact probably the daughter of a Flemish duke. She died in childbirth in 1084 at Castle Acre, Norfolk, and her body was brought back to Lewes and interred at Lewes Priory. Her husband was buried alongside her in 1088. The first houses in the road were built in 1923.

HILL ROAD

It is unfortunate that this road was not allowed to retain its original name of Miller's Walk. It would have been, at least, more pleasing than its usurper, and would have perpetuated the reason for the existence of the road. In the days when the motive power for grinding corn was provided by the wind, the parish of St. John-sub-Castro was served by an old white smock windmill which stood near the top of the present road to the old race course. The mill was reputed to have been built in 1764, and it became familiarly known as Steere's Mill, after John Steere, who owned and worked it for over 35 years, until about 1855.

When the trustees of the Offham turnpike reconstructed and brought the present Offham Road into use in 1821, the parish authorities cut a roadway to provide easier access to Steere's Mill and it was called Miller's Walk. The mill continued its useful life until the close of the 19th century, when it suffered irreparable damage by gales. The owner at that time was James Broad, tallow chandler of Lewes, who was faced with the task of demolishing the derelict and dangerous mill. He solved his problem by enlisting the aid of the 1st Sussex Volunteer Royal Engineers, who were engaged on experiments with a new type of guncotton. The army welcomed the opportunity of a little practical demonstration, and in May, 1901, the tottering structure was literally blown to bits.

*KING HENRY'S ROAD

Henry III was the monarch who was defeated by Simon de Montfort at the Battle of Lewes in 1264. Wallands was not the main site of the battle. Simon de Montfort's soldiers were deployed around the slopes of Mount Harry, while King Henry's army was stationed near the castle and priory. The king's troops divided into three divisions for the advance. Prince Edward led his men out of the castle and across the

Wallands and speedily put part of de Montfort's army to flight. However, instead of supporting his father on the westward flank, they continued to pursue their quarry for several miles, slaughtering as they went. In the meantime the other two royalist divisions were routed by Gilberte de Clare, and the king was forced to retreat to the priory. By the time Edward returned their cause was lost and he was forced to join his father at the priory. The following day the settlement known as the Mise of Lewes was brokered by the friars.

LEICESTER ROAD
Simon de Montfort, Earl of Leicester, has the signal honour of having a second road in Lewes named after him. Following his death at the battle of Evesham in 1265, his estates were forfeited and given to King Henry's younger brother, Edmund Crouchback.

MILDMAY ROAD
Audrey Mildmay was a well-known opera singer who, in 1931, married John Christie. It was her help and interest that inspired his creation of the Glyndebourne Festival Opera House which became internationally famous.

*PARK ROAD
The land on which this short road was built would have been almost in the centre of the parkland that became the Wallands estate.

*PELHAM TERRACE
This short terrace near the Pells was named in 1883 long after the heyday of the powerful Pelham family. Thomas Holles Pelham, later Duke of Newcastle, was first lord of the treasury (prime minister) in 1758, but the family had been eminent in the town since the 16th century.

Pelham Terrace is some distance from the High Street, where the family once owned a substantial amount of property, including the building now known as the White Hart: the initials TP can still be seen on a fireplace in the bar. They did not, however, actually create the fine Elizabethan mansion now known as Pelham House. The builder was

George Goring, who received some lucrative preferments in the 1570s and 1580s. The date 1579 can be seen inside Pelham House, but building probably started some years earlier.

The fortunes of the Goring family faded in time (a monument to the son of George Goring was removed from St Michael's Church in the 18th century, and it was only in 1924 that their coat of arms was replaced in the church) but the final blow to the family fortunes came in 1648 when George Goring II was commander of royalist forces at Colchester when the town fell to the puritans. He was sentenced to death, but escaped the fate of his master and was forced to sell most of his property to repay debts. Thomas Pelham bought the house in St Andrews Lane in 1654. It is now a hotel.

*PRINCE EDWARD'S ROAD
Prince Edward was the eldest son of Henry III and became King Edward I in 1272. He was taken hostage at the battle of Lewes and remained in the custody of Simon de Montfort until 1265 when he escaped from captivity and took command of the royal forces.

At the ensuing battle of Evesham in August 1265, Edward's forces inflicted a huge defeat on the earl's men. Simon himself was killed. His testicles were cut off and hung around his nose, and his feet, head and hands were then cut off and sent around the country as an object lesson to other rebels.

*QUEEN ANNE'S CLOSE
This small infill development off King Henry's Road was built in the 1970s. It is not clear which Queen Anne it was named after. Both Richard II and Richard III had wives called Anne, as did James I. Anne of Cleves, Henry VIII's fourth wife, was given a house in Southover after their divorce, although she never lived there. James II's daughter Anne succeeded her sister Mary II and brother in law William III to the throne of England in 1702. She died in 1714, having had 19 children, none of whom survived.

*RUFUS CLOSE

William II, known as William Rufus, was the third son of William the Conqueror. He died in 1087.

*SACKVILLE CLOSE

The Sackville family is of Norman origin and descends from Herbrand de Salkaville, who took his name from Sauqueville near Dieppe. He was granted various manors by William the Conqueror and his grandson's marriage to Ela de Dene brought the family extensive lands in Sussex, including the manor of Buckhurst that has been in the family from about 1200 until the present day.

Jordan de Sackville was one of the barons supporting Simon de Montfort at the battle of Lewes. The Sackville family were later of great importance in Lewes (*see* Dorset Road), and even today the family (Earl De La Warr of Buckhurst Park and Lord Sackville of Knole) are entitled to a quarter share in the manorial wastes of the borough of Lewes.

SEGRAVE CLOSE

Nicholas de Segrave was the baron to whom Simon de Montfort entrusted the force of Londoners who comprised the left (north) wing of the barons' four-pronged attack on the royalist army at the battle of Lewes. The area of this part of the conflict included the land upon which this close is built.

*TALBOT TERRACE AND TORONTO TERRACE

It was difficult to find the origin of these two street names. Talbot Terrace, Toronto Terrace, St John's Terrace and Pelham Terrace were all built on land formerly owned by the Lewes Cattle Market.

The first record of the name Talbot Terrace that I could find was on May 2nd, 1883, when there was an application by Charles Scrase to build eight houses in Talbot Terrace. There was a note to say that these houses were never built, although Mr Scrase does seem to have completed nos. 1–3. Shortly afterwards, on August 1st, the builder

E. Wells applied to build four new streets – Talbot Terrace, Torronto (sic) Terrace, Pelham Terrace and St John's Terrace – on the site of the market. These were erected over the next few years, the architect being Samuel Denman of Brighton. Charles Scrase seems to have built a lot of these houses.

The Talbot family, of whom the head is the Earl of Shrewsbury, was very influential, but there seems to be no connection with the Lewes area. However, a member of the family, Colonel Thomas Talbot (1771–1853), emigrated to Canada and became an administrator there. His position allowed him to implement a land development scheme along the shores of Lake Erie. His development grew and he carefully chose the settlers himself, ruling out Americans, Liberals or anyone insufficiently respectable! By 1836 he had title to 528,000 acres containing twenty-nine townships. The area he developed is quite close to Toronto

After I wrote to the *Sussex Express* asking for help in tracing the reason for these street names I heard from a family who is descended from Charles Scrase. It appears that originally there were two brothers who were builders. One of them emigrated to Canada and was presumably respectable enough to pass Colonel Talbot's rather rigid criteria for settlement. His brother must have missed him enough to call streets in his new development Talbot and Toronto. Charles Scrase built a house in the road for himself, which the family says was 'some kind of canteen or kitchen'.

Talbot Terrace served as the model for *The Family from One End Street*, a popular children's novel written by Eve Garnett in the 1930s.

*VALENCE ROAD
William de Valence, Earl of Pembroke, was Henry III's half brother.

5
Nevill

*The Nevill family features in the annals of Lewes history as far back as 1264 when various members of the family fought on different sides at the battle of Lewes. In 1415 Joan, Lady Bergavenny inherited a third share in the Lordship of Lewes through her brother, Thomas Fitzalan, Earl of Arundel. Since then the family has continued in unbroken ownership of the Manor of Lewes, and even today various scraps of land in the town are their responsibility.

The first houses on the Nevill Estate were built in the 1920s. The developers were singularly unoriginal in their naming of the roads – North Way was soon followed by South Way, Cross Way and East Way. Many of the houses on the estate were intended for owner-occupiers and were quickly snapped up by staff at the expanding county council offices (then in the High Street) and teachers at the various schools.

However, the estate also included the first purpose-built council housing in Lewes in Middle Way and Cross Way. The builder of these houses seems to have cut corners, and the borough minutes record concern over the concrete used in the construction. The houses on the estate all

The early development of the Nevill Estate.

had large gardens and apart from a small amount of development near the prison, the boundaries of this estate have not changed.

*CABURN CRESCENT

Taking its name from Mount Caburn, this is a British place name that was originally Caer Bryn – fort hill. Mount Caburn was an Iron Age hill fort and was the last to be abandoned in Sussex. Between 200 and 300 people are believed to have lived here in a camp covering three-and-a-half acres and enclosing 50 huts. Legend attributes the formation of Mount Caburn to a clod of earth falling from the Devil's shovel as he dug Devils Dyke.

HAWKENBURY WAY

In 1947 the prison commissioners constructed this road and built houses to accommodate staff employed at Lewes Prison. It appears that, because of autonomous powers, the normal processes of local planning consents were by-passed and there was argument at the time that the position of the houses, built on the lower slopes of the Downs, was detrimental to landscape amenities. The strong feelings prompted the decision to name the new houses Hawkenbury, which was the address of the regional government office at Tunbridge Wells which dealt with this scheme!

*THE GALLOPS

This road was built in the 1980s on the site of the sheep fair (*qv*). The children of Western Road School (formerly at the corner of Spital Road and Nevill Road) chose the name. They were doing a project on local history and regularly attended the annual sheep fair. When the site was sold for building they continued their visits and monitored the progress of construction.

Racing at Lewes probably started in the reign of Queen Anne, and a 'Horse Course' was marked on a map made in 1724. The first recorded meeting was on August 16, 1751. The King's Plate, worth 100 guineas, was the principal race. The meeting was popular with all ranks of society and the Prince Regent was a regular attender.

By the 19th century there were many racing stables in Lewes, most near the prison or St Anne's. One, covering two acres, was erected in 1780 at Spital Corner, almost on the site of the Gallops.

In the 20th century Lewes Races continued to be extremely popular and charabancs crawled nose to tail up the motor road to the course. However, in April 1963 the Horserace Betting Levy Board decided that the course should no longer receive support and decided to invest in nearby Brighton. The last meeting took place on September 14, 1964.

Training continued nevertheless, and horses were stabled in various parts of the town, accessing the training gallops by tracks leading from Spital Road. Nowadays only a few horses are trained in Lewes, and they are all kept at stables actually at the old racecourse.

*MOUNT HARRY ROAD

Called after the neighbouring hill, there are no records of this name before 1610. It is popularly supposed to be called after King Henry III, defeated there by Simon de Montfort in 1264. However, it is more likely that the name derives from the old English 'hearg,' a heathen place of worship, and the hill was therefore once the site of a heathen temple.

SHEEPFAIR

Although the cluster of dwellings known by this name is somewhat 'off target', it is good to perpetuate the memory of the great Michaelmas sheep fair which was traditionally held every September on the foothills adjacent to H.M. Prison.

The growth of Lewes as an important sheep marketing centre can be traced from before the 18th century, and the fame and perfection of the South Down lamb was firmly established by the early 1800s, when the number of sheep brought together at the annual sheep fair averaged 50,000. By the end of the century the number had fallen to less than 20,000.

*The houses were built in 1957, but the sheep fair continued until 1979, albeit with very small numbers of animals compared with its heyday. It took place on the last Thursday in September. Eventually the site was sold and the houses of The Gallops now occupy the site.

6
Landport

*The Landport estate was built by Lewes Borough Council in the late 1930s. The incentive was the Housing Act, 1930, which compelled local authorities to survey all property in their area and to clear and replace any that were unfit for habitation.

In a report of 1933 Lewes Borough Council were told that 254 properties, housing 945 people, were in an unhealthy condition and needed to be demolished. There was clearly some concern about this, because a later report reduced the number to 152. Yet another report, in 1934, reinstated the figure of 254, and the new estate was planned to replace these. Many of the condemned homes were in the North Street area and housed workers in the nearby Phoenix Ironworks. Others were near the Cliffe, around the former wharves and timberyards.

The Greenwich meridian passes through Lewes and the meridian obelisk erected in Meridian Road (*qv*) in 1938 commemorates both this fact and the opening of the estate. All houses had large gardens, coal fires and what was then the latest in kitchen equipment. Most of the roads were named after well-known Lewesians.

Landport Bottom and the prison. It is confusing that Landport Bottom is some way from the Landport Estate, which is sited near the river.

When the estate was expanded in the 1960s by the then Labour-controlled borough council, the new streets were called after local politicians – nearly all of the Labour persuasion,

The name Landport does not in fact mean an inland port. In this case 'port' meant a market place and the name, first recorded in 1296, means 'long town' and refers to the long rows of market stalls spread along both sides of a street.

*ARUNDEL GREEN

All the three greens in Landport recall the noble families that once owned Lewes. The lordship of the manor of Lewes, which still exists, is split between the Nevills of Eridge, who own half of it, the Howards of Arundel who own a quarter and the Sackvilles (the De La Warrs), who also own a quarter. The relative size of the three greens reflects this split – Eridge Green is much larger than the other two.

Arundel Castle is the seat of the Duke of Norfolk, the head of the Howard family. Despite the vast wealth and influence this family once had, Arundel Green is the only commemoration given to them in Lewes. There was once a Norfolk Street, in the North Street area, but it was a street of mean little houses swept away in the slum clearances. How are the mighty fallen!

BAXTER ROAD

When this road was named in 1939, due honour was paid to an old Lewes family whose members have left their mark upon our local heritage. John Baxter was the son of a Surrey fanner. After a brief stay in a London publishing house, he came to Lewes in 1802 and founded the well-known printing business.

His enterprise and kindly disposition won universal respect, and he was elected to the office of high constable of Lewes in 1828. He was responsible for the invention of the inking roller which superseded the old wooden press, and introduced the double-action printing machine. His reputation in Sussex was reflected in the many publications which flowed from his press. He was a keen cricketer and compiled the rules of the game, which he printed under the well-known title of *Lambert's*

Cricketers' Guide. In 1837, with his youngest son, he established and printed the newspaper which was originally known as the *Sussex Agricultural Express.*

His second son, George, achieved fame and royal patronage as an artist and engraver who invented a process of printing in oil colours. Baxter prints have never been excelled for their definition and quality, and they are greatly valued by collectors today. The town possesses a

large collection of these prints which can be seen at the town hall.

Alderman Wynne E. Baxter, of the same family, was the first to advocate a change in the form of government of the town. He was high constable under the old system in 1879 and 1880, and when in 1881 a charter of incorporation was granted, his public spirited efforts were freely acknowledged by his being elected first mayor of Lewes. Another member of the family, Reginald T. Baxter, was town clerk of Lewes from 1915 to 1925.

Wynne Baxter, the first mayor of Lewes.

*BLOIS ROAD
Monsieur le maire de Blois (M. Louis Pétré) unveiled the nameplate of this road on Landport estate on July 23, 1966, during an official visit of a civic delegation. Lewes is 'twinned' with the French town of Blois, and on June 3, 1963, a 'deed of friendship' was sealed to promote exchanges of a cultural, tourist, social and economic nature of common interest.

The connection between the towns began much earlier, in the 1940s, when boys from Lewes County Grammar school started to exchange visits with their counterparts in Blois. The scheme was soon extended to include students from the nearby girls' grammar school.

*BUCKWELL COURT

John Buckwell was a Labour member of Lewes Borough Council for many years A railway man, he was an ardent trade unionist and was chairman of the housing committee when the Landport estate was expanded in the 1960s.

Despite his long service, he never wished to become mayor. Perhaps it was his wife who wished to remain in the background. At the same time that her husband was a member of the council she was employed as the town hall cleaning lady! The borough council was nevertheless anxious to reward his many years of service. On 29th July 1970, he was created an honorary alderman, the only one ever to be made in Lewes.

*CHURCHILL ROAD

Winston Churchill was prime minister of Great Britain during the second world war from 1940–45 and again from 1951–53. He died in 1965, and Churchill Road was built shortly afterwards.

CRISP ROAD

This road was named in 1948 after Charles Doland Crisp, OBE (late alderman) who served as a member of the borough council from 1920 to 1955. He held the office of mayor for 11 years, including the war years, when he also actively served as civil defence controller. He became an honorary freeman of the borough on February 19, 1940, and he died on February 5, 1956.

*DE LA WARR GREEN

Not to be confused with Delaware Road (*qv*) this street name refers to Earl De La Warr, head of the Sackville family(*see* Sackville Close), who still live in Sussex at Buckhurst Park, Withyham. Nowadays the name is perhaps best known for the modernist De La Warr Pavilion in Bexhill which was built in 1933–36 on land owned by the family.

*ERIDGE GREEN

The largest of the three greens in Landport that recall the noble families, all descended by marriage from the De Warennes who once owned all of Lewes. The Nevill family, whose seat is at Eridge Castle near Tunbridge Wells, inherited one third of the barony of Lewes in 1415. By 1476 they owned a half of the manor of the borough of Lewes, a proportion that has continued in unbroken ownership until this day. There are in Lewes quite a number of odd patches of land where the ownership has been uncertain. Recent research for the Friends of Lewes has revealed that this land is manorial waste and that the lord of the manor owns it all.

The Friends of Lewes are currently (2010) trying to repair walls and landscape banks in Paddock Twitten, and much of this area has turned out to be manorial waste. Liaising with the current owners has proved difficult!

EVELYN ROAD

John Evelyn was born at Wotton, in Surrey, in 1620, and when he was five years old he was sent to Lewes to live with his step-grandfather, John Stansfield, a prominent citizen of the Cliffe. After his grandfather's death he resided at Southover Grange, following his grandmother's second marriage to William Newton.

Evelyn received his early education at Mr. Potts' school in the Cliffe before going to the Lewes Grammar School (then situated adjacent to Southover Grange) until 1637, when he went to Oxford. He lived in momentous times and witnessed the troubled events of the Civil War between royalists and Cromwell's roundheads, and after the restoration of the monarchy he was received at court. He laid the first stone of Greenwich Hospital and became its first treasurer. He was one of the first members of the newly-established Board of Trade and as a Fellow of the Royal Society he served on commissions for the re-building of London after the Great Fire.

His diary is a valuable guide to the history and customs of the 17th century, and his intimate friend Samuel Pepys frequently wrote of their association in his celebrated diary. As an author of repute, Evelyn is best known for his book *Sylva*, described as a 'Discourse of Forest Trees'. It became a best-seller, and his constructive proposals on afforestation, to meet the acute problem of the destruction of woodlands to feed the furnaces of the iron and glass industries, greatly influenced the character of the English landscape in following generations. During his boyhood in Lewes, Evelyn laid the foundation stone of the present South Mailing Church, which was rebuilt in 1627 by the efforts and munificence of his grandfather.

FITZROY ROAD

At seven consecutive elections Henry Fitzroy was elected member of parliament for the borough of Lewes. He served from 1837 until his death in 1860. Fitzroy first stood as a Conservative but later became a Liberal. He became a lord of the admiralty in 1845 and was a well-known parliamentary character, renowned for his eloquence. His widow, who was a daughter of Baron Rothschild, erected the Fitzroy Library at the foot of School Hill in 1862 as a memorial to her husband, who had been associated for so many years with the parliamentary history of the town. The building was conveyed to trustees who, having no endowment to maintain and manage it, leased it to Lewes Library Society at a peppercorn rent.

For 35 years this society, through its shareholders and subscribers, carried on this private library service. To commemorate the diamond jubilee of Queen Victoria in 1897, the borough council adopted the Public Library Acts and, by consent of the surviving trustees and members of the Library Society, the building was transferred to the corporation as the library authority.

In 1956 the old library building was sold and became a private house, and the proceeds were applied to the adaptation of the premises in Albion Street that were previously the Lewes Museum of Natural History and prior to that the Lewes School of Science. A purpose-built new library was built near Friars Walk in 2003, and the old library is now offices.

*FULLER ROAD

Bill Fuller was a very popular and long serving Labour councillor who was mayor of Lewes in 1974–75, the first year of the new Lewes Town Council.

*HAYWARD ROAD

Called after Frank Hayward, a staunch Labour supporter and mayor of Lewes in 1973–74, the final year of the old Lewes Borough Council. However, internecine warfare broke out in the Labour party in Lewes in the early 1980s, and Frank Hayward and some other popular councillors were deselected. They all stood again as Independents and were triumphantly re-elected. That was the end of the Labour party's dominance in Lewes, a situation that to date has not been rectified.

HORSFIELD ROAD

This road is named after a Unitarian minister, Thomas Walker Horsfield, who achieved fame as an historian of Lewes. At the age of 25 years he came from his native Sheffield in 1817 to become the minister of Westgate Chapel. He was a young man of exceptional qualities. Apart from ministering to his congregation with remarkable zeal and energy, he established and conducted a successful boarding school in St. Anne's and took a leading part in founding the Mechanics' Institute, where he lectured on a variety of subjects.

The Institute, a precursor of modern further education, stood on the site now occupied (in January 2010) by the police station. The police station will shortly move to a new site in North Street. Discussions over the future of the old building are taking place and it is hoped that the former Mechanics' Institute will be restored and that a suitable occupant will be found.

During his ten years' ministry at Lewes Horsfield was engaged in collecting a mass of material for a publication projected by John Baxter, the printer, who had recognised the exceptional abilities of this newcomer to Lewes. In 1824, the first volume of Horsfield's *History and Antiquities of Lewes and its Vicinity* was published, and the second volume followed in 1827. This comprehensive work, which was sponsored by a thousand subscribers and dedicated to William IV, gained for Horsfield a fellowship of the Society of Antiquaries. It is considered a standard work, worthy of its place in any Sussex library, and I found it useful in the revision of this book.

That this elaborate and complete record was the work of a comparative stranger to Lewes reflects upon Horsfield's great energy and industry. He accepted a ministry at Taunton in 1827, where he compiled another major work, *The History of Sussex*, which was published in 1835. He removed to Lancashire about 1835, where his career came to a sudden end when he died in 1837 at the early age of 45.

*KINGSLEY ROAD

The original entrance to the Landport estate was much closer to Wallands Crescent. Only a footpath is there now, since it was felt that a completely new entrance was needed to provide safe access to the Offham Road. Other roads in Landport have been called after prominent Lewesians. Kingsley Road does not accord to this pattern. In the lack of conclusive evidence, it is hypothesised that it is called after Charles Kingsley (1819–1875), the prominent novelist and social reformer. Best known for his classic *Water Babies*, he did much to raise the social conscience of middle class Victorians to the appalling living and working conditions of so many of the poor.

As stated in the introduction to this chapter, the Landport estate was built to rehouse people living in condemned houses in the centre of the town.

LEE ROAD

*Leslie Davey referred to a portrait of Arthur Lee that used to hang in the mayor's parlour in Lewes Town Hall. Sadly the picture is no longer there, having mysteriously disappeared in the 1970s.

Lee Road, built in 1938, commemorates a once well known and respected Lewes family, the members of which literally left their imprint upon our local scene. The Lee family were printers, and they came to notice in 1745 when two brothers, William and Arthur, established and printed the *Sussex Weekly Advertiser and Lewes Journal*. At that time it had the distinction of being the only newspaper in circulation in the whole county. For a quarter of a century it was published from Lee's printing office in Keere Street.

In 1772 the business was transferred to premises in Watergate Lane, with offices at 64 High Street. The family were also associated with the erection of a paper mill at the Pells about 1800, a project which for a time enjoyed royal patronage. The printing business was carried on after the deaths of the founders by their three sons, Arthur, Frederick and Warren. All the members of the family were talented actors and were leading spirits in local entertainment. They had lively connections with the old Lewes Theatre that stood on the site of the present police station in West Street, and they were the mainspring of the Lewes Pic Nic Society which thrived for many years, giving theatrical and musical performances which raised large sums for charity.

Arthur Lee, the younger, was particularly talented. He was the author of numerous contributions in verse, and his humour (which even today is reflected in his portrait) and witty conversation won for him a large and appreciative circle of friends. On May 2, 1842, the printing works in Watergate Lane were destroyed by fire. Although Baxter (who at that time was publishing the *Sussex Express*) immediately placed at Lee's disposal one of his printing offices, the firm never recovered from the loss, and the family association with the *Sussex Advertiser* was severed in 1843. It is a happy chance that the names of Lee and Baxter are still linked by their two adjoining roads.

MERIDIAN ROAD

On November 8, 1938, the mayor of Lewes (Alderman E. T. Hall), unveiled at Landport an obelisk erected to mark a spot through which the prime meridian of Greenwich passes.

Lewes was then the only borough in England, apart from Greenwich, which officially recognised this interesting fact. The road in which the obelisk stands was named accordingly. The position of any place on the earth's surface is fixed by two measurements – latitude and longitude – the former being its angular distance from the equator and the latter its degrees from a zero or prime meridian.

The need for a universal system of defining any position on earth was resolved by an international agreement in 1883. Up to this date, although latitudes had been commonly expressed, it had been the general practice for separate countries to have their own zero of longitude. Great Britain used the meridian which passed through the Royal Observatory at Greenwich, established by Charles II in 1675. Under the international agreement this zero became universally adopted.

The obelisk stands upon the exact spot through which the prime meridian passes. Commander Davenport of Saltdean, who was responsible for a similar obelisk at Peacehaven, made the precise observations and calculations. The column, which is about 15ft. high, was designed by Charles Butler, borough surveyor, and the bronze emblem surmounting it, representing the celestial and terrestial meridians, was the gift of John Every. Unfortunately the bronze emblem was stolen in 2008. It is hoped that it will be replaced, using a material that looks like bronze but without its scrap value.

NEWTON ROAD

Southover Grange, the fine old house faced with Caen stone taken from the ruined priory of St. Pancras, was built in 1572 by William Newton, who came to settle in Lewes from Cheshire. Sir Isaac Newton claimed descent from the same branch of the family.

From the time of its erection the house was occupied uninterruptedly by successive generations of the Newton family, and latterly by the Mabbotts with whom they married, until 1860. Over the intervening centuries the Newton's made their mark on the local scene. They were linked by marriage in 1630 with the family of John Evelyn, whose story is told in the road bearing Evelyn's name. In the 1790s the William Newton of that period frequently entertained the Prince Regent (later to become King George IV) who often rode to Lewes from the Royal Pavilion in Brighton with his entourage, accompanied on occasions by Mrs. Fitzherbert.

PELLBROOK ROAD

The river meadows at Landport are interlaced with a system of ditches and waterways which, in the past, served not only to drain the lush pastures but also to promote the industry of those days. The larger waterways have their own names. Pellbrook Cut runs from the old osier beds below Offham round to a point underneath Offham chalkpit, where it feeds into Chalkpit Cut and Papermill Cut.

The Ouse was once a busy river, navigated beyond Lindfield. The old riverside inns bear witness to this: The Anchor, The Ship, The Horse and Barge and The Sloop. Many cargoes were carried inland from the sea, including 'blue cobbles' as building material and general merchandise. Return cargoes would include iron from the old Sussex foundries of the weald, or lime and chalk from Offham, where a light funicular railway with a steep gradient was tunnelled under the Offham Road to convey cargoes to the barges lying below in Chalkpit Cut.

Papermill Cut runs parallel with Landport Lane to the Pells and, by a series of sluices, a head of water was built up on an incoming tide to serve as motive power to operate a papermill which once stood between the Pells and the river (*see* page 61). The firm of papermakers Molineux and Johnston were in business from about 1800 to 1850. The building was afterwards converted and used for a time as a flour mill.

STANSFIELD ROAD

At the time of the dissolution of the monasteries in the reign of Henry VIII, the old collegiate church at South Malling with its deanery and lands (originally part of a Saxon monastery) was surrendered to the Crown. Thereafter, its properties passed through successive ownerships until 1624. In that year, John Stansfield, a prominent and public-spirited citizen of the Cliffe, acquired the properties, but the old church had by that time become derelict. He forthwith provided funds to rebuild and endow the church. The work was completed in 1628, the year in which his wife, Jane, gave the silver communion cup which is still in use.

John Stansfield was the step-grandfather of John Evelyn, the celebrated diarist of Stuart times, who, in his *Memoirs*, recalled his childhood spent at Lewes with his grandparents and how, as a little boy, he laid the foundation stone of the new Malling Church. Stansfield also left a trust fund to benefit needy tradesmen of the Cliffe, but all trace of this charity was lost in the 18th century. When this public benefactor died in 1627, John Evelyn wrote, 'This year my Grandfather Stansfield dyed. I remember the solemnity at his funeral at All Saints.'

*WALDSHUT ROAD

Waldshut in the Black Forest, Germany, was twinned with Lewes in 1963 in a ceremony that linked Lewes, Blois (*see* Blois Road) and Waldshut. The town is now known as Waldshut–Tiengen. Tiengen is about four miles from Waldshut and the two are now officially linked.

*YARROW ROAD

When this road was named after Reginald Yarrow, three times mayor of Lewes (1960–62, 1969–70 and 1984–85) and a very popular Conservative councillor, the political balance amongst Landport place names was slightly redressed!

7
South Malling

*South Malling has an extremely long history and it is recorded that the Saxon king Egbert granted land to the archbishop of Canterbury at Malling in 838. The archbishop had a palace at Malling until 1545, and a college of canons, headed by a dean, was established there. In about 1150 Archbishop Theobald dedicated a church there to St Michael. It had a dual purpose, being both the collegiate church and also the parish church.

After the dissolution of the monasteries the church continued as a parish church but became decayed and was eventually demolished. John Stansfield (*see* Stansfield Road) paid for its rebuilding in 1628, and the present parish church retains some fragments of 14th century masonry. Some remnants of the college also survive in the fine late Stuart mansion known today as Malling Deanery. The other fine house at Malling,

Malling Street in the 1920s.

Malling House, was built in about 1650 by William Spence and was remodelled by John Spence in 1710. It is now the Sussex Police HQ.

The modern estate was built in two phases. The first phase, started in 1951, was on the land between the A26 and the then functional Lewes-to-Uckfield Railway line. Over two decades passed before the second phase of development occurred, this time on the land beyond the Police HQ that belonged to Old Malling Farm. Prior to the Conquest the archbishop of Canterbury had a palace at Old Malling, and the Domesday book records 21 closes in Lewes linked to his manor of South Malling. Many of the street names used in the second phase recall the ownership of the archbishop.

*BECKETT WAY
This name recalls Thomas à Beckett, the 'turbulent priest' who was murdered in Canterbury Cathedral. Tradition asserts that the knights who killed him stayed the following night at Malling, and there is a well known legend about the house. A heavy marble table, said to come from Malling, is still on display at Anne of Cleves house. A card on the table describes how, when the murderers put their bloodied swords on the table, it shook violently and cast the weapons onto the floor. Sadly the table was found to be of later date than 1170. It is also much more likely that the knights stayed at Malling in Kent rather than near Lewes.

*BOUGHEY PLACE
The Boughey family lived at Ringmer Park and owned the land where the New Malling Estate now is. The family moved away from the district about 25 years ago.

BRIDGEWICK CLOSE
Tucked away in the South Malling estate, this close rescues from oblivion the name of the old workings of the early 19th century chalkpit on the north-west face of the South Downs, overlooking the river valley and situated beside the road to Ringmer beyond Earwig Corner, where the other road forks to Uckfield.

*BUCKHURST CLOSE

Buckhurst Park in Withyham is the present seat of Earl de la Warr and the name has been associated with Lewes for centuries. The de la Warrs and the Sackvilles are branches of the same family. Thomas Sackville, Baron Buckhurst and later Earl of Dorset (*see* Dorset Road) was immensely influential and wealthy at the end of the 16th century. As well as his Southover property he bought the estates of Old Malling and Malling Deanery.

The Sackvilles first came to Withyham in the 12th century. There were two deer parks, and the original Buckhurst Park in the larger park was enormous – the same size as Burghley House or Knole, which also came into the Sackville family. Thomas Sackville entertained Elizabeth I here but then embarked on the construction of a second mansion in the other deer park. This house can still be seen today. Old Buckhurst fell into disrepair – only the gatehouse survives. In 1806 Humphrey Repton was commissioned to produce a Red Book, with designs for a waterfall, lakes and woods that can still be seen today. Most of his work still survives.

*CRANMER CLOSE

Thomas Cranmer was Archbishop of Canterbury under Henry VIII and the architect of the Protestant Reformation. Mary I was a fanatical Catholic, and although Cranmer signed no fewer than six recantations of his faith, Mary was determined not to forgive the man who had annulled her mother's marriage and proclaimed her a bastard. He was burned at the stake on 21 March 1556, and 283 other martyrs followed him. Seventeen of them were burned in Lewes, near where the war memorial now is, and every year on November 5th Lewes remembers them, and 17 blazing crosses are carried through the streets of Lewes to the memorial. The Martyrs' Memorial itself stands at the top of Cuilfail.

*DE GREY CLOSE

John de Grey was bishop of Norwich and a favourite of King John. When Hubert Walter, the archbishop of Canterbury, died in 1205, a dispute began between the monks of Canterbury and the king on whom should succeed him. The monks wanted their sub-prior, Reginald, to be archbishop but instead King John chose John de Grey and the monks reluctantly accepted this.

Pope Innocent III then intervened. In 1207 he dismissed John de Grey and chose another man, Stephen Langton, as archbishop. King John promptly banished him from England and the pope served an interdict on England so that that no marriages, burials or baptisms could be performed there. He also excommunicated the king. By this time the country was ready to revolt and the king reluctantly allowed Stephen Langton back into England. It was only a short reprieve for the king, and there was turmoil in the country until the Magna Carta was signed in 1215.

DUNVAN CLOSE
Although Paul Dunvan was resident in Lewes during the latter half of the 18th century, when he was assistant master at the Old Grammar School, no biographical record has survived beyond the fact that he was of French extraction. Nevertheless, he is noted in the annals of Lewes because he wrote the first *History of Lewes and Brighthelmstone,* published in 1795. It is thought that William Lee, the editor and printer of the *Weekly Advertiser and Lewes Journal*, persuaded Dunvan to undertake this work which, from a notice in that journal, appears to have first been printed in several separate instalments. The book reflects his scholarly research of the Town Books and other records, from which he gave an accurate account of the town's evolution from earliest times and its ancient form of administration.

The naming of this close nearly 200 years later was the first public recognition of his labours for posterity. He was a contemporary and friend of James Lambert, the Lewes artist, and it is fitting that their names are linked by adjacent roads on the Malling estate.

FITZGERALD ROAD
This road was named in October, 1952, after the chairman of the housing committee of the former borough council, Councillor D. J. Fitzgerald.

GODFREY CLOSE

According to the Domesday survey, the land comprising the manor of South Malling, including that upon which this close is built, was tenanted by a farmer named Godfrey. Another Godfrey is also commemorated, albeit he lived nine centuries later.

Walter H. Godfrey, architect and antiquarian, will be as well-known locally to posterity as are Dunvan and Horsfield. He lived for many years in Lewes and not only applied his professional expertise and vast store of knowledge to the recording and preservation of ancient monuments but was also the author of many works of national as well as local antiquarian interest. In 1933, he wrote what has been described as a 'concise and accurate historical presentation of this ancient town', and this work remained in print for over forty years. When he died, in 1961, the Sussex Archaeological Society, and indeed Lewes, lost one who had given unstinting devotion to Sussex, reflected in his contributions of a wealth of historical records.

HARVARD CLOSE

So far as recorded history reveals, there was but one event in the life of John Harvard that linked him with Lewes. Yet over the years the town has seen a steady flow of Americans seeking to vitalise that brief interlude.

Harvard was born in 1607, the son of a Southwark butcher. He went to Emmanuel College, Cambridge, and graduated in 1631. In 1636, he married Ann, the daughter of John Sadler, vicar of Ringmer, near Lewes. The marriage was at South Malling church which had been rebuilt eight years earlier. They emigrated to America and settled in Charlestown, Mass.

John, described as a 'godly gentleman and a lover of learning', suffered poor health and died in 1638. He bequeathed half his estate and his library of 320 books to the proposed college 'ordered to be at New Towne' (afterwards Cambridge, Mass.). With this legacy the administrators were able to commence the building of the university which was named after Harvard, he being looked upon as the principal founder.

HEREWARD WAY
The name was chosen by the town council in January, 1952, after the presiding mayor of the borough – Alderman Hereward E. Parrish. He was a member of the council for over 23 years, including 17 years as an alderman and three years as mayor. On January 28, 1970 he was admitted as an honorary freeman of the borough.

*HOOPERS CLOSE
The Hoopers were a prominent Ringmer family. At least some of the family were protestant dissenters who in 1805 were members of the congregation of the Jireh chapel. In the 18th century John Hooper and Nicholas Hooper were associated with the Spences of Malling House and leased land from them, no doubt in the vicinity of Hoopers Close.

LAMBERT PLACE
Writing in 1905, George Holman said, 'the memory of James Lambert deserves recognition as one who, by his own industry and talents, raised himself to a position of considerable merit as a landscape painter'.

James Lambert's painting of Cliffe Bridge. Compare this with the photograph on page 41, showing the same view about 120 years later.

He was born of humble parents at Jevington in 1725 but lived from early childhood in the Cliffe, Lewes, where his natural genius and skill won for him both admiration and respect as an artist of repute. His watercolours and oils of Sussex landscapes and special subjects are numbered in hundreds, many of which form part of the Burrell collection in the British Museum. He was commissioned by Sir William Burrell to portray an extensive series of drawings of churches and antiquities of Sussex.

He was also a proficient musician, and was organist at Cliffe church for many years. His oil painting, dated 1773, of the royal coat of arms of George III, formerly hung over the assize judge's chair in the old Sessions House, which until 1810 stood in the middle of the High Street. It can now be seen hanging by the stairs at the Town Hall. Lambert died in 1788 and was buried at St. John-sub-Castro, where a memorial tablet was provided by his nephew, who bore the same name and who inherited his uncle's artistic skills.

THE LYNCHETS
The name, appropriately chosen in 1951 for the new houses lying at the foot of Malling Down, recalls the primitive farming activities of our ancient British ancestors. The iron age Britons were energetic farmers, but their crude plough – a blunt stick with an iron cap – was capable only of scratching a shallow furrow in light soil. The downs provided ideal conditions for such an implement, and there are traces all over the Sussex Downs of the terraced strips of land, called lynchets, which were anciently cultivated. They are to be seen on Malling Down and the Cliffe Hills.

The lynchets appear as terraces as a result of repeated 'one-way' ploughing, the soil tending to creep down hill and bank up at the lower edges. The Saxon farmers moved from the hills to the more fertile lowlands, and the old fields thus survived the centuries and escaped obliteration by later ploughing. But since agricultural methods have been mechanised, many square miles of the downs have been brought under the plough, a development which has jeopardised the survival of many of the ancient lynchets.

*MANTELL CLOSE

Named after Gideon Mantell, a Lewes resident known as the father of palaeontology. In 1822 he published *Fossils of the South Downs*, much of the research for which was very local. In a South Street quarry he found the first fossil fish in the chalk, quickly followed by another specimen at Southerham. Malling pit produced an enormous ammonite. His house in Lewes High Street can still be seen today, with its Palladian columns adorned with ammonites.

THE MARTLETS

The coat of arms of the counties of East and West Sussex include six martlets, a martlet being a heraldic symbol for various birds. This coat of arms is said to have been assigned to the ancient kingdom of the South Saxons and it is suggested by allusion that the Sussex martlet represents a swallow (*l'hirondelle*) from which the name of the Sussex town of Arundel is derived.

The six martlets were also the armorial bearings of the de Radynden family. From the 13th century they were prominent in Sussex military and civil affairs, and as knights of the shire they were summoned to the parliaments of those days. It has been conjectured that the seal of the knight of the shire could have been affixed to a document concerning county affairs and that its subsequent adoption as the county arms came about by common usage.

*MAYHEW WAY

Two Mayhews, son and father, were mayors of Lewes. In 1981 Graham Mayhew was Lewes's youngest ever mayor, to be followed in 1983 by his father, Frank. Graham was mayor again in 1990 and 1999. Both were originally Labour councillors, but following the shenanigans in the 1980s (*see* Hayward Road) both resigned the whip and were re-elected as Independents.

*MEALLA CLOSE

The name Malling is derived from Mealingas, the people of Mealla. The name is first recorded in Sussex in 838. The territory of the tribe was

93

extensive, and while South Malling is in Lewes, East and West Malling are in Kent. There is no record of a North Malling.

MILL ROAD

About noon on September 8, 1908, a Corporation carter gave the alarm that Malling Mill was on fire. Although the fire brigade's steamer and manual raced to the scene, the lack of a sufficient water supply prevented any positive action. The whole mill soon became a furnace and was quickly gutted. Thus came to an end the windmill after which this road was named. But there remains today the miller's house and the round base of the mill, which has been converted into a residence. A windmill had existed on this site for at least 300 years and the East Sussex Record Office holds deeds of the property covering a period from 1625 to 1737.

Lewes was once ringed with windmills. It is of interest to note that they were used as late as 1881 to mark the new boundaries of the former borough upon incorporation. From the site of the old windmill (burnt down in 1760) on Cliffe Hill near the golf clubhouse, the line stretched to Malling Mill and thence across the Ouse Valley to Steere's Mill (demolished 1901) on Race Hill; then southward to Spital Mill (burnt down 1885) and across the Brighton road to the Ashcombe Smock Mill at Juggs Road, which collapsed in a storm in 1890. In 2010 a new 'windmill', actually a house, was being built on the site.

The former mill in Mill Road.

On the occasion of the traditional beating of the bounds it was customary for the miller to allow the beaters to walk right through Malling Mill, as the boundary line at that time passed through the middle of it. Early maps depict Malling Mill standing on the west side of the main road and overlooking the lane which descended to South Malling Church. The geography of the locality was materially altered in 1830 when the present main road from the former Prince of Wales Inn was cut to bypass the steepness of the former road which ran under the hill and behind the development called The Lynchets. The new road having bisected the old lane, the portion which led up to the windmill came to be known as Mill Road, and the lower section became Church Lane.

*MONKS WAY

Another reference to the archbishop's palace at Old Malling, although the two other monastic orders were not at Malling. The Cluniac Priory of St Pancras was founded at Southover by William de Warenne and in the 13th century the Franciscans established their Priory near Cliffe (*see* Friars Walk).

PECKHAM CLOSE

John Peckham, after whom this close is named, is believed to have been a native of Patcham, near Lewes. He was born about 1240 and received his early education at the school which is known to have existed in connection with the priory of St. Pancras. He later studied at Oxford and Paris and became well-known as a divine and philosopher. In 1279, he was appointed Archbishop of Canterbury, an office he upheld with diligence and dignity until his death and burial in his cathedral in 1292.

The ancient manor of South Malling with its extensive lands belonged to the archbishopric, and it was here that Peckham is said to have been a frequent visitor and where perhaps he reflected upon the obscurity of his youth in contrast to the splendour and magnificence of his changed circumstances. He paid a formal visit to Lewes Priory in 1282 where, it is recorded, he took part 'in a fine ceremonial procession'.

*PRINCE CHARLES ROAD
Prince Charles was born on November14, 1948.

*QUEEN'S ROAD
Named to commemorate the Coronation of Queen Elizabeth II on June 2, 1953.

*RUSSELL ROW
Richard Russell (1687-1759) was the son of a Lewes apothecary who married the heiress to Malling Deanery. He qualified as a doctor and is most famous for his prescription of seawater as a cure for all of nature's ills. He believed that the ocean was a defence against all 'bodily corruption and putrefaction'. His patients had to both drink and bathe in seawater and were rubbed with fresh seaweed. He is buried in Malling Church, where his memorial can be seen.

SPENCES LANE
Malling House, now the headquarters of the Sussex constabulary, was from 1656 for more than two centuries the family seat of the ancient family of Spence. In 1824, it was described as 'an elegant and spacious building, standing on a gentle eminence, and encompassed with rich and extensive grounds'.

Spences Lane probably originated as a bridleway, or droveway, hugging the perimeter of the river marshes, which were subject to tidal flooding. It developed into a parish road which led more directly to the parish church than the main road route by way of Malling Hill. It was a convenient detour for heavily laden horse-drawn vehicles that could not negotiate Malling Hill which, prior to its being diverted and reconstructed in 1830, rose steeply behind the old windmill sited at the top of Mill Road.

In the 1880s, a large residence in this lane, originally called Spences but later the Grey House, was the home of a gentle Quakeress, Miss Rickman, a lover of horses. She rescued them in their old age and gave them good pasture and stabling, and buried them in special graves in her field adjoining the house. One particular favourite named Charlie was given a grand monument – a high conical mound (the centre solid concrete) with a spiral path to the top, where an inscribed granite slab was placed. This mound, together with the Grey House, its stabling and pastures, have now all disappeared and a cul de sac called Spences Field now occupies the site

*STONEHAM CLOSE
Upper and Lower Stoneham farms straddle the Uckfield Road just beyond Malling. Some of the land from Stoneham was taken to build the first homes on the estate in 1952, although Stoneham Close itself was not built until 1980. The name means 'settlement on stony ground'.

*WAITE CLOSE
Many Malling place names have connections with the archbishop of Canterbury, and Terry Waite was the archbishop's special envoy in the 1980s. Lewes District Council records say that Waite Close was built in 1985, two years before Terry Waite was kidnapped in Beirut in January 1987. He was imprisoned for 1760 days and finally released in November 1991.

It seems likely that the discrepancy in dates is due to the fact that planning permission was given well before the close was actually named. Unfortunately the file recording reasons for naming streets in the 70s and 80s cannot be located.

*WILLEY'S BRIDGE
This well-used footbridge, opened in 1965, links the Malling Estate with the Pells and the town centre. It replaced an elegant iron suspension bridge, slightly further up the river, which provided a short cut from Malling Deanery to the town centre. The suspension bridge, the foundations of which can still be seen, itself replaced a wooden latticed bridge in the early 20th century. This bridge was known as Admiral Curry's bridge after the then owner of Malling Deanery.

The suspension bridge was generally kept locked but was opened on bonfire night to allow revellers a quick route to the Cliffe bonfire site which was on Malling Hill for many years. Len Willey was a popular Lewes councillor.

Fishing and boating by the former Admiral Curry's bridge, before 1906.

8
Houndean and Winterbourne

*The whole of the Winterbourne area was originally part of the Saxon manor of Houndean and for century's there was very little development in this area. The ownership of the manor changed several times. After the conquest it was granted to the Fitzalans and the de Warennes and, like much of Lewes, eventually became largely the responsibility of the Nevills.

Lewes Prison was built in 1853, and about fifty years later three large houses, Warren House, Barons Down and Clevedown were built opposite. They were all demolished in the 1970s and 80s. Some more large houses were built along the Brighton Road in the 1930s, and Houndean Rise was built after the war. Further down the hill there was no building on the western side of Winterbourne Hollow until the 1930s, when Dale Road and Valley Road were built by Lewes Borough Council. Private developers completed the rest of the estate over the next twenty years.

A military camp at Houndean Bottom in 1910.

*BERKELEY ROW

The only connection of the Berkeley family to Lewes appears to relate to their entitlement for about 150 years to one fourth of the barony of Lewes. The way they inherited their share in the barony is enshrined in one of the most infamous stories in English history. During the 14th and 15th centuries, as we have seen, the lordship of Lewes was divided, in differing proportions over the centuries, between the Mowbrays, Earls of Arundel and later dukes of Norfolk, and their kinsmen, the Nevills, the lords Abergavenny.

By 1475, Richard, Duke of Norfolk, younger brother of Edward V, was entitled to one half of the barony, but he was murdered in the Tower of London, along with his brother the king, on the orders of his uncle, who became King Richard III. Despite the fact that Richard was only eleven at the time of his death, he was already married, and his estates passed to his wife Anne, who unsurprisingly survived him by only a month. Her share of the barony then passed to her kinsmen, John, Lord Howard, and William Berkeley, Earl of Nottingham.

The next hundred years was a turbulent time for the nobles of England, and estates were constantly being attainted by the Crown and then restored to successors when conditions changed. The Berkeley quarter share of the barony finally passed in 1566 to the Sackville family, who still hold it today (*see* Sackville Close).

DELAWARE ROAD

On May 14,1964, the mayor of Lewes in the state of Delaware, USA (Mr Otis H. Smith), formally named this road to commemorate his visit to the town on the occasion of the battle of Lewes 700th anniversary celebrations.

*GLEBE CLOSE

One might expect Glebe Close to have been built on former glebe land, but in this case the street naming committee seem to have been out by quite a margin. Glebe land was owned by the church and the income from it went to the parson. Old maps show that the St Anne's Glebe Field lay north of the Winterbourne stream, more or less on the site of the former St Anne's school. Glebe Close is several hundred yards to the west. In 1882, Lewes Town Council bought 'St Ann's Rectory Glebe Field in Rotten Row' for £1500 in order to cut a new road to the cemetery. Road works brought the total expenditure to £2230. Three building plots were then sold for £1334, leaving a deficit of £896.

HILLYFIELD
The development built on the steep rising land on the south side of Bell Lane perpetuates the name by which it was known before the houses came. The right of way from Winterbourne to the top of the hill has been preserved, and it gives access to the now forgotten Jubilee Gardens and to the old pathway known as Love Lane, which leads down to Haredean and the Pewetts (now enclosed by the gardens of Winterbourne Close).

The southern bypass road has literally carved out of existence the escarpment called the Folly, known in the past as Cowslip Hill, leading from Hope-in-the-Valley up to the 'Old Duck' and 'Rosary' windmills which once adorned the brow of Juggs Road.

*HOUNDEAN RISE
The word Houndean means 'hounds' valley', but for hundreds of years the lands of the manor of Houndean covered an extensive area. Following the Conquest, the Saxon manor of Houndean was retained by the lords of Lewes, the Warennes and the Fitzalans. It certainly included the medieval parishes of St John Without, St Peter Without and St Mary Without, and in 1065 it also probably included Southover parish.

By 1615 the lands of the manor were still extensive. It included 1200 acres of arable land and sheep-run at Landport, the Wallands and the 'Fludds' (now the Nevill estate), as well as Houndean Bottom, Ashcombe, Winterbourne, Haredean and Littledown. It also held water meadows bordering the Ouse from Landport down to the Lewes borough boundaries, as well as those on the other side of the borough in Southover.

*MONTACUTE ROAD
This is another name from the Nevill family. In the early 15th century

Richard Nevill (who died about 1460) married Alice de Montacute, heiress to the Earl of Salisbury. The title was assumed by the Nevills and remained in the family for almost two centuries.

In the turbulent politics of the time, a later Earl of Salisbury fell out with the sovereign and lost his head. The title was forfeited and recreated for the Cecil family. However the Montacute name is still in use in the family – the present marquis's father was Rupert Charles Montacute Nevill and his father, the 4th Marquis, was Guy Temple Montacute Nevill (1883–1954). The land on which Montacute Road stands was, like so much of Lewes, owned by the Nevill family. The family eventually sold the land, and the Montacute Nevill name appears in the deeds of some of the modern houses.

There is another Lewes connection with Montacute, although it may not have been in the minds of the planners when they named the road. Montacute House is in Somerset and was built in 1580 by Thomas Phelips. It remained in the family for over three centuries. Sir Edward Phelips was the speaker of the House of Commons who was sitting in state when Guy Fawkes was creeping below in the vaults. His was the first speech at Guy Fawkes trial, and the original minutes of the gunpowder plot enquiry were kept at Montacute until the early 20th century. The Nevill family owned land in Montacute Norton, Somerset, for many centuries and no doubt still has some manorial waste there.

*WARREN DRIVE
Warren Drive and Warren Close were built on the site of Warren House, a large mansion demolished in 1983. Warren House was owned by Major H.G Lang and was built around 1900 on land largely owned by William Nevill, Marquis of Abergavenny. It was originally called 'Holme' and was later owned by the Nicholl family who were popular doctors in the town. The Nicholls also owned Castle Lodge, which they bought from the infamous Charles Dawson, perpetrator of the 'Piltdown Man' hoax.

Mrs Gladys Nicholl sold Warren House to the county council in 1962 for 'road improvements'. These improvements never materialised. It was intended to build a link from the southern bypass to Nevill Road, much of which would have been in the form of a massive flyover above Southover and Winterbourne Hollow. In this case the protests of the residents of Lewes were successful, and the county council abandoned their plans. They then used Warren House as offices for the next twenty years before selling the site (there were originally five acres of gardens) for development. The county council also acquired the neighbouring Barons Down House, which was also used as offices prior to its demolition.

Warren House.

Bibliography

I am fortunate to have a large collection of books on Lewes and Sussex. I was therefore able to do a lot of the research needed in the comfort of my home and without too much resort to the internet, which, in my experience, takes much longer than checking a well indexed volume.

Beamish, Tufton   *Battle Royal*, 1965

Blaauw, W.H.   *The Barons War*, 1871

Brent, Colin and Rector, William   *Victorian Lewes*, 1980

Brent, Colin   *Georgian Lewes 1714–1830*, 1993

Brent, Colin   *Pre-Georgian Lewes c890–1714*, 2004

Coates, Richard (ed)   *Locus Focus*, forum of the Sussex Place-Names Net

Clark, Kim   *Lost Lewes*, 2002

Cobb, Ruth   *Travellers to the Town*, 1953

Davey, L.S.   *The Inns of Lewes, past and present*, 1977

Ekwall, Eilert   *Concise Oxford Dictionary of English Place-Names, 4th edition*, 1960

Godfrey, Walter H.   *The High Street, Lewes*, Sussex Archaeological Collections, Vol XCIII, 1955

Godfrey, Walter H.   *The Official Guide to Lewes*, 1962

Glover, Judith   *The Place Names of Sussex*, 1975

Hague, William   *William Pitt the Younger*, 2004

Horsfield, Rev T.W.   *The History and Antiquities of Lewes*, 1824

Lower, Mark Anthony   *The Worthies of Sussex*, 1865

Salzman, L.F. (*ed*)   *The Town Book of Lewes 1542-1701* (Sussex Record Society 1945)

Smith, Verena (*ed*)   *The Town Book of Lewes 1702-1837* (Sussex Record Society 1972)

Smith, Verena (*ed*)   *The Town Book of Lewes 1837-1901* (Sussex Record Society 1975)

Domesday Book, Sussex

Kelly's Directory of Sussex, 1966

Parish of Withyham, Millennium Map

Whitakers Almanac, 1953

Index of Place Names

Eridge Green	77	Jenner's Way	46
Evelyn Road	77, 83	Juggs Road	16, 56, 101
Farncombe Road	44	Keere Street	20, 41, 58
Ferrers Road	65	King Henry's Road	66
Fisher Street	15, 56	Kingsley Road	81
Fitzgerald Road	89		
Fitzjohn Road	65	Lambert Place	91
Fitzroy Road	79	Lancaster Street	21
Foundry Lane	45	Landport	74, 84
Friars Walk	14, 16, 94	Lansdowne Place	22, 25
Fuller Road	18, 79	Lee Road	81
Fuller's Passage	18, 22	Leicester Road	60, 67
		Love Lane	56, 101
Garden Street	55	Lynchets, The	92
Glebe Close	100		
Godfrey Close	90	Malling Hill	95
Green Lane	18, 32, 58	Malling Street	41
Greenwall	14, 19	Mantell Close	93
Gundreda Road	19, 65	Market Street	22, 30
Guy Road	60	Martlets, The	93
		Mayhew Way	93
Ham Lane	55	Mealla Close	93
Harvard Close	90	Meridian Road	74, 82
Hawkenbury Way	72	Middle Way	71
Hayward Road	80, 92	Mildmay Road	67
Hereward Way	91	Millers Walk	66
Hillman Close	45	Mill Lane (Southover)	56
Hill Road	66	Mill Road (Malling)	94
Hillyfield	101	Monks Way	95
Hoopers Close	91	Montacute Road	101
Horsfield Road	80, 92	Morley Close	56
Houndean Rise	99, 101	Morris Road	45, 46
		Mountfield Road	55
Ireland's Lane	19, 39	Mount Harry Road	73

CW00661987

Systems Thinking for Business

Capitalize on Structures Hidden in Plain Sight

Rich Jolly

RichJolly.com

SYSTEMS
SOLUTIONS
PRESS

Portland, Oregon

Copyright © 2015 by Richard Jolly
All rights reserved.

Rich Jolly at www.RichJolly.com

Published by Systems Solutions Press, Portland, Oregon.
Systems Solutions Press is an imprint of Systems Thinking Solutions, LLC.
www.SystemsSolutionsPress.com

PDHMDY11bb1f

The text is set in Calibri font. The headings are set in Cambria font.

No part of this publication may be reproduced, stored in, or introduced into a retrieval system, or transmitted, in any form, or by any means (electronic, mechanical, photocopying, recording, or otherwise), without the prior permission of the publisher.

Publisher's Cataloging-in-Publication data

Jolly, Rich.
   Systems thinking for business: capitalize on structures hidden in plain sight /
   Rich Jolly.
   p. cm.
   Includes bibliographical references and index.
   ISBN 978-0-692-35334-9
   1. Management theory. 2. Complexity (Philosophy). 3. Success in business. 4. Strategic planning. I. Title

HD58.8.J6535 2015
658.4'06—dc22 J685
Library of Congress Control Number: 2014960308

This work is dedicated to the countless researchers and scientists who have strived to develop the ideas described in this book.

Let's put that hard work to good use!

Table of Contents

Systems Thinking for Business

Capitalize on Structures Hidden in Plain Sight

Rich Jolly

RichJolly.com

1. Introduction: A New Way of Seeing

The Value of Systems Thinking for Business

Systems thinking can provide a substantial edge in business and in your career. And, in the world of business, any competitive advantage is valuable. What type of tangible effect might arise from systems thinking? Would finding unique and unanticipated solutions or products interest you? How about avoiding unproductive options or actions that may have damaging side effects? And how about your career? First, let's recognize that in the workplace there's a complex interplay between cooperation and competition between employees (something we will explore in great depth). Whenever there is more than one employee at a company, there is some allocation of limited resources (e.g., salary), and employees who have special skills are the most valuable.

You may think that college education, business training, and experience have prepared you for the situations you will face in business. Your experiences may well prepare you for 90% of the situations you are likely to face, but what about the other 10%? Although these exceptional experiences may occur infrequently, they could be disproportionately impactful and could be crucial turning points for your organization or your career. In these cases, the systems methods can be of great benefit.

So what is *systems theory* or, as some people might call it, *complexity theory*? The simplest explanation is that it is the study of interactions. In many theories and models, interactions are assumed to be negligible. Usually this is a reasonable assumption and is likely necessary for the associated mathematical derivations. But in some cases, the interaction may be integral to the phenomenon. Consider for example, an ant hill. How exactly do these hills get built? Is there a master foreman ant who is directing the other ants? No. While ants may be extremely strong for their weight, they're not particularly smart. Instead, the ant hill is built from the interactions between the ants, who are acting based on their own simple set of rules. Interaction can also be in time. Feedback and delays are something from the past that is affecting the present. The term we use for the unanticipated result from these interactions is *emergence*.

While not all interactions create emergent effects, when emergence does occur it is difficult, if not practically impossible, to predict based on the study of the components of the system. From this standpoint, one might characterize systems thinking as the antithesis of reductionism. To illustrate the difficulty of predicting emergent effects, consider this thought experiment. A Martian landed on Earth and brought a single ant back to Mars. By studying it for years, could the Martian anticipate that a colony of these creatures would produce an ant hill? As an ultimate example of emergence, consider your own consciousness that is emerging from the connections of neurons in your brain. In addition to unanticipated results, consideration of system effects might also provide you with unanticipated solutions. Subtle high points of leverage may be uncovered with systems thinking. Figure 1 gives a symbolic description of the essence of systems thinking.

Figure 1. The Essence of Systems Thinking

Carpenters need hammers, saws, and drills to be successful. But while these tools are necessary, they are not sufficient without the skills of the carpenter who can use these tools successfully. So this book will also talk about how to properly use the tools of systems science. We will talk about ideas on forecasting and judging causality in complex systems. Systems thinking can lead to questioning simple causality and, perhaps, even turn it on its head. To really gain insight of complex systems, one must have some understanding of the agents operating in that system; in business, the agents are humans. So we'll touch on human judgment and decision biases, and strategize on how to use that knowledge. Finally, we will spend time on how to use models. Either not using or over-relying on models can be hazardous, so we will talk about how to tread this dangerous slippery slope. To illustrate systems thinking, let's explore a few examples.

The rise and fall of the airline People Express provides many interesting insights into systems thinking. People Express is discussed in Chapter 8 of Senge's *The Fifth Discipline (1990)*. People Express was a low-cost airline that had a meteoric rise in the early 1980s, only to see a symmetric gut-wrenching fall in the mid to late 1980s (Figure 2).

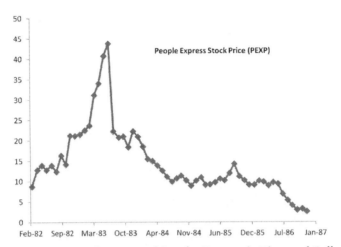

Figure 2. People Express' Stocks Dramatic Rise and Fall

One of the cornerstones of People Express' strategy was the reinforcing feedback loop shown in Figure 3. To be a low-price carrier, People Express needed a low-cost structure. Salaries are a large component of costs, so People Express used an incentive based salary structure. Management gave employees a low base salary along with stock incentives. If People Express stock did well, then employees were very well compensated, even with a low base. This created the feedback loop as shown in the figure. The low employee base salaries allowed People Express to charge low ticket prices while still delivering excellent customer service. These low prices allowed air travel to compete with other transportation businesses such as buses and trains. As consumers switched from buses to People Express flights, the total available market for airlines grew. In the early 1980s, People Express was the primary low-cost carrier and garnered most of this new traffic. That led to growth in People Express' revenue and margin. As People Express' revenue and margin grew, their stock price increased. As the stock price increased, the employees cashed in their incentives and, correspondingly, grew in enthusiasm. This reinforcing feedback loop would be characterized as a *virtuous* feedback loop since the growth around the feedback loop is helping achieve the company's goals.

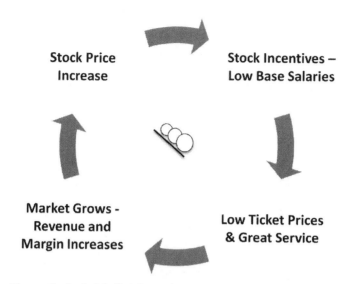

**Figure 3. An Initially Virtuous Reinforcing Feedback Loop
Present at People Express**

But a reinforcing feedback loop need not be virtuous, and this was a lesson People Express learned the hard way. While the low ticket prices initially grew the market quickly, the company soon came face-to-face with the S-shaped curve of market growth (to be described in detail in Chapter 3). As the market growth from reduced ticket prices started to level off, People Express' revenue and market growth slowed. As the revenue and market growth slowed, stock analysts became concerned about People Express' future prospects for growth and became bearish on the stock. As the stock price began to drop in 1983, the incentive based pay structure of employees changed from generous to painful. The unhappy employees were no longer delivering such great service. This service decrease impacted customers' choices and subsequently People Express' revenues. The reduced revenues and margins then impacted stock price, which further impacted the total compensation of employees. The loop shown in Figure 3 was now amplifying a characteristic that was not helping People Express achieve their goals. The virtuous feedback loop had changed into a *vicious* feedback loop! If People Express management had understood this feedback loop, and the problems it would create when it changed its nature, they could have gradually changed their compensation system to raise the base salaries and reduce incentives as the market growth started to slow. The negative effects of virtuous turned vicious loops is an extremely important lesson to keep in mind.

As an example of emergence from the aggregation of interactions, consider the information assimilation ability of markets. In Chapter 4 we will discuss the aggregation of information by markets in quite a bit of detail. While markets may have some potential problems, they also have extraordinary information assimilation capabilities. Consider the reaction of the equity prices for the primary contractors to the Space Shuttle immediately after the tragic explosion of the *Challenger*. On January 28, 1986 the *Challenger* Space Shuttle launched from NASA's facility. Just seconds into the flight, the shuttle exploded. It was not until many months later that the trigger event for the explosion was conclusively attributed to the solid rocket boosters. In fact, at the end of the day of the tragedy, *The New York Times* noted that there were no clues to the cause. However, the actions of the stock prices of the contractors tell a different story. Within minutes of the explosion, the stocks to the primary contractors for the shuttle, Rockwell International, Lockheed, Martin Marietta, and Morton Thiokol, were down between 3% to 6% from their opening prices for the day. But, within an hour of the explosion, the behavior of the contractors' stocks began to behave differently from one another. First, the stock of Morton Thiokol halted trading due to extreme imbalance between buy and sell orders. When trading began about an hour later, the stock of Morton Thiokol dropped precipitously compared to the other contractors. By the end of the trading day, Morton Thiokol's stock had suffered a 12% decline while the stock of the other contractors had only been reduced by 3%. So, *the market* was able to *figure out* the most likely cause of the accident within about an hour (Maloney & Mulherin, 2003).

Next, consider a practice commonly used by human resource groups to illustrate strategic thinking. Many organizations use 360 evaluations as part of the employee performance review process. With this process, employees are asked to provide an assessment on the performance of other employees. The idea is that the manager has limited visibility on an employee's contributions and other employees can provide an important perspective on performance.

Consider this situation:

> Tom and Bruce are individual contributors (that is, they do not manage anyone) in Jill's group. Jill has asked Tom to provide a 360 evaluation on Bruce, and Bruce to provide a 360 evaluation on Tom. Jill is given a focal budget to distribute to her group of eight people. She will apportion this budget based on a number of factors, one of which is the 360 evaluations she receives. Both Tom and Bruce are struggling with their personal finances and have concerns about supporting their families.

> About a focal budget: This is a pool of incentives given to a manager to distribute to their group. It may include an amount of base salary, an amount of bonus salary, stock options, etc. You should assume for this situation that the budget is fixed (that is, Jill can't ask for more budget because her group is exceptional), and all of the budget will be allocated to the group.

From Tom and Bruce's perspectives, what are the strategic systems thinking issues?

The framework of game theory (explored in depth in Chapter 5) can be used to understand the considerations of these two group members. To assess the situation, assume that the 360 evaluations are the only considerations in the reviews (they are not, but it makes the analysis easier and still valid). Further, Jill is somewhat predictable in the relationship between how she allocates budgets based on evaluations. Tom and Bruce understand that Jill targets about 25% of the focal budget to the two employees. But, she will allocate slightly more if they both have good evaluations, and slightly less if they both have bad evaluations. Tom and Bruce estimate the focal payouts as:

- If both receive good evaluations, they will get 30% of the focal budget, split as 15% for each.
- If one receives a good evaluation and one a bad evaluation, then the two will receive 25% of the focal budget, split as 18% and 7%.
- If both receive bad evaluations, they will get 20% of the focal budget, split as 10% for each.

Consider the situation from Bruce's perspective (it is the same for Tom, something we call symmetry in game theory). Given this structure, what should Bruce do? Bruce could think about the situation under two scenarios: Tom gives him a bad 360 evaluation, or Tom gives him a good 360 evaluation.

If Tom gives him a bad evaluation then:
- If he gives Tom a good evaluation, he will get 7% of the focal budget and Tom will get 18%.
- If he gives Tom a bad evaluation, both will get 10% of the focal budget.

In this situation, considering only the financial aspects, the analysis would recommend that Bruce give Tom a bad evaluation.

If Tom gives him a good evaluation then:
- If he gives Tom a good evaluation, both will get 15% of the focal budget.
- If he gives Tom a bad evaluation, he will get 18% of the focal budget and Tom will get 7%.

In this case, again considering only the financial aspects, this analysis would recommend Bruce give Tom a bad evaluation.

This analysis argues that Bruce's best course of action is to give Tom a bad evaluation irrespective of what Tom does[1]. From the symmetry, it also argues that Tom should give Bruce a bad evaluation. So, both team members will get bad 360 degree evaluations and 10% raises. However, had they both given good 360 degree evaluations they could have had 15% raises! In fact, as we will see in Chapter 5, this situation has the same structure as the well-known Prisoner's Dilemma game! Do the human resources managers at the companies using 360 evaluations realize they are producing a Prisoner's Dilemma that could drive employees to deliver negative evaluations?

---

[1] Readers may argue that people do not make these decisions purely on financial aspects. This is true for some employees and is discussed in detail in Chapter 5 under behavioral aspects and utility. However, one may still see this effect manifested as a statistical tendency across a large number of employees. Also, some readers may assert that their organization does not do 360 evaluations within a work-group exactly for this reason. But, the effect may still be present in their organization (although much subtler) since the argument holds across groups (as the entire organization's focal budget is fixed at some level).

Finally, consider a situation that Domino's Pizza experienced in 2009 that illustrates the power of networks and the dynamic flow of information. Two Domino's employees had a funny idea to make a video, using their cell phones, of themselves making pizza with nasal mucous and other unsettling toppings. They decided to post this video on YouTube so their friends could get a chuckle. A silly, stupid, prank, which has played out countless times throughout human history, had a radically different impact this time. The video went viral on YouTube. The movie makers' friends loved the video and shared it with their friends. And their friends did the same. The video spread through the network of friends of friends and then out to the world. Today, most major corporations have groups monitoring social networks for content related to their business. It is a necessary reaction to the reality of a connected small world (a concept we explore in depth in Chapter 7). Does your business have this type of monitoring in place? Should you?

What's Wrong With My Current Way of Thinking?

The human mind is simply amazing. Starting with simple, single-cell organisms, in the matter of a short 3.5 billion years or so, nature has developed the human brain! But one of the messages that will be covered in Chapter 6 on evolution is that the analyst must consider the path that the system has followed. What artifacts have been left over from this evolutionary process?

There won't be space in this book to do justice to the topic of human psychological judgment and decision biases. However, there are excellent accessible works of psychologists, and particularly the book by Daniel Kahneman, *Thinking, Fast and Slow* (2011), will be referred to frequently in this work. However, the topic of human judgment is extremely important to our systems thinking ability. First, humans are the key agents in the systems of interest for business, so we need to have a basic understanding of their psyche. Second, and just as important, we, the system analysts, are human. So, we need to understand something about how our own mind works and where our systems thinking blind spots may be.

To illustrate these blind spots, consider the fascinating *Invisible Gorilla*[2] experiment by the psychologists Christopher Chabris and Daniel Simons (discussed in their book *The Invisible Gorilla,* (2009). In this experiment, subjects are shown a short video of two teams of three players each passing basketballs amongst the team members. One team is wearing black shirts and the other team is wearing white shirts. Subjects in the experiment are asked to watch the film and count the number of passes made by the team in white shirts. Towards the middle of the film a person in a gorilla costume walks into the frame, strolls to the center and proceeds to pound their chest, and then walks out of the frame on the opposite side. Thousands of people have seen this video and only about half see the gorilla.

The Invisible Gorilla experiment exposes a fundamental paradox of the mind. On the one hand, the human mind can conceive of theoretical physics, propose the Higgs boson, engineer the Large Hadron Collider at CERN, and find supporting evidence for the Higgs boson. On the other hand, we can't see a gorilla walking across the screen!

Kahneman helps us to grapple with this paradox with his construct of a two-layered (system) mind. In this model, Kahneman uses the idea of the two mind systems working together. First, sensory inputs are fed into System 1. System 1 takes the inputs and makes initial sense out of them. System 1's analysis is then fed to System 2. System 2 is the primary component of what we consider consciousness. The processing by System 2 completes the analysis of information within your mind. Some human actions (like counting passes by the white team) are susceptible to errors introduced by this System 1/System 2 mind. Effective systems thinkers need to understand and adapt to these inherent processes. The biases of the human mind will be discussed much more in Chapter 2.

The Goal: A New Way of Seeing

What is the goal of this book? The aim is to arm you with a toolbox filled with systems ideas and then help you to reprogram your System 1 mind to be able to quickly recognize system effects. Is this type of reprogramming possible? Consider Figure 4, a chess grandmaster

---

[2] As of this writing the video was available on Chabris and Simons' web site at http://www.theinvisiblegorilla.com/gorilla_experiment.html

simultaneously playing dozens of games. The grandmaster has a different way to think about the chess game than his opponents. An idea of the different cognitive processes at work are given by Larry Evans in his book *New Ideas in Chess* (2011). In this book, Evans describes analyzing chess boards as a pattern recognition process while noting conditions like control of center squares, weakness in pawn structures, etc. The grandmaster has learned these patterns, and how to effectively use them in a game, through a very long learning process. It will take *time* and *practice* to reprogram your System 1 mind to quickly recognize system effects.

Figure 4. A Grandmaster Playing Multiple Simultaneous Games in an Exhibition

Ultimately, systems thinking can give you a very different way of seeing the world. Recall the scene near the end of the movie *The Matrix,* right after Neo has been shot by the agent and where he finally can see the matrix as the code itself rather than the physical representation. In the same way, situations will look different to you as you start to see the interactions that are present and as you learn to be suspicious of the simple causal relationships that might have seemed obvious before. That metaphor is the driving force behind the graphic of Figure 5. We are moving towards a new way of seeing!

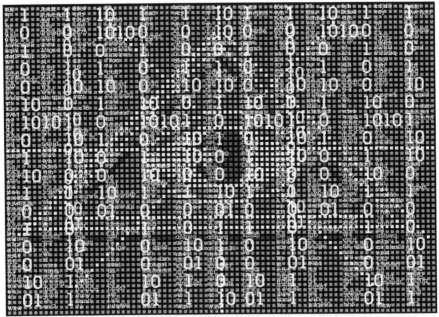

Figure 5 . Systems Thinking: A New Way of Seeing

System Effects and the Tools of Systems Thinking

This book provides you with a valuable set of tools and frameworks for use as summarized in the graphic of Figure 6. Each sub-diagram is a key idea graphic that will be explained in detail later in the book. A downloadable color version of this figure is available (RichJolly.com/STBdownload) and is a great reminder to place on your office wall. The core components of the toolbox are modeling techniques of dynamic interactions (feedback and delay loops) and aggregated agent-to-agent (or agent-environment) interactions. With this foundation, the tool set layers on several important systems thinking concepts including systems simulations, strategic behavior (including game theory), evolutionary process (such as the genetic algorithm), networks, and more. These tools will be woven into a comprehensive tool set, and then will be clearly demonstrated so you can apply them to your business situation.

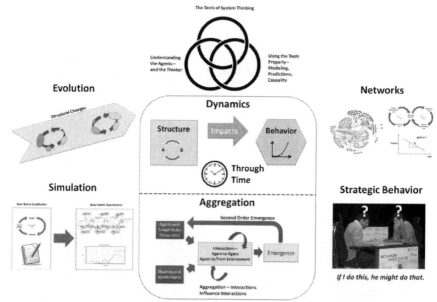

Figure 6. The Tools and Framework of Applied Systems Thinking

Essence of the Book

Why this book? Certainly there are excellent resources available that can explain the scientific work I will discuss (in fact, I'll be pointing these out to you as we go along). But, some of these works lack adequate guidance on application, especially for a business audience. The lack of business application can be traced to the deep cross-disciplinary nature of systems theories. That is, systems theories apply to so many areas (economics, business, psychology, sociology, political science, and more) that authors may be hesitant to focus their application examples to a single area. In some cases, other works may focus on just one area of systems science. This book will compile the systems ideas that are most impactful to business and focus the application examples to business situations.

A primary goal is to make this book an effective use of your time. Basic ideas are presented as efficiently as possible—a crash course, if you will— but plenty of examples and references to dig deeper are provided. While the primary audience is the average business reader, ample references are included for researchers. The focus of the book is *application*. The aim is to get you using these tools effectively and as quickly as possible. The book summarizes a tremendous amount of empirically developed science, not opinion. This scientific work is pulled together and organized into a structure that directly applies to business. There is value here for every discipline of business: management, marketing, sales, finance, human resources, information technology, and more.

The book will introduce the reader to simulation software tools in this field, such as Vensim (dynamic simulation) and NetLogo (agent-based simulation). The goal of this introduction is to help you understand and appreciate their application, not for you to gain simulation proficiency.

A PhD in systems science, along with a career as a senior business leader, have given me the knowledge and perspective for this project. The book is based on a University class I teach that is targeted to MBA candidates. Based on these classes, the material has been fine-tuned for the business audience.

Hopefully, this introduction has sparked your interest. The structure of the rest of the book is as follows:

- Chapter 2 presents the systems thinking framework. The systems thinking framework lays out the map to the proper use of the systems models (the tools).
- Chapter 3 explores dynamics and the science of feedback loops and delays, as illustrated briefly in the People Express example.
- Chapter 4 discusses aggregated interactions and agent-based modeling, which was illustrated with the stock market reaction to the *Challenger* explosion.
- Chapter 5 lays out strategic behavior and game theory that is illustrated by the case of 360 degree evaluations.
- Chapter 6 discusses ecosystems and evolution in the business context.
- Chapter 7 defines the science of networks and delineates what this science means for business, as illustrated in the Domino's Pizza example.
- Chapter 8 introduces a technique known as TOP (Technical, Organizational, Personal) multiple perspectives. This technique is deeply insightful and valuable for those in business.
- Chapter 9 will pull the systems thinking skill set together.

As mentioned, the goal is to provide you with immediately useful skills as efficiently as possible. Let's get going!

2. Systems Thinking Framework

We can't expect to hand someone a set of carpenter's tools and anticipate they will produce beautiful handcrafted furniture. In the same way, learning a set of systems thinking models will not necessarily produce great systems thinking. We also need a clear understanding of how those tools should be used. The framework for using the system tools is the focus of this chapter.

Applied Systems Thinking Framework

Two critical elements to the application of the tools of systems thinking are identified. The graphic in Figure 7 provides a useful image for this relationship. The three key components of applied systems thinking are:

1. The tools of systems thinking—The systems science models (where we will spend the bulk of our time).
2. Understanding the agents—Gaining an understanding of relevant human cognitive processes.
3. Using the tools properly—Appreciating the issues around the use of models in the understanding of business situations.

The Tools of System Thinking

Understanding the Agents — and the Thinker

Using the Tools Properly — Modeling, Predictions, Causality

Figure 7. Applied Systems Thinking Framework (Represented by the Borromean Rings)

The image here, from the mathematical field of topology, is known as the Borromean rings, and they have a special characteristic in the realm of systems science. The unique feature of these rings is that by removing any one ring, the other two will fall apart. The rings represent a three-way interaction that cannot be reduced. This may sound a bit abstract, so let me give you a simple concrete example. Consider a family consisting of a father, mother, and son. By understanding the father-mother interactions, father-son interactions, and mother-son interactions, we still may not understand the dynamics of the family when all three are together. In the same way, we must understand all three of the components of applied systems thinking and the way they work together.

There are two aspects of understanding the agents; that is, the human cognitive processes. First, since the systems we will be modeling in the business realm are primarily human systems, it is necessary to have an understanding of the agents in those systems. But also, you, the system analyst, are human. You must understand your own cognitive biases to assess if they may be limiting your ability to properly understand the system under analysis.

The final aspect, the proper use of tools, is somewhat philosophical in nature (note, being philosophical in nature does *not* mean that it can't have deep practical use). Here we will delve deeply into the proper use of models: the mental models and the mathematical (or computer simulation) models. We will also consider many aspects around making predictions and judging causality from models in complex systems.

The Tools of Systems Thinking

Figure 8 gives an outline of the book's organization of systems thinking tools. At the core, we cover the emergent effects from the dynamics of feedback and delays (Chapter 3) and the aggregation of interactions (Chapter 4). With this core, we will layer on strategic behavior (Chapter 5), ecosystems and evolution (Chapter 6), networks (Chapter 7), and finally the multiple perspectives of TOP (Technical, Organizational, Personal - Chapter 8).

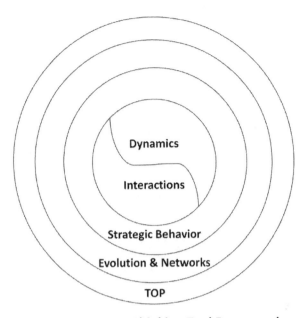

Figure 8. Systems Thinking Tool Framework

Systems Science and Complexity

Systems science and complexity science are often used synonymously, but there could be some subtle differences. Unfortunately, neither terms are rigorously defined. Some view systems science as a superset of complexity science. Systems science encompasses all of game theory, dynamics, cybernetics, information theory, complex adaptive systems, chaos, and many more theories dealing with interactions. Many complexity experts would not include the entirety of these theories into complexity science.

Complexity can be categorized into two types: combinatorial and dynamic. An example of combinatorial complexity is building an airline schedule. For example, United Airlines must build a flight schedule with thousands of airplanes, many airports, thousands of crews, etc. There's nothing inherently difficult in conceptualizing this problem, but it is extremely complex because of all the options. Combinatorial complexity is well understood and can be tackled in an engineering fashion. For example, the airline schedule is usually built using a technique called *linear programming*. In the case of dynamics, changes through time create the complexity, like the anthill we discussed in the first chapter. In this case, engineering techniques may struggle. Dynamic complexity is the topic addressed by systems thinking.

Understanding the Agents

We need to have an understanding of human cognitive processes. We need this insight in our systems thinking process to effectively model human decisions and judgment. But, we must also understand human thinking processes to see our own blind spots in the analysis process. We will look to evolution and the mechanisms of intelligence to gain insight into these processes. Then, we will cover a brief list of the biases of which we must be cognizant.

A Simple Model for the Evolution of Higher Intelligence— Efficient Survival

Having an intuitive idea of the mechanisms that generate decision biases is helpful in the integration of these ideas. To that end, a hypothesis is presented for the development of human judgment and decision biases. There is a rich literature on these ideas. To get an overview, and a pointer to more references, see the article in the journal *Science* by Emery and Clayton (2004).

To understand this basic hypothesis, we need to go back in time and look at the evolution of intelligence. Humans have a lot of difficulty understanding processes that encompass very long time periods. For many years people did not understand that the Grand Canyon was etched by the flow of a river. This is primarily because people could not comprehend that such a massive structure could be formed over very long time periods by the flow of what seems, in scale to the structure, a very small amount of water. Similarly, it was not until the late 1800s that Darwin was finally able to understand biological evolution. Again, this is at least partly due to the long, in relation to a human life span, time periods involved. To understand and frame the characteristics of the mental processes of humans, we need to look across the time span of animal evolution[3]. To have survived and prospered in evolutionary history, higher intelligence must increase fitness.

---

[3] We explore the idea of using a system's evolutionary history to understand current relationships more fully in Chapter 6.

Figure 9 gives a log-log plot of the brain weight versus body weight of various animals. One can speculate that a larger body mass, with more cells, nerves, muscles, etc. to control will require greater *compute* capability in the brain; hence, greater brain mass. However, in the plot, several animals lie well above the trend line. Notably these are humans, apes, dolphins, and ravens. These species have certain characteristics that scientists often describe as higher intelligence.

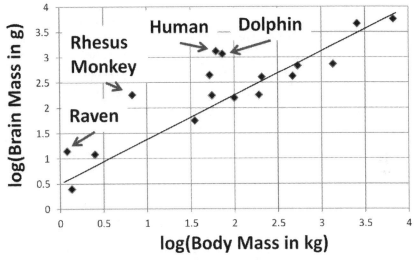

Figure 9. Log-Log Plot of Brain Versus Body Weight of Various Animals

Scientists have noted that animals that exhibit higher intelligence have two notable descriptive differences. First, these animals are capable of using tools. Second, they tend to live in complex social structures.

One simple model for the process of intelligence in the creation and use of tools is illustrated in the upper row of boxes in Figure 10. Here, the first step is to make sense of reality. By making sense of reality, simple causal relationships can be understood. This understanding of causality, in turn, allows for prediction and finally the use of tools. The Nova documentary *Inside Animal Minds* provided an excellent illustration (Russell, 2014). A worm was placed, floating, in a beaker half filled with water. A raven, who loves these worms, was shown the beaker and given some small stones. The beaker was narrow and deep enough that the raven couldn't reach the worm. The raven picked up the stones and dropped them in the beaker. This raised the water level to the point where the raven could grab the floating worm. Next, the raven was shown the same beaker half filled with sand and a worm on top of the sand. Even though the raven had small stones at its disposal, it did not attempt to drop the stones into the beaker. Apparently, the raven had made sense of the situation and understood the simple causal relationship between the stone sinking in the water and the water line in the beaker increasing. This allowed the prediction of what would happen when the beaker was filled with water and what would happen if the beaker was filled with sand.

The upper chain shown in Figure 10, while simple, is extremely powerful. It has led to ravens using simple tools, to early man creating stone weapons and wheels, and eventually to modern man creating the Large Hadron Collider. However, while powerful and effective in evolution, there are side effects. Figure 10 also shows these side effects, which are the focus of this section.

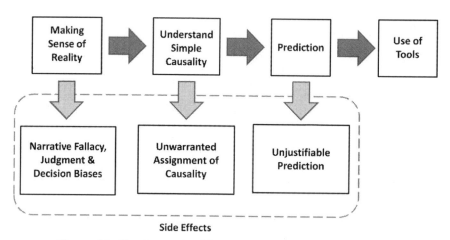

Figure 10. The Sense-Making Process and Its Side Effects

While evolution is optimizing overall system (animal) fitness, there are metrics we might use to get a handle on a subsystem performance. If higher intelligence is contributing to the fitness of the animal, then efficiency of that subsystem would likely be valuable as a metric of interest. To define efficiency we have the following equation.

$$Efficiency = \frac{Performance}{Cost}$$

Improving performance or minimizing costs will increase efficiency. Performance would be measured in terms of improving the animal's fitness. So, higher intelligence allows the animal to use tools that increase the probability of survival. Costs may come in direct or indirect forms. Use of energy to perform a task is a direct cost. In a typical human, the brain is using 20% of the resting calories while comprising only 2% of the body weight.

One of the centerpieces of efficient intelligence is mental heuristics. Sometimes referred to as a *rule of thumb,* a heuristic is a mental shortcut. Here, the brain is increasing efficiency by minimizing cost (energy use) as well as improving performance. Performance may be increased by reducing the thinking time. This may be an important characteristic in the context of fitness. For example, in quickly escaping a predator. Of course, to be efficient, the heuristics must generally produce correct results.

System 1/System 2 and Judgment/Decision Heuristics

Out of the 200,000 or so years that humans have been around, we've primarily been simple hunter-gatherers. It shouldn't surprise us then that the human mind has been evolving to perform well in that role. And, it also shouldn't surprise us that the mind could have a few *issues* when suddenly (in evolutionary terms) placed into the modern era. As mentioned in Chapter 1, Daniel Kahneman has developed a model of the mind he calls System 1/System 2[4]. The preceding section has provided a hypothesis for the evolutionary basis of this mental system. Using this framework can provide insight into human actions.

System 1 is the *fast* in Kahneman's book *Thinking, Fast and Slow.* If you have an engineering perspective, you might consider it the first stage of information processing. The primary objective of System 1 is to keep us alive in a dangerous world, at least long enough to reproduce. Kahneman notes some important characteristics of System 1.

- WYSIATI—Kahneman's acronym stands for "What You See Is All There Is." Essentially, it means that System 1 primarily uses the available sensory input in its sense-making process.
- It is biased to believe and confirm.

---

[4] Keep in mind that like all models, System 1/System 2 is not reality. If you dissect a human brain, you will not find a System 1 section and a System 2 section linked by synapses. These are tools to help us understand.

- It may substitute an easier question: one that it can answer quickly.
- It attempts to build a story from available information as part of its processing method.
- It overweights low probabilities.
- It is loss averse.
- It infers (and invents) causes and intentions (closely related to the mechanism of building a story).

Taleb (2007) proposes a hypothesis for another reason the brain attempts to build stories and assign causality. Information is costly to obtain, so the brain should attempt to keep it. But information is also costly to store. The more orderly and patterned the data, the easier it is to store. Furthermore, information is costly to manipulate and retrieve. This is a problem most database users have run across. Fundamentally, it's an indexing problem. Storing information as a story, linked with causality, could help meet the biological need to efficiently store, retrieve, and reduce the dimensionality of information.

The System 1 characteristics contribute to the manifestation of the judgment and decision heuristics and biases that Kahneman spent most of his career exploring. Understanding these biases is a crucial component of effective systems thinking. Table 1 gives a list of just some of these human judgment and decision heuristics and biases.

Heuristic/ Bias	Description	Example
Anchoring	Using a data point, which may or may not be relevant, as a starting point (anchor) for an estimate	Basing your offer on the asking price
Availability	Overweighting the probability of examples that are easily recalled from memory	Overestimating the risk of flying after a recent and well publicized plane crash
Confirmation	Search for data that confirms existing beliefs (rather than alternatives)	Noting white swans while trying to prove all swans are white
Representative- ness	Judging the probability of an event by how it resembles the typical case	Thinking all PhDs are nerds

Table 1. A Very Small Sample of Human Judgment and Decision Biases

Table 1 references: Anchoring Bias - (A. Tversky & Kahneman, 1974); Availability Bias - (A. Tversky & Kahneman, 1973); Confirmation Bias - (Nickerson, 1998); Representativeness - (A. Tversky & Kahneman, 1974).

Constructing mental models is another artifact of the System 1/System 2 mind. One can think of mental models as heuristics the mind uses to simplify the sense-making process. The actual characteristics of complex systems can often be quite different from these mental models. These discrepancies are important to keep in mind as we evaluate a complex system because our System 1/System 2 mind will be trying to assert the simple mental models. Figure 11 shows just two examples. The human mind will normally assume trends are linear. However, in most complex systems, trends tend to be nonlinear. Similarly, the human mind will attempt to describe spatial characteristics in simple geometric patterns while actual complex systems tend to develop fractal-like patterns. We will explore these discrepancies throughout the book.

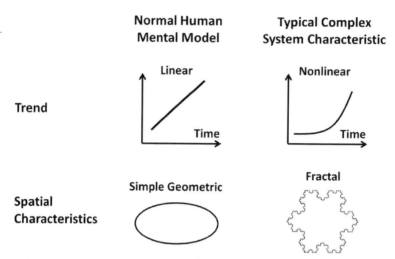

Figure 11. Comparing Mental Models to Complex System Characteristics

System 2 takes the output of System 1 and produces the thoughts we refer to as consciousness. As you read this passage, it is System 2 that is doing the final interpretation. System 2 burns a lot of fuel (glucose from the bloodstream), and the tendency to accept the recommendations of System 1 reduces its overall fuel usage. Reducing fuel use tends to make the System 1/System 2 complex more efficient. While Kahneman describes System 2 as *lazy*, an *efficient* moniker may be more descriptive.

Narrative Fallacy

One of the more nefarious ramifications of the System 1 mind's predispositions is the narrative fallacy. The idea comes from Nassim Nicholas Taleb's important book *The Black Swan* (2007). Taleb defines the narrative fallacy as taking a sequence of facts and binding them together in a story. The created story invariably includes arrows of causal relationships between the facts. This process allows humans to more easily remember and make sense of facts. Unfortunately, as we will discuss in depth later, assigning these direct causes may be misguided. An important result of the narrative fallacy is to push humans to the mental conclusion that a rare event was predictable since the precedent events are all clearly linked together in the mind. This then adds support to the human belief in predictability of future rare events. Some of the other direct results of the narrative fallacy are:

- Assigning a larger role to skills (or lack of) and intentions.
- Reducing the importance of randomness.

- Focusing on things that happened and neglecting things that didn't happen.

Example: Human Decision Bias

Here are a few examples described in Kahneman's book that illustrate human decision biases.

Read the statement below and speak out your immediate response.

> A bat and ball cost $1.10
> The bat costs one dollar more than the ball.
> How much does the ball cost?

Did you say 10 cents? This is the most common answer. But, if the bat costs one dollar more than the ball, then the bat must cost $1.10. So the bat and the ball together would cost $1.20. The correct answer is 5 cents. 10 cents was the suggestion from your System 1 mind.

This famous example was developed by Kahneman and Tversky. Read the paragraph below and answer the associated question.

> Linda is thirty-one years old, single, outspoken, and very bright. She majored in philosophy. As a student, she was deeply concerned with issues of discrimination and social justice, and also participated in antinuclear demonstrations.

Which alternative is more probable?
- Linda is a bank teller.
- Linda is a bank teller and is active in the feminist movement.

The majority choose the second, "Linda is a bank teller and is active in the feminist movement." Kahneman calls this a *conjunction fallacy.* The group of people who are bank tellers is larger than the group of people who are both bank tellers and active in the feminist movement. Further, the group of bank tellers completely contains the second group. "Linda is a bank teller" must be more probable.

Here's an example from Chapter 10 of Kahneman's *Thinking, Fast and Slow* .

A study of the incidence of kidney cancer in the 3,141 counties of the United States reveals a remarkable pattern. The counties in which the incidence of kidney cancer is lowest are mostly rural, sparsely populated, and located in traditional Republican states in the Midwest, the South, and the West.

What is going on in your mind? Have you been thinking about what is the circumstance of these people that could lead to a low incidence of cancer? Is it the locale? Their lifestyle? Could being Republican lead to lower cancer?

Now read the next section:

Now consider the counties in which the incidence of kidney cancer is highest. These ailing counties tend to be mostly rural, sparsely populated, and located in traditional Republican states in the Midwest, the South, and the West.

Are you thinking "how can this be?" What is going on here is an artifact of the research. To understand, consider the following experiment. An urn is filled with 50% red and 50% blue marbles. Jack repeatedly draws four marbles from the urn and records the number of times that all four marbles are the same color. Jill draws seven marbles and also records every time she draws all seven marbles of the same color. Now, you can clearly see that Jack will record many more of the extreme situation where all marbles are the same color (12.5% for Jack versus 1.56% for Jill, on average). Was your System 1/System 2 complex busy making a story out of the facts even though the data was due to an experimental artifact?

Using the Tools Properly

The third Borromean ring of the Applied Systems Thinking Framework (Figure 7) is the proper use of tools. A cornerstone of this section is the proper use of models. This includes proper concern for the assertions of causality and use of models for predictions.

Models

All models are wrong, but some are useful.

George E. Box (Box & Draper, 1987)

> The Dao that can be told is not the eternal Dao.
>
> Lao Tzu, First verse of *Tao Te Ching*[5]

Understanding and, more importantly, the proper use of models is a crucial skill in applied systems thinking. To begin, let's define the modeling process:

> Modeling—a *process* to develop a *representation* of reality to understand, communicate, or predict.

Process is emphasized because in most cases the process of building the model (e.g., understanding relationships, collecting data, etc.) can bring valuable insights and understanding into the modeler's issue. Representation is emphasized because one must always remember the model isn't reality and therefore the analyst can't rely on the model's outputs.

Figure 12 is a graphical representation of the modeling process. In the modeling process, data and knowledge are used to construct the model. The model is then used to extract some type of information and conclusions. George Box's quote above encourages one to integrate into their thinking to never take a model as reality; but if the analyst understands the model's limitations, the model can be quite valuable.

Data & Knowledge ⟺ Filter / Transform **Model** ⟺ Information / Conclusion **Audience**

Figure 12. The Modeling Process

---

[5] The *Tao Te Ching* is a classic Chinese text written around the 6th century BC. According to tradition it is attributed to the sage Lao Tzu who was an advisor in the Zhou dynasty. The actual authorship is debated by scholars. The current Chinese character text is compiled from transmitted versions, commentaries, and ancient manuscripts. In addition to the exact text being difficult to pin down, there are many English translations of the characters. Sabbadini's (2013) effort to compile the various interpretations is recommended.

An important consideration in model construction is the approach used in the interaction with the real world, the data source. To illustrate, consider these two business situations. First, an advertising executive is reading Kahneman's *Thinking, Fast and Slow* and is intrigued by the idea of loss aversion. She infers that advertisements that focus on loss prevention would be more impactful than those that focus on gains. So, she devises an experiment to test this idea—this hypothesis. She runs two versions of a new advertisement in two different geographical areas that have similar demographics. One advertisement frames the message in terms of preventing a loss. The second advertisement frames the message in terms of increasing profits. After the advertisements have finished their runs, she does survey testing in the two areas to determine the impact of the advertisements. Based on this survey data, she either supports or rejects her hypothesis. This result is then used to tailor the nationwide advertising campaign.

Now, consider a second situation. A retail sales analyst is studying sales data. He runs a data mining program to look for groups in the data. He notices that customers have purchased two products together frequently in the past. The classic data mining example is that beer and diapers tend to be purchased together. The analyst then builds a possible explanation for this type of behavior. For example, he may propose that this behavior is due to young fathers stopping at the store on the way home from work to pick up diapers and using the shopping trip as an opportunity to purchase an after work libation. Based on the observed pattern and proposed explanation, the analyst may make a recommendation. In this case, the analyst may recommend that stores place beer next to diapers on an aisle endcap.

Knowledge (Explanations)

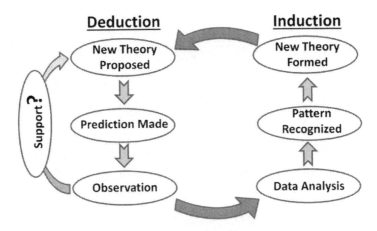

Data (Observations)

Figure 13. Reasoning Frameworks

These two examples illustrate different ways of understanding the real world and building knowledge about it. The advertising executive is using deductive reasoning, and the retail sales analyst is using inductive reasoning. Figure 13 illustrates the two types of reasoning. Deductive reasoning, the bedrock of the scientific method, begins with a new theory which leads to a prediction (a hypothesis). The real world is tested and observed to determine if the theory is supported. One can think of deduction as being top down or theory driven (or general to specific). Induction, on the other hand, begins with observations from the real world. Based on these observations, patterns are recognized and new theories proposed (specific to general). The different methods have important implications on model construction.

In the deductive reasoning process, the test for support of the hypothesis is a critical feedback mechanism. Induction, on the other hand, does not have an implicit feedback mechanism. As practical systems thinkers, we understand that real-world knowledge accumulation uses a complicated mixture of both methods. In fact, the support mechanism for deductive logic is an inductive process. Figure 13 illustrates the symbiotic relationship between the two methods as a large feedback loop. For example, examining the experimental results from a hypothesis test of the deductive process may spur an inductive process of searching additional data for new patterns. Theories about these new patterns might prompt a new hypothesis and a second deductive process.

Model construction will typically involve elements of inductive and deductive logic. It is important to understand the implications of the use of these methods. Models constructed with deductive processes that replicate the behaviors of the real world have strong explanatory power. This has been described by Epstein and Axtell (1996) as generative science. Their argument is that if you can build a simulation using the characteristics of the real world and your simulation produces behavior that is consistent with what you see in the real world, then you have supported your argument about the system mechanisms. This idea will be expanded with examples as we proceed.

In many modeling processes, real-world data is used to adjust model parameters to allow the model to match observed real-world behavior. This general process is called calibration, and it is inherently inductive. Processes in the workplace tend to drive the construction of models that match historical data. At a superficial level, models that match real-world behaviors appear more credible. A precarious tendency of model developers is to add more elements to the model in an effort to create a better match to real-world behavior. This process could lead to overfitting, and will be discussed in depth in the next chapter.

Inference is the process of coming to logical conclusions based on premises or patterns of data. Each step in the processes of induction and deduction requires inference. If data is involved, the field of inferential statistics can help quantify the conclusion. In inferential statistics, the distribution of data sampled from a population is analyzed to provide the probability of seeing the observed data if the hypothesis is true (known as the p value[6]). Inferential statistics is the most common method of assessing if the observations support the new theory in the deductive reasoning process. Inductive inference is a powerful instrument in our

---

[6] This is often written as $p(Data|Hypothesis)$ or $p(D|H)$ and read as probability of data given the hypothesis. It is important not to confuse $p(D|H)$ with $p(H|D)$. The p value is the former and not the latter. This confusion is a subtle, but crucial, mistake sometimes made by students of inferential statistics.

reasoning arsenal. But—and this is an important but—the limitations need to be clearly understood. Observations that support the hypothesis only provide support. The hypothesis cannot be proven to be true. On the other hand, a single data point can disprove the hypothesis. We will revisit this again shortly in the section on Black Swans.

Even though making predictions is listed as a use of models, understanding the limitations of this use will be paramount. A critical point that will be made again and again in this book is that predictions are quite difficult in complex systems. In complex systems, outcomes are often dependent on system effects (interactions, feedback, strategic behavior, etc.) that are difficult to accurately model. For example, in terms of a structural model where feedbacks and delays are involved, one must consider the following factors.

- Have all feedback loops been included? Some may be dormant.
- Are all parameters of the model correct? Some system models are highly sensitive to changes in model parameters.
- Are human decision processes modeled appropriately? Have issues like the decision biases mentioned above been considered and included?
- Are other effects crucial in this phenomenon (aggregated interactions, networks, and so on)?

The limitation on model predictions can be troublesome because, in many cases for non-systems thinkers, prediction may be the primary purpose of a model. Consider, for example, the gross domestic product (GDP) economic models built by the Federal Reserve Bank. Predictions are integral, and essentially the primary purpose of these models.

Causality

Understanding simple causality is critical in the use of elementary tools, as depicted earlier in Figure 10. Understanding that "if I push this stick in this hole I may catch a termite" is essential for a monkey or raven in using the stick as a tool. However, this underpinning of tool usage can be misguided when applied to complex systems. With effects that may emerge from interactions in time or space, there may be no simple *cause* to an observed effect. We must caution *ourselves* from summarily accepting simple explanations since our System 1/System 2 complex will be at work constructing possible causes. We should also be aware that others will seek simple causes for emergent effects.

It is particularly useful to understand how humans judge causality; that is, having a descriptive model. In a landmark paper, Einhorn and Hogarth studied the psychology of causality (1986) and compiled a complete theory from all the existing research. They found several important cues that people use to understand causality.

- Change from Normal—For example, hitting a watch crystal with a hammer and the watch crystal breaking.
- Temporal Order—Causes preceding effects.
- Contiguity (post hoc)—How close in time are cause and effect. For example, some primitive cultures don't understand what causes pregnancy because of the time lag involved.
- Strength of Explanatory Chain—How strong the links are between perceived events.
- Similarity in Duration, Magnitude, Physical Characteristics—For example, bear tracks look like bear paws, or difficultly in understanding germs cause sickness.
- Covariation—Correlation between cause and effect as illustrated in the table below.

	Effect = True (Subject had lung cancer)	Effect = False (Subject did not have lung cancer)
Suspected cause = True (Subject smoked)	Cause and effect relationship confirmed	Cause and effect relationship not confirmed
Suspected cause=False (Subject did not smoke)	Cause effect relationship not confirmed	Cause effect relationship confirmed

Einhorn and Hogarth (1986) noted that poor judgment of covariation can lead to several problems.

- Superstitious Behavior—This arises from false positive signals. Here, spurious correlations are mistaken for causality. The classic example is from B.F. Skinner's experiment where he put several very hungry pigeons in cages and set a dispenser that released food at regular intervals. Six of the eight birds had developed curious repetitive body movements (e.g., spinning counter clockwise) that they had been performing, by chance, when the food pellet was delivered (Skinner, 1948).

- Illusion of Control—For example, gamblers bet more at craps if they are rolling the dice.

Example: Causality

The first example illustrates the psychological desire to assign simple causality. In *The Black Swan,* Taleb recounts a particularly insightful example of the sometimes desperate search for causes. On December 13, 2003, the U.S. forces captured Saddam Hussein. At around the same time the price of U.S. Treasury bonds rose. In a search for the *cause* of this bond price change, the *Bloomberg News* flashed the headline "U.S. Treasuries Rise; Hussein Capture May Not Curb Terrorism." But half an hour later, bond prices fell (bond prices can move up and down most days) and *Bloomberg News* issued a new headline: "U.S. Treasuries Fall; Hussein Capture Boosts Allure Of Risky Assets." Clearly, Hussein's capture could not simultaneously cause opposite effects. The journalists felt the need to link the events into a causal relationship.

Further, our ideas about causality in complex systems may be misguided. For example, many subscribe to the idea that the following is a path to good investments:

1. Read and study the financial newspaper to learn about important things happening in business, the economy, and the market;
2. Armed with this knowledge, you decide on the best strategy to invest your money; and
3. Lo and behold, your investing efforts lead to a growing nest egg.

The implication here is that using the newspaper can predict future stock returns.

Now let us look at this situation differently—through a lens of systems thinking. As illustrated in Figure 14, we first consider the markets as powerful information-gathering devices, as illustrated in the market reaction to the *Challenger* disaster. Markets collect bits of information from around the globe and from individuals with diverse perspectives who have real *skin in the game*. The market assimilates all this information into a single price. Journalists, eager to write newspaper-selling stories, watch the stock market, observe large changes in a particular stock, and build probable simple causes for what they observe.

Perhaps you have heard the saying, "I could make money if only I had tomorrow's newspaper today." By looking at the markets today, you *can* have tomorrow's newspaper! Finally, consider what effect those newspaper articles might have on stock market participants[7]. Now we see a feedback loop where a final stable equilibrium may not be possible.

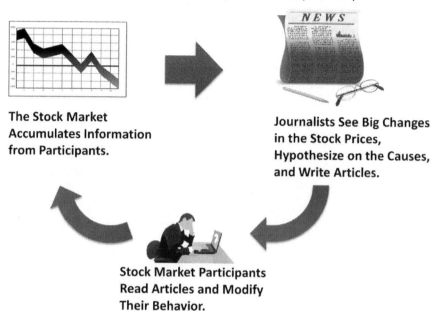

The Stock Market
Accumulates Information
from Participants.

Journalists See Big Changes
in the Stock Prices,
Hypothesize on the Causes,
and Write Articles.

Stock Market Participants
Read Articles and Modify
Their Behavior.

Figure 14. Systems Diagram of the Influence of Media
on the Stock Market

Prediction

A theme we will revisit often is that prediction is very difficult in complex systems. But in the model of higher intelligence from Figure 10, prediction of simple effects is a crucial step in tool use. It is natural for humans to look for ways to predict the future. If we look at the world of engineering, we have plenty of support for the hypothesis that complicated things are predictable. For example, NASA says that they are tracking over 500,000 pieces of space debris orbiting the earth and have been able to keep the International Space Station out of the way of this junk. But a crucial factor of this system is that interactions *are* negligible. The orbits of the 500,000 pieces of space junk rarely affect one another. In effect, this example is

---

[7] Chapter 3 will examine the effect of stock price changes on participant's actions; that is, the loop in the opposite direction.

combinatorial complexity. As we move through the different phenomenon of complex systems, from feedback loops, aggregation of interactions, strategic behavior, and so on, we see more and more possible reasons why a prediction of future behavior is so difficult in human complex systems where interactions are important. The final chapter (Chapter 9) will provide some very direct advice on prediction.

Example: Could We Have Predicted the 2008 Financial Crisis?

Could the 2008 financial crisis have been predicted? Let's look at some of the key points for the debate[8].

Support for the argument that the crisis could have been predicted (knowledgeable individuals who correctly predicted the crisis):

- Nouriel Roubini, an NYU professor, made numerous comments about an impending crisis including a talk given at an International Monetary Fund (IMF) meeting.
- Peter Schiff, a noted financial analyst, repeatedly predicted the crisis.
- Ron Paul, a former congressman, predicted the crisis.
- Dean Baker, senior economist, predicted the housing bubble and also predicted that the bubble's collapse would lead to a severe recession.
- Med Jones, economist and strategist, predicted the financial crisis.
- Nassim Nicholas Taleb, *The Black Swan* author, warned of the coming crisis and specifically warned about Fannie Mae and the unhealthy interlinking between large banks.
- Henry Paulson and others made extensive speculative investments that would gain in value in the case of a crash (Lewis, 2010).

Support for the argument that the crisis couldn't have been predicted (knowledgeable individuals who predicted no crisis):

- Ben Bernanke, chairman of the Federal Reserve Board, issued the statement, "Strong fundamentals support a relatively soft landing in housing. I think we are unlikely to see growth being derailed by the housing market."
- George Soros, considered one of the greatest investors, made an investment in Lehman Brothers just prior to its collapse.
- Warren Buffet had substantial losses in his portfolio from the crash.

---

[8] Google any of these names with a phrase such as "predicted 2008 financial crisis" to see more about what they said.

- Some of the crucial information needed to see the scope of the problem was either hidden or obscure. For example, there was little transparency on large investment bank holdings. Also, modeling errors in the valuation[9] of Credit Default Swaps (CDS) and Collateralized Debt Obligations (CDO) due to poor assumptions were largely unknown and required a PhD in financial engineering to even understand.

One might argue that Bernanke had strong suspicions of a crisis but had to make positive statements to avoid panic. However, the examples of Soros and Buffet, where they were putting their money on the line, indicate they were not expecting a crash of this magnitude.

If you do some of your own research on this topic you will run into articles that paint a picture of clear predictability. These authors will focus on the predictions and ideas of the people who predicted the crisis, and will exclude the predictions and ideas of those that predicted no crisis. This is an example of a narrative fallacy.

Black Swans

The idea of a *Black Swan* event has become a common concept in the world of business (and elsewhere). The idea was described by Nassim Nicholas Taleb in his important book *The Black Swan* (2007). A Black Swan event has three important characteristics.
1. The event is unexpected, or considered improbable, to the observer.
2. The event has a major impact on the observer.
3. In hindsight, the observer rationalizes that they "should have seen it coming." This, then, is a narrative fallacy as described earlier in this chapter.

Many times in current dialogues, the Black Swan is described as a characteristic of the data set. However, at its core, the Black Swan is a *modeling* problem. The observer has deemed the event improbable based on their existing experiences which serve as their current data set. Europeans considered all swans white based on their observation of only seeing white swans. The *all swans are white* hypothesis is based on inductive reasoning. The scientific method asserts that one cannot prove

---

[9] The error was basically the assumption of Gaussian characteristics in the Copula function. This is essentially the error of the Bell Curve (chapter 15 in *The Black Swan*) that Taleb spends so much time discussing, expanded to multiple dimensions.

a hypothesis, only disprove it. Seeing more white swans may strengthen the hypothesis, but seeing a black swan can disprove it. The confirmation bias, the search for data that confirms existing beliefs (versus alternatives), accentuates this effect in humans.

Taleb's foremost example is the turkey on a turkey farm. The Thanksgiving Day *surprise* is the Black Swan event. Imagine that the turkey is a master modeler. The turkey has formed the hypothesis that *humans are benevolent towards turkeys*. As the days go by, and the farmer dutifully feeds and cares for the turkeys, the turkey's hypothesis is supported. If the turkey is statistically inclined, he may be computing p values (or confidence levels), which are increasingly meeting statistically significant levels. Finally, on Thanksgiving Day, when the turkey needs it the most, his model horrifically fails him. It's important to note that the Thanksgiving Day surprise is *not* a Black Swan to the turkey farmer. After all, the whole reason for the farm is the Thanksgiving Day surprise. It's also worthwhile to note why Taleb chose the turkey farm to be the symbol for the Black Swan event. One of the motivations for Taleb's book is to help prevent us from being turkeys.

Emergence

Emergence has been mentioned but not precisely defined. While there isn't an agreed-upon definition, here is a working definition:

> Emergence: A phenomenon where an interaction among objects at one level generates new types of objects at another level. The emergent characteristic requires a new descriptive category at that next level.

An illustrative example is in statistical mechanics, where laws of gases, such as Boltzmann's law, emerge from the interactions of the gas molecules. Descriptions at the micro-level (molecules) versus the macro-level (gasses) require different constructs. Similarly, temperature is an emergent property of the motion of atoms. While an entity which is a collection of atoms has temperature, a single atom has no temperature.

System scientists might debate if emergence is subjective or objective. Philosophically, this may equate to an epistemological versus ontological viewpoint[10]. In this book, I take a broad subjective view on this topic in that an unanticipated result from an interaction of entities can be considered an emergent effect. No matter the definition or viewpoint, emergence is a powerful concept that will serve us well in business analysis.

The Value of Systems Models

Finally, in using models, we recall George Box's refrain that all simulations are wrong but some are useful. We've discussed where to exercise caution when using models. Where, then, are the areas of use?

Identify leverage points: Just as the small movement of the captain's wheel can change the course of a half-million ton oil tanker, complex systems may contain points of high *leverage*. System models and simulation tools allow the exploration of a system's sensitivity to changes in various parameters. A large sensitivity to parameter value indicates potential for high leverage. Often, in complex systems, the location of high leverage points may not be intuitive. *Using system models to identify high leverage points is the primary method of finding unanticipated solutions!* Also, prior system behavior, identified in the course of gathering model data, may give subtle clues to points of high leverage.

Recognize modes: Systems models afford the user the chance to *characterize the basic modes* of the system. For example, are certain variables exhibiting exponential growth, approach to an asymptote, or perhaps oscillation? Comparing model behaviors to the observed data from the real system can help in understanding the nature of the system relationships. Further, the model may expose potential behavior of the system that had not been anticipated. Thus, the model may help avoid unexpected results.

Communicate: Models are very valuable to *communicate and teach*. Simulations can be a very impactful tool to illustrate an effect to managers and colleagues. If the simulation can be interactive and provide instant feedback to questions, all the better. Simulation models can also be excellent learning tools when used as management flight simulators.

---

[10] A variant of this debate will be revisited in the discussion of system boundaries in Chapter 3

Some of you may have participated in strategic role play using one of these simulation tools.

The process: There's great value in *the process* of building a systems model. This process will entail doing a series of interviews with managers in the organization, collecting historical system performance from corporate databases, and so on. This model-building process will help to identify feedback loops, delays, areas of important heterogeneity, etc., that may produce emergent effects. So this process of gathering data and thinking deeply about it may provide valuable deep insights and be one of the prime benefits of building a model.

Generative: System models based on deductive reasoning may be able to provide support for your ideas about why a system is behaving as it is. Scientifically, we would say one is trying to build support for a hypothesis. This has been described by Epstein and Axtell (1996) as *generative science*. Their argument is that if you can build a simulation using the characteristics of the real world and your simulation produces behavior that is consistent with what you see in the real world, then you have supported, but not proven, your argument about the system mechanisms.

Summary

Systems thinking and systems models can be powerful tools, but they must be used properly. The systems thinking framework of Figure 7 gives a roadmap of three related components to effective systems thinking: The tools of systems thinking, understanding the agents, and using the tools properly. These concepts will continue to develop throughout the book.

Further Reading

The amount of topics we need to cover is so extensive that only brief introductions can be provided in this book. So, each chapter will include a prioritized list of further readings related to the chapter's content.

Certainly *Thinking, Fast and Slow* by Daniel Kahneman (2011) must be first in this list. In this important work, Kahneman has made this academic topic completely accessible to all readers. The entire book is valuable, but if you are pressed for time, the priority is to read Part I and then Part II. Part IV, which goes into prospect theory, will be highly valuable later for the Chapter 5 discussion on strategic behavior.

A close second is the important work by Nassim Nicholas Taleb, *The Black Swan* (2007). Many consider Taleb to be one of the greatest critical thinkers of our day. But some people are put off by this book. Taleb is not one to *sugar coat* anything. And he does have a habit of making some rather disconcerting, sweeping generalizations. When you read this book, take an appropriate mindset where you can examine the arguments but not be put off by some of the controversial statements.

Chapter 6 of *The Origin of Wealth* by Eric Beinhocker (2006) provides a nice introduction to some of the human decision biases.

Questions

Questions will be provided throughout the book to help cement the ideas of the chapter. Commentary on each question will be on the next page. Thinking about these questions can help with the learning process.

1. In the discussion on models, a quote from the *Tao Te Ching* (listed below for quick reference) was introduced. Discuss how this verse might apply to models.

> The Dao that can be told is not the eternal Dao.
>
> Lao Tzu, First verse of *Tao Te Ching*

2. Epstein and Axtell call their techniques generative. They say that being able to explain a phenomenon is being able to grow it in an artificial environment. Why doesn't this provide a definitive explanation of the phenomenon?

Discussion of Questions

1. One characteristic of the *Tao Te Ching* is that it is abstract enough that multiple interpretations are possible from any given verse. Here's my interpretation of this verse. The Dao, the total reality of the world, is too extensive to be completely described in any human form. I believe Lao Tzu was reminding us, in the very first verse, that our conception of reality is only a subset of all reality. Additionally, as I read the *Tao Te Ching*, I see a great deal of practical systems thinking advice. I believe a lot of this ancient wisdom has been moved out of the mainstream thinking in the scientific revolution.

2. You can only definitively disprove a hypothesis. Otherwise, you are providing support. That's a fundamental underpinning of empirical science. Even though a simulation shows that the mechanism being modeled generated the phenomenon seen in the real world, there may be other (or even multiple) models that can generate the same behavior. Your model may not be correct, and the actual mechanism may be related to one of these other models.

3. Dynamics

Dynamics is one of the key components in the systems thinking toolbox. Along with aggregation of interactions, dynamics forms the core of the tool hierarchy in Figure 8. We will discuss dynamics in two parts. First, we tackle the qualitative aspects of dynamics and look at the relationships that use the concepts of feedback and delays. Later in the chapter, we look at the quantitative aspects of dynamics and will take the more abstract relationships and quantify them. This second effort will be taken to the point of building dynamic systems simulations.

Qualitative Dynamics

In the area of qualitative dynamics, we seek to understand how dynamic factors, feedback and delay, may affect behavior. The term *qualitative* is used in the sense that qualitative research is differentiated from quantitative methods. In qualitative dynamics, the focus is on the identification of feedback loops and delay instantiations and how they affect behavior. In a later section, we expand on these ideas and look at ways to quantitatively describe and study the relationships. While there are many researchers who pioneered the ideas of qualitative dynamics, Peter Senge, in his significant book *The Fifth Discipline* (1990), pulled the early ideas together and fortified and constructed them into an actionable framework. This book is high on the Further Reading list. One of Senge's key ideas is that certain connections of feedback and delay regularly occur in complex human systems. He calls these common sets of connections *archetypes*. Archetypes will be described later in this chapter.

Simple graphics can be an aid for learning and memory. For each component of the toolbox, a simple graphic is provided to focus the concept to its essence and to aid in the assimilation process. For qualitative dynamics, the key idea is that structure impacts behavior through time as depicted in Figure 15. Structure is composed of the feedback loops and delays that have developed from the processes that are present in the situation. How this structure impacts behavior is the key concept.

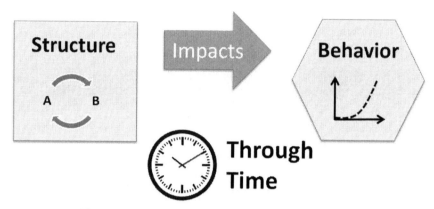

**Figure 15. Key Idea for Qualitative Dynamics:
Structure Impacts Behavior Through Time**

Feedback loops are a primary component of the structure shown in Figure 15. Feedback is a process where information from the past has influence on that same phenomena in the present. Feedback has an effect through a loop, a complete path through the system in time and space. Feedback has two types. *Reinforcing feedback*, also called positive feedback, occurs when a disturbance will be amplified as it travels around the loop. The other type of feedback is *balancing*, also called negative feedback. For balancing feedback, a disturbance of the system will decrease as it travels around the loop, so the values will eventually settle and thus achieve stability.

A reinforcing feedback loop is shown in Figure 16. In this figure, a system variable is shown in a feedback loop and its value over time is plotted in the curve on the right. As time progresses, a fraction of the system variable is fed back into the system variable. To get a handle on this important idea, consider the common example of a bank account earning interest (with neither deposits nor withdrawals). Given an initial balance, the bank computes an amount of interest as a percentage of the balance. This amount of interest is deposited back to the account and adds to the initial balance. The next time the bank calculates interest, the balance has increased so the account owner will earn interest on the prior interest. As time proceeds, the feedback loop causes the account balance to grow without bounds and in a nonlinear fashion. Following Senge's convention, a reinforcing loop will be illustrated with the symbol of a snowball rolling down a hill and growing as it captures more and more snow. Notice that the system variable has an exponential growth rate. While the increase in the system variable at a given time point is a linear process (in the bank account example, the interest is simply the bank balance times the interest rate) the accumulation process makes the balance grow exponentially. This is the *emergent* property in this system.

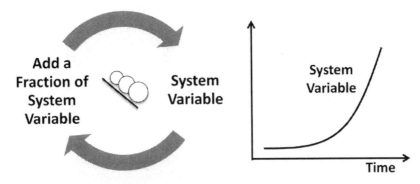

Figure 16. A Reinforcing, or Positive, Feedback Loop

Figure 17 shows a balancing, or negative, feedback loop. As time progresses, a fraction of the system variable is removed from the system variable. To continue the bank account analogy, consider a bank account where the owner spends 20% of the balance each week (with no interest accumulation or deposits). For example, if their current balance is $1000, then they will spend $200 the first week. As the balance declines, the account owner's weekly spending will decrease. As seen in the graph on the right of the figure, the system variable, the account balance in this example, again decreases in a non-linear manner. The bank balance will approach, but never reach, zero. Following the convention of Senge, a small see-saw will be used as the symbol of a balancing loop.

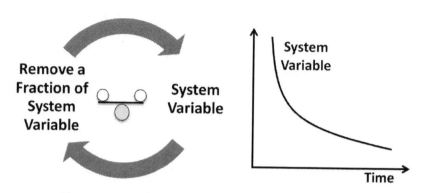

Figure 17. A Balancing, or Negative, Feedback Loop

Delay is another crucial component in the structure of dynamic systems. In most cases, the process of feedback is not instantaneous. As the delay of the change process increases, the potential for the delay to impact the system behavior increases. Figure 18 illustrates a dynamic system with a delay explicitly shown. In this balancing feedback loop system, the value of the system variable is compared to a target level for this variable, labeled here as a goal. If the system variable is lower than the goal, a mechanism adds a quantity to the system variable. If the system variable is higher than the goal, a quantity of the system variable is removed. However, there is an amount of time delay before these increases or decreases are realized. The quintessential example is someone taking a shower and adjusting the hot and cold water valves to tune the water temperature to their preference. When the bather turns the valve, there is no immediate change to the water temperature. If the bather grows impatient, they may turn the valve even further. This can create oscillations of scalding water, followed by showers of icy cold water after the bather over-reacts to the temperature extreme.

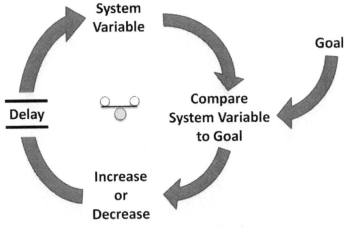

Figure 18. Delay in a Feedback Loop

Example: Feedback Loops—Margin Calls

To illustrate the dynamics of feedback loops, let's examine the effect of stock declines on portfolio margin as depicted in Figure 19. Imagine at some point the stock market has a large drop. This drop will decrease the equity value in portfolios. If the account was using a margin loan to finance some of the stock purchases, then the drop of equity value may drop the equity-to-loan ratio below the limits set on the account. In that case, the broker issues a margin call. The margin call asks the customer to immediately put equity into the account to restore the equity-to-loan ratio. If the customer fails to do this by the (short) deadline, then the broker has the authority to sell stocks in the account to raise cash and bring the equity-to-loan ratio back to the prescribed limit. However, this selling pressure may cause, in turn, greater stock drops in the marketplace. The new stock drop may create a further drop in the equity-to-loan ratio, and the cycle repeats. This feedback loop is a positive or reinforcing loop. Evidence has supported the assertion that this effect was a contributing factor to the 1929 stock market crash.

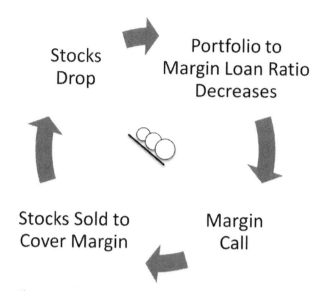

**Figure 19. Positive (Reinforcing) Feedback Loop
Driving Stock Prices Lower**

Linked Feedback Loops

Having two linked feedback loops is very common. In this section, we examine the case of two linked feedback loops in detail. In Figure 20, a reinforcing loop has been paired with a linked balancing loop. Here the impact of the value of the system variable on the system resources is modeled. A crucial parameter in this system is the carrying capacity. In biological systems, the carrying capacity might be the amount of food available for a species in an ecosystem. In a business system, the carrying capacity might be the total available market. Or, if the system being modeled is product development in an organization, the carrying capacity might be related to the total number of engineers in the organization. As the system variable increases and the use of resources approaches the carrying capacity, the rate of increase in the reinforcing loop is decreased. This makes the second feedback path a balancing loop.

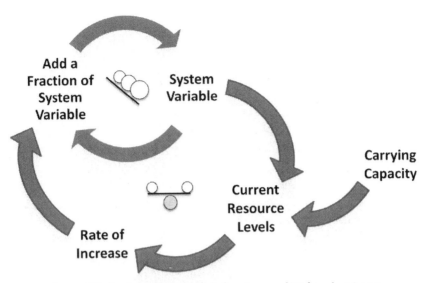

Figure 20. An Interlinked Reinforcing and Balancing Loop

The common structure of Figure 20 has the interesting characteristic that the dynamic behavior is very dependent on the specifics of the structure and its parameters. Figure 21 shows some of the types of dynamic behaviors that this system might demonstrate. The left figure shows the very common S-shaped curve. In business, we may see this shape in a product sales chart. The sales may increase quickly as the installed base and word-of-mouth advertising grows. Subsequently, the sales will plateau as most of the available market is reached and replacements dominate the sales. If delays are substantial, the system may oscillate as it approaches the carrying capacity limits. If there is a feedback mechanism between the system variable and the carrying capacity, then the system could subsequently collapse. In Chapter 4 of his book, John Sterman (2000) provides a Vensim model that is capable of simulating all of these dynamic behaviors by changing the model parameters.

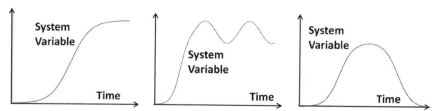

Figure 21. Some of the Different Dynamic Behaviors a Linked Reinforcing and Balancing Loop Might Produce

Multiple linked feedback loops make the diagnosis of solutions difficult. For the linked feedback loops of Figure 20, the slowing of growth resulting from the enhanced impact of the reinforcing loop may be a source of concern to the business that is depending on continued growth. The manager's intuition is often to enhance the reinforcing loop. For example, adding sales people, increasing advertising budgets, etc. However, there may be more leverage in reducing the impact of the balancing loop, for example, altering product features to reduce customer's concerns.

The dynamic behavior of these linked feedback loops can lead to some important errors in forecasting as illustrated for the S-curve dynamic in Figure 22. Primarily, this effect comes from the tendency to fit a linear trend onto the nonlinear system characteristics. Early on, the balancing loop has little effect and the reinforcing loop dominates, leading to exponential growth. In the early stage of exponential growth, data will be scarce. This scarcity makes the data much more susceptible to random fluctuations. With less data, participants may be easily swayed by outside factors such as news stories, opinions of experts, and emotional issues. Thus, the linear fit may either under or overestimate in this time period. This phenomenon is often seen in new markets. For example, in the early days of smart phones, manufacturers *hoping* for sales to cover their development costs may have overestimated the actual growth by predicting a linear, and faster growing, shape to the sales curve.

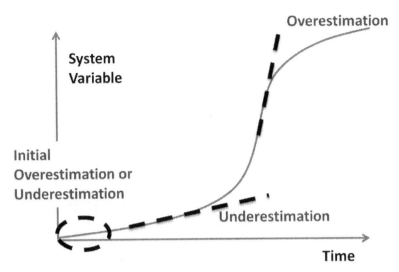

Figure 22. Illustration of Common Forecasting Errors Over the S-Curve Life Cycle

As the market gains traction, the installed base starts to have an impact on sales. Here, attempts to fit a linear trend to the data will typically underestimate growth. In the mid-1990s, Apple missed the nonlinear trend in demand for the Power Macintosh, and the lack of production capacity resulted in $1 billion of unfilled orders.

Finally, as sales slowly taper, there is a tendency for overestimation. This overestimation is a result of not recognizing the emerging balancing feedback loop. For example, in late 2011 several solar energy companies were caught with extreme excess capacity. The solar energy market demand had slowed as the balancing feedback loop driven by competition with other energy sources kicked in.

This example illustrates an important identification issue. In the early phases, the structure exhibits exponential growth. This identifies the reinforcing loop. However, the balancing loop is effectively dormant. It's only later in time that the balancing loop reveals itself in the data set. This leads to errors in misidentifying the system and errors in predicting the future state of the system. And this example is for a model with just two linked feedback loops. In real life situations, there are often many feedback loops present, with perhaps several dormant feedback loops lying in wait.

System Boundaries and Endogenous and Exogenous Variables

What defines a system? This seemingly simple question is at the center of considerable debate in the systems science field. One school of thought is that system boundaries are natural. For example, our solar system might represent a complete system with the vast distance to the next solar system being the factor that defines the system (philosophically this could be considered an ontological view). Others might argue that the system boundary is defined by the modeler and can be wherever the modeler chooses (this may, by contrast, be an epistemological view). For our applied purposes, we will skip this debate and declare both correct. Generally, the modeler should look for natural boundaries of the system to capture the most important and impactful structure. But the modeler has the latitude to include or exclude any portion of the system in their definition.

Systems reside in a nested structure; that is, each component in a system is a system in itself. And every system we are modeling resides within other systems. This nesting leads to the critical concept of endogenous versus exogenous variables. The word endogenous derives from the Greek *coming from*. An endogenous variable is generated within a system. For the system of Figure 20, the **System Variable** is endogenous as it is created within the system. Exogenous variables, by contrast, are generated outside the system. From Figure 20, the **Carrying Capacity** is exogenous.

One of the important systems thinking perspectives is to view variables that are usually considered *out of our control* (that is, exogenous) as parts of the system (or endogenous). In fact, this is one of the important messages from the key idea graphic (Figure 15). System variables are frequently not being uncontrollably manipulated by outside agencies like puppets on a string, but rather are responding to the hidden structures (feedback and delay) contained in the system.

Archetypes

Senge (1990) introduced the idea of system archetypes as being connections of feedback loops and delays that are frequently seen in complex human social systems. The small number of common structures is due to human complex systems having the same building blocks: human psychology, incentive structures, laws, regulations, and other aspects of human society. Senge listed nine archetypes:

- Balancing Process with Delay—A single balancing loop with delay.
- Limits to Growth—Linked reinforcing and balancing loops. (The linked feedback loop structure discussed in the last section is an example of this archetype).
- Eroding Goals—Two linked balancing loops where one loop has more delay than the other.
- Escalation—Two linked balancing loops with different balancing rates.
- Success to the Successful—Two linked reinforcing loops.
- Fixes That Fail—Linked balancing and reinforcing loops with a delay in the reinforcing loop (representing unintended consequences).
- Shifting the Burden—The eroding goals structure (two linked balancing loops where one loop has more delay than the other) with a third reinforcing loop.
- Growth and Underinvestment—Somewhat related to limits to growth, this structure has three interdependent feedback loops (two balancing and one reinforcing).
- Tragedy of the Commons—The most structurally complex archetype includes four linked feedback loops.

In Appendix 2 of *The Fifth Discipline,* Senge gives an excellent description of each archetype with examples. If you don't have the book, Wikipedia.org gives a brief description of each archetype (under "System Archetype"). The following examples will detail some of the more important archetypes for business.

Example: The Impact of Delays—The Beer Game

The beer game is a business simulation game created in the 1960s at MIT to provide training to business school candidates in the principles of supply chain management. There are a number of resources to learn about the beer game with perhaps the best being Chapter 3 of Senge's *The Fifth Discipline.* The game features three levels in a distribution chain where retailers sell beer to consumers, wholesalers sell the beer to retailers, and the manufacturer bottles the beer and sells to wholesalers. The game begins with the stages of the supply chain in a temporary equilibrium. There is a sudden increase in consumer demand in one particular beer due to, as we find out later, a music video that features that beer.

The beer game example is illustrative because it highlights the importance of delays in a feedback loop. The case highlights the *bullwhip effect*. As demand quickly outstrips stock, players order more inventory. Due to the delay in the system, the stock cannot be resupplied fast enough. Internally generated pressure provokes the player to order even more product. When the additional supply finally starts to arrive, it quickly builds up into excess inventory. This is an example of Senge's first archetype, balancing process with delay. The system diagram is shown in Figure 23.

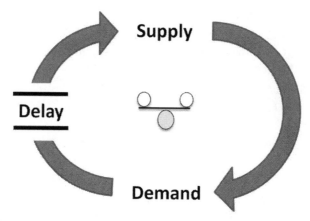

Figure 23. System Diagram for a Stage in the Beer Game

The narrative in Senge's Chapter 3 is interesting and educational. All of the decisions seem rational at the time. For the most part, the participants have the impression "that other guy is doing this to me," whether it be not delivering beer when their customer's need it, or delivering too much beer as the inventory piles up. But, when we step back and see the entire supply chain and the processes at work, it becomes evident that the shortages and inventory overstock are due to the inherent system attributes. The game has been repeated many times with MBA students, professors, and professionals, and the results are usually the same: The system structure drives the effect of shortages followed by stockpiles.

This example is also illustrative in the use of qualitative feedback loops as shown in Figure 23. When the analyst starts to graph out this feedback loop, it becomes apparent that the loop itself is heterogeneous—part of the loop is physical inventory (beer) and part of the loop is information (orders). This situation is quite common in qualitative loop diagrams. As we move into quantitative dynamics, we will be much more explicit about the feedback loops.

What could the participants do to improve the situation? Improving information flow is one reasonable approach. For example, giving the brewer some visibility into what's happening at the wholesaler could improve their planning. This bullwhip effect was at least partly a driving force in the development of vendor-managed inventory (VMI) systems in supply chains. With a VMI system, the wholesaler would take part in the management of inventory at the retailer, restocking shelves based on changes to inventory.

Example: Success to the Successful—VCR Wars and Intel

The home video cassette recorder (VCR) started gaining significant use in the mid-1970s. The new ability to *time shift*, to watch a program at the time of your choice rather than the time it was aired, was highly appealing. As the VCR market grew, the rental of movies became an important use for VCR owners. Two incompatible tape formats (one type could not play in the other machines) of VCRs were available: Betamax (Beta) and VHS. Beta was developed and sold by Sony. VHS was developed by JVC and licensed to a number of other manufacturers. While generally similar in design, there was one crucial design difference. The Betamax engineers optimized the design for higher quality recording whereas the VHS engineers gave up some recording quality to extend the maximum recording time. Quality versus record time turned out to be a crucial distinction when the movie rental business became important. The History Channel produced an excellent short video summarizing the VCR market. As of this writing, the video was available on YouTube (search for "Betamax versus VHS emergence of dominant design").

Two linked, reinforcing feedback loops evolved in this market, as shown in Figure 24. The open licensing of VHS enabled the reinforcing feedback loop on the left. Sales of VCR units is the key state variable. As sales increase, new entrants, makers of consumer electronics, become interested in the potential for profits. As new manufacturers join the market for VHS machines, competition increases. This competition, in turn, tends to decrease VCR prices as market participants attempt to gain market share. This drop in VCR prices now makes the technology even more affordable for consumers, and more price-conscious shoppers can afford machines. These new customers increase the sales even further. This reinforcing loop can be called a virtuous cycle since most of the participants, manufacturers and consumers, are benefitting. The consumers are getting lower prices and the manufacturers are getting a bigger market (which is likely offsetting the lower unit prices).

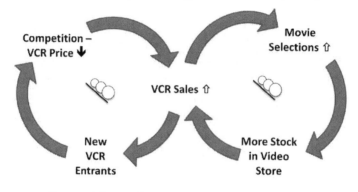

Open Licensing   Recording Length

Figure 24. The Two Powerful Interlocked Reinforcing Feedback Loops in the VCR Example

The feedback loop on the right of the figure relates to rental of movies. This business was nascent in the early stage of the market but grew to become large and influential in setting market direction. As non-replacement VCR units were sold, the installed base of VCRs (all the units that had been sold so far and were still in use) grew. As producers and distributors of tapes responded by producing more movies (drawn by the potential for more rentals and more profits), the selection of movies for consumers increased. Consumers who were considering the purchase of a VCR machine would be influenced by this greater rental movie selection, which, in turn, would increase VCR sales volume. This reinforcing feedback loop was also a virtuous cycle in that all participants, movie producers, rental stores, and consumers, benefitted from the growth.

In the competition in this market between the two formats—Beta and VHS—these two loops proved crucial. VHS technology could be licensed while Beta could not. So only VHS sales could benefit from the loop on the left. This increase in sales and installed base activated the loop on the right and drove VHS tapes to dramatically outnumber Beta tapes at the movie rental shops. The feedback loop on the right painted decidedly different pictures to VHS and Beta. As VHS sales grew, VHS movie selection also grew and influenced higher VHS sales, which became a virtuous cycle. However, for Beta, another version of the story emerged. As consumers chose VHS instead of Beta, the relative installed base of VHS increased over Beta. The movie distribution and rental firms responded to the decreasing installed base ratio by reducing the relative number of Beta movies to VHS movies in the rental stores. New consumers who would be using machines to view rented movies responded by favoring VHS because of the greater selection, and thus negatively impacted Beta VCR machine sales. This again dropped the relative installed bases, and the loop continued. For Sony and the owners of Beta VCRs, the loop is a vicious cycle.

The structure of Figure 24 had a huge influence on the dynamics of the VCR market in the 1970s and 1980s. While Sony introduced Beta first and held the dominant market share, VHS quickly caught up and overtook Sony in share. According to Wikipedia, by 1981 Beta's market share had dropped to 25%. By 1986 Beta's share had dropped to 7.5%.

The structure of this market competition is an example of Senge's *Success to the Successful* archetype (Figure 25). For alternatives competing for a common resource, customers in the VCR example, the relative success of one alternative creates even more success in the future. The two reinforcing loops take on different natures: virtuous to the successful and vicious to the unsuccessful.

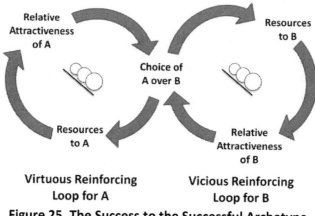

Virtuous Reinforcing
Loop for A

Vicious Reinforcing
Loop for B

Figure 25. The Success to the Successful Archetype

The Success to the Successful archetype is quite common, and very important in business situations. Two more examples of the Success to the Successful archetype will be provided, both from Intel. The first example involves the installed base of the Intel x86 processor architecture (the 286, 386, 486, Pentium, Pentium Pro, and so on). All x86 processors share a common basic mechanism to execute base level programs, called *machine code*. While high level software compilers can produce code for many types of base machine architecture, software developers usually need to make some level of modifications to their software, which depends on this base level architecture. Since software developers have limits on their resources, they will naturally target the machine codes with the largest market—the largest installed base—first. Since software is the reason why consumers purchase a computer, architectures with more software will be chosen more often. This Success to the Successful structure has limited non-x86 architectures for many years. It is one of the prime reasons that Apple Macintosh computers historically had a very hard time competing against PCs: The Apple Macintosh computers were based on non-x86 processors and were not able to run the same code. This translated into a delay in the introduction of software for a Macintosh compared to the x86-Windows version. Today Apple uses x86 processors in their Macintosh computers, mitigating this issue.

The next Success to the Successful example details a situation within Intel. Here the state variable is the resources for a chip design project. Creating a new x86 processor requires a large array of engineers, architects, technicians, and programmers. These highly skilled individuals are usually in limited supply. Consider the situation where two chips are being developed simultaneously at Intel. One project is an x86 processor, the other project is another microchip. The x86 processor in development would be expected to bring high margins into Intel. The potential profit of the other microchip would be much less certain. If the x86 processor development suddenly fell behind schedule, the tendency would be to divert resources away from the second microchip development to shore up the development of the x86 processor. This is one of the reasons that Intel's revenues are primarily driven by x86 processors and they've had difficulty getting new products into the mobile computing market such as cell phones.

The resource diversion situation was noticed at Intel. In fact, the CEO at the time, Craig Barrett, used the example of the creosote bush to try to explain this to the company and to mitigate the effect. Craig Barrett was based in Arizona and enjoyed exploring the desert and studying the flora and fauna. The creosote bush is a very interesting example of desert fauna. It looks normal, but one might notice nothing is growing underneath the bush. In the hot desert this is unusual as the shade provided by the bush is a beneficial environment for plants. But the creosote bush drops sap on the ground and kills any other plants except itself. Mr. Barrett used this analogy for the x86 processor killing other types of programs that tried to develop around it. Even though the effects of Success to the Successful were well understood within Intel, the archetype is so powerful that its effects are hard to mitigate.

Example: Markets With a System Dynamic Lens

The construct of feedback loops can be used to build a model of a market's pricing mechanism. Figure 26 shows a loop diagram of the classical market perspective of rational expectations and efficient market hypotheses.

Figure 26. System Dynamic View of Markets Under the Rational Expectations Theory and Efficient Market Hypothesis

Consider the case of the market determining the price of a particular stock. First, there is a large collection of **All Relevant Facts**. A relevant fact is anything that could impact the supply and demand of this particular stock. These facts can derive from factors that impact the overall economy, current issues in the geopolitical landscape, the prospects of the company, and so on. It is very possible, even likely, that many of the relevant facts may not be known by anyone who is participating in the market. And if so, these facts would be unable to influence the price of the stock until they became known to the market[11]. Each individual who participates in the market has access to a subset of this vast collection of relevant facts, **My Information**. For example, an individual investor may have read some of the financial reports, read some industry analysts' reports, and perhaps had some direct experience with the company's products. Using this subset of all relevant facts, the investor forms an expectation about the price of the stock, **My Expectation of Price**. Now, the investor logs into their trading website and checks the market price of the stock. If the stock is trading below expectation, then the investor has the tendency to buy the stock. If the stock is trading above expectation, and the investor is holding shares, there is the tendency to sell the stock. As investors take action, their buying and selling impacts the share price. Buying will tend to increase share price, and selling tends to reduce share price through supply and demand. As buying in the market increases the

---

[11] This is the basis of the levels of insider information in the efficient market hypothesis.

price of the stock, the expectation of profit is reduced. This, in turn, reduces the buying. Thus the buying and selling impact on market price form a balancing feedback loop. The model of Figure 26 depicts what economists call the *rational expectation theory* and the *efficient market hypothesis*. As new information becomes available to market participants, it is quickly integrated into the market price through this structure.

Consider now the potential impact of changes in **Market Price** on **My Expectation of Price**. For example, the consistent increase in the prices of houses in the United States in the early 2000s likely influenced the expectation that prices would continue to rise in the future. This effect has been called *herding*, but could also be considered a rational form of observational learning (we will discuss this much more in Chapter 4)[12]. The loop from **Market Price** to **My Expectation of Price** to **Buy/Sell/No Action** is reinforcing since buying on expectation of a price increase will increase prices from supply and demand considerations.

Figure 27 shows the original model of Figure 26 with the new feedback loop of **Market Price** to **My Expectation of Price** to **Buy/Sell/No Action** added. It illustrates the nested reinforcing and balancing loops. The interplay between the strengths of the two loops can create a vast array of dynamic behavior of the market price over time.

Figure 27. Market Price Model

---

[12] This situation can describe a type of technical trader often called a *trend follower*. Note that there could be a type of behavior that is exactly the opposite. These traders are sometimes called *contrarians*. When a contrarian sees the market price being driven up, they may expect it to decline in the future.

Finally, it is worth noting that in the real world there are always more feedback loops at work. For example, there exists another loop that accounts for the impact of **Market Price** on **All Relevant Facts**. As market prices increase, investors' portfolios will increase. As individuals see their net worth increase, they may be more apt to make purchases. These extra purchases increase the profits of the companies selling those purchased products. As these profits are reported to the market, the relevant facts have changed and may increase the price of the stock from the efficient market model of Figure 26. This feedback loop is sometimes referred to as the *wealth effect*. Clearly, there will be a long delay involved in this feedback loop.

Qualitative Dynamics: Action Plan

Qualitative dynamics and archetypes are one of the most powerful instruments in the toolbox. The key idea that was summarized in Figure 15 is that structure impacts behavior over time. In this figure, structure is specifically feedback loops and delays. Archetypes were also introduced as a powerful tool to help us make sense of the dynamic complexity.

Recognizing feedback loops presents a number of challenges to the ideas of simple causality. If a variable is in a feedback loop, then a *chicken and egg* dilemma presents itself. Did changes in other parts of the feedback loop *cause* the variable to change? Or did the change of the variable *cause* changes in the other parts of the feedback loop? Further, in real-world business situations, the variable we are usually interested in may reside in many, perhaps dozens, of feedback loops. *How can simple, direct causality be ascertained from this web of dynamic relationships?*

Qualitative system dynamics is a powerful tool to help categorize behaviors as endogenous or exogenous with respect to the system under study. In the beer game, the human tendency is to blame the shortages that are followed by large stockpiles of inventory on forces outside one's control ("that wholesaler is out to get me"), when they are in fact endogenously created by the participant's actions and the inherent delays in the system.

The major steps in qualitative dynamic analysis are:

1. Identify the System—Perhaps the most important aspect here is specifying the system boundary. Generally, our goal is to specify the boundary wide enough so that the behavior of interest is generated endogenously. For example, if you are the brewer in the beer game, the system needs to include the customers, wholesalers, and the factory in order to gain an understanding of the mechanisms that lead to shortages and overruns of product inventory.

2. Identify Feedback Loops and Delays—In the beer game, participants must recognize that there is a certain amount of time to get an order to the wholesaler, and there's also a delay in the wholesaler to the brewery. The modeler must identify that the flow of information (orders) followed by the flow of product (beer) forms a feedback loop.

3. Look for Building Blocks—Look at your diagram of feedback loops and delays to identify potential building blocks, either linked feedback loops or archetypes. The linked reinforcing and balancing loop of Figure 20 is very common. Perhaps you have drawn a reinforcing loop and haven't identified a balancing loop. This could be because the balancing loop's effects are small and the loop is effectively dormant. If you have identified several feedback loops, then review the archetypes in the appendix of Senge's book. It is very possible that your situation is described by one of these archetypes.

4. Sketch Out Possible Dynamic Behaviors—Given the structure you have identified, what possible dynamic behaviors can be produced? Compare those to what has been observed to build support for your initial model. Does the model support the observed data? If not, there may be unidentified loops or delays present.

5. Search for Leverage Points and Potential Unintended Consequences of Interventions—When a model produces dynamic behavior like the real system, start to examine the model for insights. Are there key leverage points in your model? In the beer game, reducing the delays in order flow or gaining more information on inventory across the distribution channel are important leverage points. Where might potential unintended consequences lie? In the beer game, ordering in the face of shortages leads to massive inventory buildup.

6. Consider if the model may be a useful communication or training tool for the organization. A model, especially one that is interactive and with graphics, can be particularly valuable to educating others on the system's structure.

7. Remember It's Only a Model—Always remember George Box's excellent advice, "All models are wrong, but some are useful." The feedback and delays you have identified are only part of the picture. There may be tens or hundreds of feedback loops and delays that have not been identified. Further, there are many more types of system effects (as discussed in the remaining chapters) potentially at work.

Quantitative Dynamics: System Dynamic Simulations

Now we will build upon the understanding of qualitative system dynamic models by taking the analysis to the next level of detail and constructing simulation models. This will entail taking the qualitative model and adding a level of specificity. Recall that the goal of this introduction to system dynamic simulation is to help you understand and appreciate the applications, not for you to gain simulation proficiency.

Quantitative dynamics is a rich field that primarily developed at MIT. The founder of this work is Jay Forrester. John Sterman, one of Forrester's students, has been a primary driver of the field after Forrester and has written the most extensive text on the topic, *Business Dynamics* (2000). It is worthwhile to browse online videos and watch these two luminaries speak on this topic. There's also a very active system dynamics society with an excellent annual conference. The conference papers are published and are a great resource.

The key idea graphic for this section is shown in Figure 28. On the left is a graphic representing the qualitative analysis of the beer game. Here we used the Senge archetype (Balancing Process with Delay) to gain a basic understanding of the nature of the shortages and stockpiles in inventory. This qualitative analysis afforded an understanding of the endogenous nature of these inventory aberrations. It showed that the participant's own actions were as much to blame as those of the others in the supply chain. It also gave some clues as to possible avenues to improve the situation (e.g., focus on improving information flow across the channel, reducing delays and avoiding reactionary behavior). In this section, we will build actual simulation models as depicted on the right side of the figure. Here, data from the system under analysis is collected and dynamic simulation models are created. When we feel that the model has validity, then various simulation studies can be performed to examine model sensitivities and potential interventions.

Beer Game Qualitative   **Beer Game Quantitative**

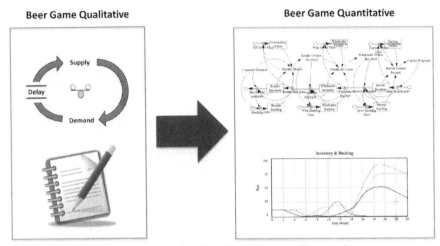

Figure 28. Key Idea for Quantitative Dynamics

To explain the process of building a system dynamic simulation model, the feedback loop of a bank account accumulating interest, as shown earlier in Figure 16, will be used. The first step in the process is constructing a loop diagram[13]. Here, the qualitative loop diagram is taken to the next level of detail. Figure 29 shows the loop diagram for the bank account accumulating interest which was discussed previously. The individual bank account is represented as an oval labeled **Individual Account**. Interest can flow into the account per the arrow from the variable labeled **Interest Payment**. The exact value of this interest is determined from two factors: the interest rate at the time of the calculation (**Agreed Interest Rate**) and the level of funds in the account. The interest payment itself comes from the bank's coffers indicated by the variable **Bank's Funds**.

---

[13] Many in the field call these *causal loop diagrams* or CLDs. However, here the term *causal* has been removed because it might imply to the general reader that a high level of causality can be ascribed in complex systems. The causal in causal loop diagram refers to the direct link between two items in the diagram and does not imply broader causality.

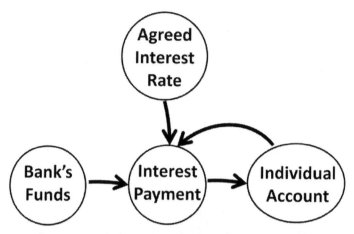

Figure 29. Loop Diagram of Bank Account Model

Once the loop diagram is complete, the simulation model can be specified in the simulation software. There are a number of software applications available to create system dynamic simulations. Vensim is particularly useful because a student evaluation version is available for free download. The free version does not have any inherent limits (e.g., data size) but this version doesn't have some of the more advanced features of the for-purchase versions. Figure 30 is an annotated Vensim model of the bank account accumulating interest. The **Money in the Bank Account** block on the right is a stock. One can think of a stock as a container for something. For example, a bathtub is a container for water. The value of a stock variable is measured in units (in this case dollars). The double arrow going into the **Money in the Bank Account** stock is called a *flow*. It represents a channel for items to move into the stock. One could think of water flowing through the faucet into the bathtub as a flow. Flows are measured in units of the stock items per unit of time. For this example, the interest is flowing as dollars per month (or whatever the frequency of the interest payments). The hourglass shape in the flow line is a flow control. It modulates the flow into the stock. Imagine the valve that controls the flow of water into the bathtub. The single arrow from the stock **Money in the Bank Account** to the flow control **Interest Payments** is an influence line. These usually represent the flow of information. In this example, the current account balance is used in the determination of the interest payment. The final component in Figure 30 is the cloud symbol to the left and is an infinite (for the purposes of the simulation) sink or source of the material of the flow. Here, it is the bank's funds used to pay account interest.

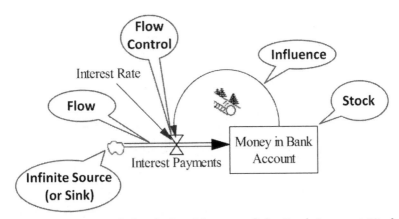

Figure 30. Annotated Simulation Diagram of the Bank Account Model

Simulation tools provide the ability to specify all the details of the model. The flow control points allow input of equations to specify the relationship between the influence factors and their effect on the flow. The initial condition of stocks can be set. Dynamic simulators create the behavior of the system by solving the imbedded sets of differential equations using mathematical approximation techniques. Once the model is specified, Vensim allows the dynamic behavior of the system to be simulated. Figure 31 shows a simulation of the model in Figure 30. This graph is the value of the money in the bank account over time.

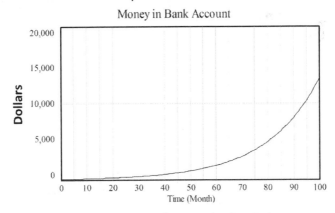

**Figure 31. Output of Dynamic Simulation:
The Bank Account Grows Exponentially**

Example: Building a Dynamic Simulation—The Beer Game

Rather than spending a lot of time discussing the methods of building a simulation model, let's take a hands-on approach and walk our way through the construction of a dynamic simulation of the beer game. This is a moderately complicated model and will give us a chance to introduce a number of challenges and approaches in the process. Further, this model represents a greatly simplified model of the real situation. Thus, the model could be used to build insights into real-world situations. The actual Vensim model is available for download at RichJolly.com/STBdownload.

Recall the discussion in Chapter 2 on deductive versus inductive reasoning methods and their application to model construction. The dynamic simulation designer needs to decide on an approach in their modeling process. Being more deductive, or generative as Epstein and Axtell would describe it, increases the explanatory power of the model. But, a deductive approach may impact the ability of the model to fit historical data, and thereby superficially impact its credibility. Adding more elements and parameters, an inductive approach, will improve the ability of the model to match real-world data at the risk of overfitting. The tradeoff represents just one of many yin-yang relationships the systems thinker must confront. In this example, the modeler has attempted to strike the balance by building model elements from fundamental analysis of the system, and using calibration techniques to allow the model to match real-world behavior. The process shown is not meant to be the *right* approach. The choice of approach depends on the specific situation.

First, a detailed loop diagram is created. Figure 23 showed one stage of the supply chain at an abstract level. In the detailed loop diagram, all elements and their relationships need to be specified. This detailed diagram for one stage is shown in Figure 32. First, note that here, as in many business situations, the main feedback loop is heterogeneous. That is, information (orders) flows in the direction towards the factory, and the product (beer) flows from the factory to the consumers. This forms a large feedback loop all the way from the customer orders through the retailer, the wholesaler, up to the brewer, and then the feedback loop completes as beer comes back down the supply chain. Since backlog and inventory will be used in order size decisions, these variables need to be added to the diagram. Backlog and inventory will be modeled as stocks because they are values within the system that are measured in units. Sales and product delivery will be flows because they're movements of either information or product. The diagram details that orders to the supplier will depend on orders from customers, the current inventory, and the backlog. Order quantity is the primary decision to model for the retailer and wholesaler.

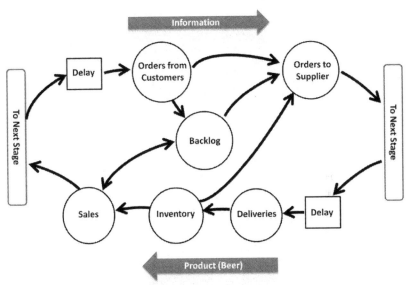

Figure 32. Beer Game Participant's Detailed Loop Diagram

Once the detailed loop diagram is complete, the next step is to convert it into the simulation building blocks of stocks, flows, controls, etc., as illustrated in Figure 30. The model for the wholesaler is shown in Figure 33. Here, outstanding orders, inventory, and backlog are modeled as stocks. Retailer orders received is a parameter in this section of the model, but will be an output of the retailer section when the complete model is built. Similarly, wholesaler orders will link to the factory section of the model when fully assembled.

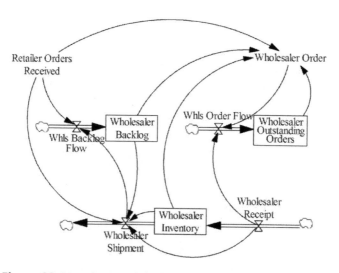

Figure 33. Vensim Model of the Beer Game Wholesaler

Each section (retailer, wholesaler, and factory) is modeled, and the sections are linked together to form a complete model as shown in Figure 34 (download a full sized copy of this figure from RichJolly.com/STBdownload). The next task is to describe the exact nature of the relationships. Specifically, that means building the equations that will populate the flow gates and decision models. With these equations complete, the parameters and initial conditions are specified and the model tested.

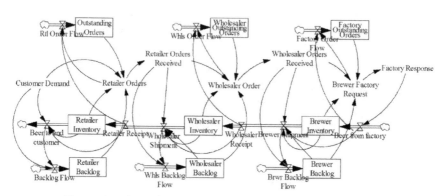

Figure 34. Complete Vensim Model of the Beer Game

Completing these final steps will require data from the system being modeled. For this example, data given in Chapter 3 of Senge's *The Fifth Discipline* was used to complete a data table. At the beginning of the chapter, and the early stages of the story, Senge describes the situation at the retailer. So the retailer's demand, inventory, sales orders, and delivery are well understood early in the chronology. However, for the later weeks the text gives very little data about the retailer. Data for the wholesaler and factory are sprinkled through the chapter. The result is a sparsely populated matrix of data.

The next step will require a bit of detective work and interpretation of the text. Senge gives clues to the specific nature of many of the relationships. A complete set of data (Figure 35) is generated using these relationships and interpolation between data points. In system dynamic simulation, this data set is referred to as the *reference behavior pattern* (RBP). Note that this sparse data is quite common when building simulations of real business situations. Often data for the system is incomplete, and the modeler must make assumptions and interpolation to get a complete data set. The RBP data is available for download at RichJolly.com/STBdownload.

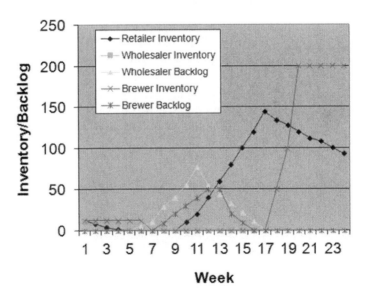

Beer Game Behavior

**Figure 35. Complete Beer Game
Reference Behavior Pattern (RBP)**

The next major task is to specify the decision models. The most crucial decision is the order size for any link in the supply chain. The order size in the model is described as a relationship based on four factors: inventory, backlog, outstanding supplier orders, and weekly customer orders. In the real system, this is likely a nonlinear relationship, but there isn't nearly enough data to fit a nonlinear model, and it would be difficult to fit a nonlinear model even if there was some idea of the relationship. The option used here was to perform multiple linear regression. This does not take into account interactions (e.g., a factor such as backlog multiplied by inventory) between these variables. The linear model for orders used is:

$$Our\ Orders = a_1 * C + a_2 * B - a_3 * I - a_4 * O + a_5$$

The variables are:

Symbol	Factor	Effect on Orders
C	New customer orders	As new customer orders grow, weekly orders increase.
B	Customer order backlog	As backlog grows, weekly orders increase.
I	Inventory	As inventory grows, weekly orders decrease.
O	Cumulative outstanding orders to supplier	As outstanding orders grow, orders decrease.

Now multiple regression techniques can be used to fit the parameters of the model. Using the RBP data, the following coefficients can be extracted for the wholesaler's order model:

$$Wholesaler\ Orders = C + B - 0.3 * I - 0.08 * O + 4$$

The next task is specifying the remaining model equations and parameters. Equation models must be specified for every relationship, and parameters throughout must be specified. As was described above for orders, flow gate equations can be simple linear models. When each equation has been specified and a value to each parameter has been assigned, the modeler can begin fitting the model's behavior to the RBP. In almost all cases, this will require changing parameters from the initial assumptions. Some of the advanced versions of Vensim have a maximum likelihood fitting capability to estimate parameters. With the free version of Vensim, the modeler can work through a process of trial and error to find the best parameters. For models of this complexity, there will be multiple sets of different parameter sets that can match the RBP, a crucial topic we will discuss in much more detail later. After fitting parameters, the final simulation model behavior is shown in Figure 36. This is seen to be a good fit with the RBP data of Figure 35.

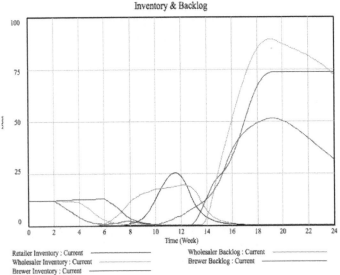

Figure 36. Vensim Simulation of the Beer Game

Once the model is complete and representative of the RBP there are several uses:

1. Sensitivity Analysis—Individual parameters can be varied to assess their impact on key system variables. The variables with the largest impact are the key leverage points in the system. These variables would be a focus for further study of the real system.

2. Intervention Analysis—Different potential strategies for improving troublesome system variables (such as inventory buildup) can be tested with the model. In this example, different strategies for improved information flow across system elements could be added. For example, a link could be added from retailer inventory to the factory to represent the

brewery making direct contact with retailers to assess system wide inventory.

3. Communication—The model could be used by members of the supply chain to communicate the nature of inventory shortages and oversupply. This education may modify behavior, which could potentially change the decision models used by participants and improve the performance of the system.

Considerations in Building Simulation Models

When building any type of fitted model, be it a system dynamic simulation or a machine learning regression model, there are a number of important considerations.

Testing a system dynamic model for *correctness* has two distinct components: verification and validation. The first step, verification, is a process of determining if you have built what you intended to build (that is, your conceptual model). This process is dominated by correcting any errors in the model connections, equations, and specification of parameters. By analogy, if you were writing a report, this process of correcting errors would amount to a check of spelling, grammar, and logical completeness. The second procedure is validation and is the process of testing how well the model matches the real-world system. Perhaps the most common validation method is breaking the real system data into two sets: a training set and a test set. The training set is used to determine the parameters of the model. Then, the completed model's behavior is compared to the test set data to assess validity. For example, if Ben Bernanke's team were building a model of the economy, they might use the economic data from 2012 to determine the model's parameters, and then test the model validity with data from the first half of 2013. We will later see a serious question that must be considered when using this ubiquitous validation procedure (see Chapter 6, Question 7).

A simulation model of a complex system that fits the real-world system's behavior may not be unique. That is, there may be other models that can fit the given reference behavior. We can quickly see the nature of this phenomenon from a very simple algebra problem. What is the solution of $x^2 = 9$? If you said 3, your math instructor would remind you that there are two possible solutions. Both 3 and -3 meet the relationship. In the same way, there may be multiple, perhaps even an infinite number, of other models that can fit the RBP to the same level of accuracy.

A crucial issue that tends to get little discussion in the system dynamic modeling field is model data fit. This is intimately related to the discussion in Chapter 2 on deductive versus inductive reasoning in model construction. Specifically, the issue is *underfitting* versus *overfitting* of a model (often called *bias* versus *variance* in mathematical modeling). Figure 37 illustrates this phenomenon. Consider a collection of *x* and *y* data as shown by the dots. Fitting this data with a straight line (simple linear regression) yields a reasonable fit. But we can see this straight line is not as good as the parabolic shape of the middle figure. The figure on the right exhibits overfitting. The error between model and data is minimized, but instinctively we expect this more complicated model is just fitting to noise in the data and not the nature of the underlying relationship. In the same way, overfitting in a system dynamic model, while quite satisfying when comparing model performance to RBP data, will reduce the explanatory power of the model and make it very poor at predicting future behavior of the system. For system dynamic models, adding more stocks, flows, relationship lines, etc., all add to the complexity of the model and risk of overfitting. Each added component should be carefully considered in terms of parsimony. Remember Albert Einstein's famous quote "Everything should be kept as simple as possible, but no simpler."

| Underfit | Good Fit | Overfit |

Figure 37. Illustration of Underfitting and Overfitting

Dynamic System Simulation: Action Plan

As depicted in Figure 28, the key idea graphic, we've moved from the insightful qualitative analysis of system dynamics and discussed the construction of system dynamic simulation models. We went into a rather lengthy discussion of building the beer game model to understand the process in some depth. The process begins with a gathering of information to understand how all the pieces fit together, and then pulling together a set of data that is to be used to fit the model. As complicated as they might seem, the models themselves are great simplifications of reality. The beer game is a greatly simplified case of reality. For example, the diversity of many different beer stores is modeled as one homogenous retailer. Also, complicated, and often emotional, human decision models, such as order quantity, have been drastically simplified. Since we rarely have full visibility into all aspects of the model, the data set will need to be completed with a certain amount of intuition and interpolation. Despite these limitations, there is still great value in the modeling exercises.

First, a model can help with understanding. The rigor of building a model helps us to focus our thinking about a real-world situation. We will formalize the exact nature of the feedback loops. For example, in the beer game we need to formalize the loop as a flow of information (orders) up the supply chain, and a flow of product (beer) down the chain. With the process of modeling, the importance of backlog is highlighted. Simulations allow you to look for leverage points by testing the sensitivities of model variables to parameters. Models may give insight into lurking patterns of behavior such as oscillations and exponential growth.

Communication is another key benefit of a system dynamic model. When we have an insight into a system from dynamic analysis, a system dynamic model can be an outstanding tool to illustrate the idea to colleagues, customers, management, and so on. If a simulation can be made interactive, its ability to foster the integration of knowledge by your audience will be enhanced.

Using a system dynamic simulation as flight simulators for management training is an outstanding use of the technology. Management flight simulators are a cost efficient way to get managers training in business situations with minimal company resources.

There's a tremendous value in the process of building the simulation model. The process provides a structured checklist to examine a system. The collection of data can be quite insightful. Important data that is not being collected in a meaningful way may be discovered. Collecting real-world data requires many meetings with people in an organization. When getting the data, the discussions are likely to yield interesting insight into decision processes, and perhaps into factors that might not have initially been considered.

Systems models can build support for the system affects studied. This *generative science* idea, originally proposed by Epstein and Axtell (1996), argues that being able to generate a phenomenon with a model adds support for the assertions of the model. For example, we are asserting that the dramatic changes in inventory in the beer game, from shortages to dramatic overstock, are the result feedback loops with delays. By reproducing the phenomenon in our simulation model, we have supported this assertion. Note that due to the nature of inference, we can't *prove* that feedback loops are responsible.

Invariably, when system dynamic models are shown, a business audience imagines the tools being used to predict the future states of the system. The allure of this option is strong, and these tools often find some role in this usage. But extreme caution must be used. First, the inherent simplification from the real-world system means that predictions from the model may not represent future states. One specific area where prediction may be valid is *scenario development*. Running the model may show possible system states that weren't on your radar before. For example, in the early days of the beer game, when beer was hard to get, the idea of huge stockpiles of inventory may not have occurred to the participants. If the model predicts scenarios you hadn't considered, you may wish to examine if your organization is ready for these situations and how it might respond.

Further Reading

In a prioritized list of further reading on this topic, there is no question what comes first: Peter Senge's *The Fifth Discipline*. The key sections to read are Part I and Part II, along with Appendix 2. The ultimate focus of Senge's book is organizational development. If that topic interests you, then the rest of the book is highly recommended as well.

For quantitative dynamics, John Sterman's work ranks the highest. Sterman's 2001 article in the *California Management Review*, "System Dynamics Modeling: Tools for Learning in a Complex World" (2001) is an excellent summary. His book, *Business Dynamics* (2000) is excellent and, although a textbook, quite readable.

If you are pressed for time, then Chapter 5 of Beinhocker's *The Origin of Wealth* (2006) is a valuable short discussion.

Questions

1. Is the demise of dinosaurs from an asteroid impact an exogenous effect? (Think this one through carefully).

2. It's 1984 and you have just graduated with your business degree. Thanks in part to your exceptional interviews (where you impressed the team with your systems thinking skills), you have landed a job as a general manager at Sony. When you report to work, you learn your role is GM of the Betamax unit (where the previous GM has suddenly left to "spend more time with his family"[14]). After a very short honeymoon period, your boss demands that you reverse the market share trend and grow shares to 45%—or else! Your best option is:
A. To license Beta and start your own virtuous cycle.
B. To use the concepts of feedback loops and the Success to the Successful archetype to educate management on the market situation and renegotiate a goal.
C. To spiff (incentivize) movie distributors to increase the flow of Beta tapes to video stores.
D. To focus on niches where Beta quality has an edge and start market demand programs in those areas.

---

[14] Generally "left to spend more time with their family" is a business euphemism for "resigned rather waiting to be fired."

3. The efficient market hypothesis (EMH) is frequently mentioned in the discussion of financial markets. As discussed, this theory asserts that all available relevant information has already been incorporated into the equity price. It's also an important idea for prediction markets, which will be discussed in Chapter 4. The EMH would assert that no one could consistently achieve above-average market returns given available information (since that information is already incorporated into stock prices). The EMH prompts trading strategies such as investing in simple stock index funds. With this strategy, the investor gets the average market return and reduces costs as much as possible.

The EMH follower who considers the stock system to consist of those who buy and sell stocks (the stock exchanges, brokers, institutions, individuals, etc.) but not the economy itself believe that:
A.   Stock prices change due to exogenous events.
B.   Stock prices sometimes change due to endogenous effects.
C.   Stock changes are simply random fluctuations within the system.

4. Another school of thought in investing is *technical analysis*. Technicians (those using technical analysis) look at historical stock prices and make trading decisions based on those prices. You might hear them discuss resistance levels, support, trend lines, and so on. According to the EMH, technicians should not be able to make above average returns because historical stock data is publically available.

The technical analyst who considers the stock system to consist of those who buy and sell stocks (the stock exchanges, brokers, institutions, individuals, etc.) but not the economy itself believe that:
A.   Stock prices only change due to exogenous events.
D.   Stock prices sometimes change due to endogenous effects.
B.   Stock changes are simply random fluctuations within the system.

5. In the late 1980s, Intel decided that they must address the market for 64-bit instruction set computing (the current x86 was limited to 32 bits). The team decided that the existing x86 architecture simply couldn't be extended successfully to 64 bits (although there was a minority report that suggested otherwise). This launched what was to become known as the *Itanium* program, which was a completely new instruction set processor. While the Itanium processor could not natively run x86

programs, the idea was that it would be launched into the high-end segments of the market (for example servers in big data centers) where code compatibility is less important. Intel believed Itanium would eventually work its way down into the lower-end segments (desktop computers and laptops). In essence, the plan was that Itanium would supplant x86. What Senge archetype would you advise Intel to pay special heed to? (For an excellent account of this situation, see the insightful book by the Intel architect Robert Colwell *The Pentium Chronicles,* (2006).

6. Which of these concepts from this chapter have the potential to lead to a Black Swan event for a company?
A. A powerful dormant feedback loop that suddenly activates.
B. Exogenous inputs that are far outside of the range considered normal.
C. Companies using system dynamic model results as predictive forecasts of the future.
D. All of the above.
E. None of the above.

7. Critics of system dynamic simulation might argue that a major shortcoming of the method is that it generally models neither diversity (e.g., all customers are the same) nor randomness. Do you agree or disagree?

Dynamics

Discussion of Questions

1. It all depends on how you define the system. If your system is the earth and its atmosphere, then yes, the asteroid is exogenous. If your system is the solar system, then no, it is an endogenous event because the asteroid is part of the solar system.

2. A) This is probably not a good idea at this time. It's not likely to help with market share and it will reduce margins.

B) That's the best option. Feedback loops and archetypes are great for communication. You may have a chance. But, you may want to polish up your resume when you have a chance because there is no guarantee that your manager will renegotiate.

C) It might help, but the issue is that consumers who have VHS machines will demand these tapes at the video stores. That will dictate what the distributor can sell.

D) This is a pretty good strategy (essentially a cash cow), but there's little hope of getting a 45% share. You may bring in some good margin to the company, but your manager can still implement the *or else* clause. Perhaps you could try to renegotiate this as the goal using Option B.

3. The EMH states that stock price changes are due to new information becoming available and being integrated into the price. Since the question states that EMH followers consider the economy to be outside the system, then the price changes are exogenous. The EMH argues these changes are unpredictable and appear random so the third option is quite tempting but not correct.

4. Technical analysts believe that historical price changes can foretell and influence future price changes. In these cases, price changes would be an endogenous effect. In fact, trend followers often have the mantra of ignoring the news (which is precisely where EMH followers believe *all* changes are coming from).

5. This was a costly mistake by Intel. Intel underestimated Senge's Success to the Successful archetype. The successful here was the x86 architecture. This is despite the fact that this archetype led the company to their

greatest success (as discussed in the example of this chapter)! So, the industry structure (the archetype) treated the Itanium processor just like all the competitor products that came before it (MIPS, SPARC, and other processor architectures). AMD, on the other hand, asked their engineers to extend the x86 to 64 bit, and the engineers succeeded. AMD was first to release a 64 bit x86 architecture to the world, and for the first time (but not the last), Intel was a follower to AMD. Intel eventually extended their x86 processors to 64 bits. Today, Itanium is a small part of the server market used exclusively by Hewlett-Packard (who eventually shared in the development costs).

6. Recall that a Black Swan requires:
1. The event to be unexpected or considered improbable to the observer.
2. The event has a major impact on the observer.
3. In hindsight, the observer rationalizes that they "should have seen it coming." This, then, is a narrative fallacy as described earlier in this chapter.
Both A and B have the potential to make a system dynamic model incorrect. But, the company must be relying on the model to generate its expectation of the future for them to have a major impact. Thus, D, All of the Above, is the correct response.

7. Well true. However, I'd tell them that it's not our intention to model reality; the goal is to study particular aspects of reality.

4. Aggregated Interactions

The second core component of our systems thinking toolbox—aggregated interactions—will now be explored. Studying this phenomenon and modeling with agent-based modeling (ABM) is fascinating and really catches the interest of many systems thinkers.

Key Idea

Figure 38 is the key idea graphic for this section. The concept of aggregated interactions centers around the action of agents. Each agent acts based on their own unique situation using a set of guiding principles called *rules* in ABM. These rules allow the agent to adapt to the situation as other agents act or as the state of the environment changes. As the agents act, their actions, in turn, influence the actions of other agents. Thus, these interactions between agents are being aggregated, and, through time, the emergent effect presents itself.

Randomness can play a crucial role in the process of emergence. Different random variations can create totally different outcomes. Diversity will also be crucial. Diverse characteristics across the agents may be the driving force behind the emergent effect.

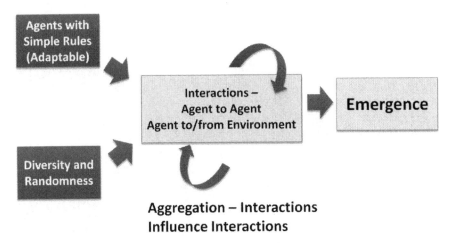

Figure 38. The Key Idea in the Aggregation of Interactions

Emergent phenomena from the aggregation of interactions are decentralized self-organized processes. Decentralized meaning there's no central authority directing the efforts. A central authority is not telling the individuals what to do; they're organizing themselves based on these processes. This is important for the business world. Corporate culture is an example of an emergent process. We can think of the *Dilbert* cartoons where the managers in the conference room write a corporate culture statement. In fact, large corporations do that. But the culture will not be dictated by a statement of the official corporate culture. The corporate culture will be built by the way senior managers act, and the way these actions affect managers and employees below them. Crowdsourcing is another example of an emergent phenomenon from the aggregation of interactions. Wikipedia and open-source software, such as Linux, are excellent examples of crowdsourcing.

The emergent phenomena happen from the bottom up. To understand aggregated interactions requires a constructionist analysis; that is, to see these effects you may need to build them up or simulate them. There may be no other method of determining what could happen. By the same token, they're nondecomposable. When the emergent effect is complete, it may be virtually impossible to deconstruct how all those interactions had aggregated. There can be either temporal or spatial emergence. Emergent phenomena from aggregated interactions are very path-dependent: Depending on the starting conditions, you could end up at very different emergent patterns.

Aggregated interaction effects can be simulated in software in a process referred to as agent-based modeling (ABM) or agent-based simulations (ABS). These simulations can be performed with any object-oriented programming language. Alternately, some specially designed ABM graphical environments are available. This book will use NetLogo, an easy to use, free, graphical programming and simulation environment. Agent-based models typically feature a grid, usually called patches, which represent the environment. Also, the models typically contain one or more agents. These agents represent actors in the environment. Agents can move on the grid and interact with other agents and the environment. The NetLogo environment affords the modeler a simple graphical means to run the model and change the characteristics of the simulation. These programs run on discrete time steps, dynamically running mini-programs within each agent and environmental patch.

There are various types of processes that rely on the aggregation of interactions:

- Sorting—Agents change locations. We will explore this mechanism in detail in the next example on segregation.
- Recruitment—Agents recruit other agents. An example of this process is ants recruiting other ants to collect food. We will explore this shortly.
- Assimilation—Agents assimilate information. An example of assimilation is the integration of information by market participants. We will explore this in detail as we examine *The Wisdom of Crowds*.
- Synchronizing (peer influence)—Agents alter their preferences. Fads and fashion fall into this category. We'll explore this in some detail as we look at Granovettor's model later in the chapter.

Understanding these processes is important in the business world. If a phenomenon in the business system is being driven by aggregated interactions, then the techniques of this chapter are needed to understand them because the standard business techniques will be inadequate. Also, these effects may provide valuable business tools. For example, crowdsourcing may supply valuable project resources. Or, prediction markets may be used as a tool for organizational knowledge management.

Sorting—Ethnic Segregation

Ethnic segregation had perplexed sociologists for many years. Figure 39 shows an ethnic diversity map of New York City. The shades represent households of a given ethnic background (see the full color view at RichJolly.com/STBdownload). The figure illustrates the very heavy concentration of ethnic groups in the area. What perplexed sociologists was that the reported preferences for similar ethnic groups from surveys was markedly different from the actual density of the groups observed.

Figure 39. Ethnic Diversity Map of New York City

By investigating the way individual actions aggregate, it is possible to gain insight into this phenomenon. We will follow in the footsteps of the Nobel Prize winning economist and sociologist Thomas Schelling in this example. This example will also be used to introduce agent-based simulation using NetLogo. To begin, we define a percent similar metric as shown in Figure 40. Here the agent in the center red square has three red neighbors, four green neighbors, and one vacant patch. The similarity metric for the agent in the center square can be calculated as three similar neighbors divided by seven total neighbors (since there are seven total possible neighbors), or 43%.

Red	Green	Vacant
Green	Red	Red
Green	Red	Green

Figure 40. In this Example of the Similarity Metric, the Percent Similar for the Agent in the Center Square is 3/7 (43%)

First, the NetLogo screen, Figure 41, will be explained. On the right, the large square is the simulation frame. The dark dots represent agents of the red variety. The light dots represent agents of the green variety. Each space on the frame represents a potential location for an agent. In this case, there are nearly as many agents as possible locations. On the top left we see two sliders and two buttons. The slider on the top is labeled **Number** and the little bar can be moved with the mouse left and right to change the number of agents in the simulation. The slider below, labeled **% Similar Wanted**, is used to set the similarity metric as discussed above and shown in Figure 40 . By pressing the button labeled **Set Up**, a new simulation will be initialized with the characteristics set by the sliders. When the **go** button is pressed, the simulation will commence. In the bottom left there are two graphs. The top graph will plot the average of the percent similar (the similarity metric as shown in Figure 40) over time. The second graph will plot the percent unhappy. An agent is unhappy if their similarity metric is less than the desired value as set in the **% Similar Wanted** slider. This simulation is available in the NetLogo models library (Social Science/Segregation).

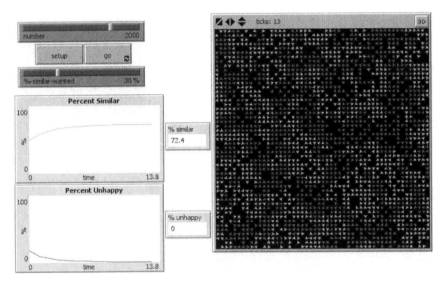

**Figure 41. NetLogo Screen for the Segregation Example
After Running the Simulation**

At the beginning of the simulation, when the agents are randomly placed on the frame, the percent similar is approximately 50%, and the percent unhappy is approximately 15%. Agent-based simulations run on discrete time steps. When the **go** button is pressed, the simulation will assess each agent, and if any agent is unhappy, will attempt to move them. When every agent in the frame has been assessed, and moved if required, the time period ends. The simulation will continue to the next time period where again each agent will be assessed for their percent similar wanted versus the percent similar actual, and moved if unhappy. In this simulation, that process will continue until the **go** button is pressed again to stop the simulation.

In this example, a **% Similar Wanted** setting of 30% seems small. This means that these agents would like to see at least three agents of the same type around them out of a possible seven. In other words, they would be happy if there were more different type agents than similar agents around them (4 versus 3). We might say that they are very tolerant of different types of agents. And we would not expect this type of preference to lead to highly segregated results.

But running the simulation produces a very unexpected result, as shown in Figure 41. After a number of time periods have been run in the simulation, we see that the percent similar and percent unhappy metrics have stabilized. The percent unhappy is zero but, curiously, the percent similar is 72%. That is despite the preference being only 30%. This surprising result mirrors what is seen in real life (e.g., Figure 39) and was the source of the paradox for sociologists. This is a prime example of an *emergent* effect. Although Thomas Schelling, the Nobel Prize winning economist, did not have NetLogo at his disposal, he famously was able to mimic the simulation we just performed using gridded paper and coins as agents (Schelling, 1971).

Recruitment—Foraging Ants

To illustrate recruitment, this section will depart from the world of humans and explore a situation from biology: foraging ants. This example is particularly illustrative in the mechanisms of agent-based simulation (ABS).

This model is called *Foraging Ants* and is also available in the NetLogo models library (Biology /Ants*).* The interface is shown in Figure 43. The agents are ants that can move across the landscape. The circle in the middle is the nest, and the outer circles are food sources. There are two control buttons in the upper left. **Setup** is pressed once to reset the simulation. This creates food sources and positions all ants in the nest. When **go** is pressed, the simulation proceeds. On each time step, each ant runs its program once. There are three slider controls also in the top left. These allow changes to the parameters of the simulation. In the bottom left is a graph that shows the amount of food over time at each of the three food sources. In addition to moving and collecting food, the simulation ants can deposit and sense pheromones—just like real ants. These pheromones will help guide ants to food, or the nest. In the simulation, the chemicals both diffuse away from the location they were dropped, as well as evaporate. As seen in Figure 43, the food chemical is shown as lighter shades on the dark background. Lighter shades have a greater concentration of the chemical. The rates of diffusion and evaporation can be controlled with sliders.

The ant's goal is to collect food and bring it into the nest as efficiently as possible. The ants follow chemical gradients to lead them to food or back to the nest. Each ant follows the same simple set of commands. One can think of it as a computer program. Figure 42 illustrates the ant's simple program (in pseudo-code). First, the ant evaluates if it is currently carrying food. If so, then it will move one patch towards the nest (following the nest chemical gradient) and also drop a unit of the food pheromone. If the ant does not have food, then it will next check for the presence of a food pheromone. If there is a pheromone, then the ant will move in the direction of the food. If there is no pheromone present, then the ant will make a random rotation and move one patch. In either case, if the ant ends up on a food patch it will collect the food. The ants just continue to *run* this program over and over.

Do I have food?
Yes
        Move one patch towards nest
        Drop food chemical
No
        Is there a food gradient here?
            Yes
                Move one patch towards food (in direction of strongest pheromone). Collect food if present.
            No
                Random rotate
                Move one patch. Collect food if present.

Figure 42. The Ant's Simple Program (in Pseudo-Code)

Now, given the simplicity of this program, what would you expect to happen? By clicking **setup**, we can start a new simulation. With the default parameters, 125 ants are created and located in the center of the nest. Three food sources are also created at varying distances from the nest.

At this point, consider what your intuition suggests might happen. One might expect the ants to fan out from the nest, pick up the food, and start bringing it back into the nest. You might expect the closest food source to be found first. But, you also might expect the other sources to be found shortly thereafter. Further, you might expect the sources to be transported to the nest simultaneously, and that the food depletion, as measured on the graph in the bottom left, might show something of a linear decrease over time for each of the food sources. Now, let's find out what really happens.

As we click **go,** ants begin streaming out of the nest. Since their directions are randomly set, they come out in all directions. Figure 43 shows the simulation after a number of time periods have passed. As our intuition expected, the ants do find the closest food first. However, the rate of decrease of the three food sources is not matching our intuition. We see that the nearest food source is decreasing very fast and in a nonlinear fashion. As we examine the grid, we see a bright, wide swatch of pheromones from the nest to the first food source. This ant *superhighway* is collecting any ant that happens to wander by and recruits them into the food collection of the closest source. When an ant deposits their food at the nest, they immediately head right back to that food source. This channeling of ants is the prominent emergent effect.

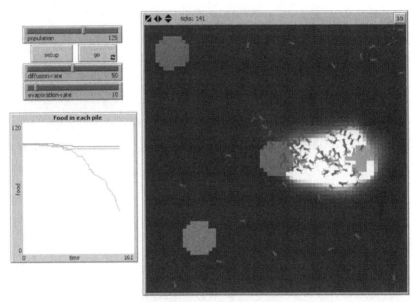

Figure 43. The Early Stages of the Foraging Ants Simulation

The ant superhighway results in the colony quickly consuming the closest food source while barely touching the other two food sources. When the closest food source is fully consumed, the ants construct a superhighway to the next closest food source. In similar fashion, they quickly carry the entire second food store into their nest.

This is a simple model but it has an interesting emergent feature. The food sources get depleted in a very nonlinear manner as the pheromone highways are generated. Anyone who has had a picnic in the park has experienced this ant superhighway as a line of ants gets your picnic food. An interesting aspect of this emergent phenomenon is that a critical number of ants are required to create and maintain that trail to keep the pheromone from diffusing and evaporating away. If you get this program and download it, you can change the population levels and the diffusion and evaporation rates, and get many different effects.

Assimilation—Wisdom of Crowds

The stock market reaction to the *Challenger* Space Shuttle explosion was discussed in Chapter 1. The market seemed to *figure out* what happened within a few hours, while the experts were publicly saying that they had no ideas. In this section, we will dig deeper into this *wisdom of crowds* with a focus on the aggregation of interactions. The term wisdom of crowds was coined by James Surowiecki who wrote an outstanding book on this topic with this title (2005).

For business, there are two important areas where this wisdom of crowds effect is relevant. First, internal to the organization, knowledge management programs have the challenge to aggregate information and get all employees access to the vast storehouse of knowledge. Yet, as discussed shortly, there are some very structural challenges to this effort. Lew Platt, while CEO of HP, said, "If only HP knew what HP knows, we would be three times more productive." Understanding information aggregation mechanisms may help these knowledge management efforts. External to the organization, businesses must deal with financial markets. Finance departments may need to access capital, or business development groups may make investments. So, understanding the workings of markets is important for these efforts.

The core idea behind the wisdom of crowds effect is that diverse knowledge and expertise is being collected and aggregated. Essentially, it argues that a group of people can be more accurate than individuals, even the best individuals. Scott Page, one of the leaders in the field, with one of his graduate students at the University of Michigan, built a mathematical framework that, given a set of conditions, shows that the collective prediction error of a group is less than the average individual error (Hong & Page, 2004). Surowiecki outlined four conditions that characterized wise crowds:
1. Diversity of opinion
2. Independence
3. Decentralization
4. An aggregation mechanism

The first two items specify the need for diversity and independence across the group. Decentralization indicates that that there are different areas of specialization and different local knowledge that's available to the group. The aggregation mechanism is typically a market of some type. For organizational knowledge management, a prediction market is a potential aggregation mechanism.

Prediction markets (also *called predictive markets, information markets, decision markets, idea futures, event derivatives* and *virtual markets*) are a type of market, typically a futures market, used to harness the wisdom of crowds. Usually, an instrument (e.g., a futures contract) is created whose final value is tied to the future event. The current market prices can be interpreted as predictions of the probability of the event or the expected value of the parameter. An example use of prediction markets by organizations is as an aid in demand forecasting (Hopman, 2007). Prediction markets are the topic of several current books (e.g., Abramowicz, 2007; Hahn & Tetlock, 2006). Also of note, analyst firms, such as Forrester Research, which do research, analysis, and consultation for IT organizations, have recommended prediction markets as a business tool (Young, 2008).

Prediction markets may offer a financial incentive for organizational members to participate. Page (2007) argues that incentives are important, as they drive out less accurate predictions and more heavily weight accurate ones (as long as the predictors understand how accurate they might be). Anonymity is another critical characteristic of some prediction markets. Anonymity addresses some of the barriers to sharing (Jolly & Wakeland, 2009) as well as some of the group deliberation biases as described by Sunstein (2006).

Figure 44 will be used to illustrate the mechanism of assimilation of information. The large oval on the left represents all the information that is relevant to some question. For example, consider that someone is trying to forecast the sales of a product in a company. Relevant information for this task includes the economic trends of the countries the product is being sold in, the relationship between the company and customers, the state of the product inventory and production capabilities, the status of competitors, and so on. Now consider a group of individuals as represented by the three people in the diagram. These three people know some subset of this total relevant information set, as represented by the dashed ovals.

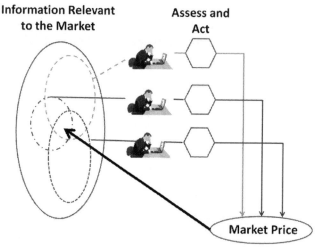

Figure 44. A Market Viewed Through the Lens of Aggregation of Interactions

Imagine the first person is a sales manager from Asia. He may have an in-depth understanding of the local customers, the local economy, the local government rules, and so on. Envision the second person to be in the finance department. He may have some in-depth knowledge about forecasted GDP growth rates[15], the Federal Reserve policies, markets, and trends. And, imagine the third person is in the engineering department. He may have in-depth knowledge about the capabilities of the product and how the capabilities stack up against the competitors. These three have subsets of the relevant knowledge. There will also usually be some overlap (that is, they have common information) but typically each individual has some unique information to contribute.

The assimilation of information has two distinct components: collection and aggregation. In the collection process, each individual is using their own information set to make an assessment. If the assimilation mechanism is a market, in this case say a prediction market, then there will be a price metric. This price metric will be known by all who are participating in the market, and so it will be a piece of common information. The feedback of price into the information space is

---

[15] Let's hope he has read this book and uses care with forecasted values!

represented by the arrow from the market back into the information oval. As market participants see the price, which they understand to be generated by the knowledge of other participants, their own judgment is modified. So, we see the market is not only collecting relevant information, but also jointly making a judgment of how that information relates to the subject of the market (in our example, a sales forecast). This second process may be called *aggregation*, and it is the market's method of figuring out what the collected information is telling it about the relevant question. The combination of the collection and aggregation leads to assimilation by the market, and is described by the pseudo-equation (=> could be read as *leads to*):

Collection + Aggregation => Assimilation

Since each participant knows the market price, a feedback loop is formed among the market, the information space of the participants, and their actions.

The feedback loop of price, market information, and participants, which enables the market to assimilate the collected information, can also create issues. The excellent book *Madness of Crowds* by Charles Mackay (1841) describes many market bubbles and ensuing crashes. For example:

- Tulip Mania—A bubble in the price of tulips in Holland in the 17th century where the price of a tulip could reach the price of some houses. The bubble was followed by a subsequent, and sudden, crash.
- The South Sea Company—Another famous bubble and crash that happened in England during the 18th century. Isaac Newton lost his fortune in the crash that ensued.

In more recent times, many of you may remember the dot com bubble and subsequent crash. We have already discussed the 2008 financial crisis. Given these types of potential pathologies, can a manager trust a prediction market? To paraphrase Surowiecki and Mackay, there can be a fine line between the *Wisdom of Crowds* and the *Madness of Crowds*.

One potential mechanism underlying these pathologies is observational learning. To illustrate observational learning, consider this familiar example. You are attending an out-of-town conference and want to go out to dinner. You do not travel often to this city and you don't know it very well. You walk out of the hotel and see a couple of restaurants. One restaurant has just a couple of diners. The second restaurant is full and there is a short line of people waiting. Which one would you choose? If you are like most people, you would pick the crowded restaurant. You (and perhaps a lot of the others) chose that restaurant because you assumed that the people dining there knew something about the two restaurants when they made their choice. This is observational learning and, generally speaking, it's very valuable and valid. But there are situations where it can go awry.

Imagine you chose the second restaurant and ordered dinner. You sit down and prepare to enjoy a nice meal. But, as the meal progresses you are disappointed in the food. Furthermore, you overhear other diners complaining about their meals. What could have happened? Roll back the clock to the restaurants' openings. A few hungry hotel guests (who have just flown in from the East Coast) head out and see two empty restaurants. They randomly choose one restaurant (perhaps by type of cuisine or the decor). Shortly thereafter, a few more hotel guest filter out in search of dinner. They see the few early birds in one restaurant and no one in the other, so they decide to choose the more populated restaurant. This phenomenon is called an *information mirage* or *information cascade* (Banerjee, 1992; Bikhchandani, Hirshleifer, & Welch, 1992). An information cascade can develop from rational thinking (following Bayesian statistics) on the part of the participants. Information cascades can develop from characteristics of the data and randomness. In this sense, an information cascade represents a case where individual rationality results in collective irrationality. We will see examples of this collective irrationality again in Chapter 5 when we discuss the Prisoner's Dilemma. My recent paper (Jolly, Zwick, Wakeland, & Woods, 2015) presents experimental evidence supporting the hypothesis of information cascades in markets, as well as supporting the role of collection and aggregation mechanisms.

What's important about markets for organizational use? They have a great ability to assimilate diverse information, but the evidence suggests that they can exhibit pathologies, namely bubbles. They're potentially valuable for organizations but the design and proper use is key.

Example: Prediction Markets—Google

The Harvard Business School case, *Prediction Markets at Google,* outlines Google's use of prediction markets for internal processes. Additionally,

Google has been generous by allowing the scientists to publish much of their research (e.g., Cowgill, Wolfers, & Zitzewitz, 2009). We have just briefly discussed the use of prediction markets as part of an organization's knowledge management repertoire. This example affords the chance to examine some important questions associated with that use.

How Well Do Prediction Markets Work?

This question will immediately come to the mind of any manager considering the use of a prediction market. The short answer is extremely well. Researchers have several excellent vehicles to study this question. One market, the University of Iowa's *Iowa Electronic Market* has been using prediction markets to forecast the winner of various U.S. elections for over 20 years. This market, which trades real money, was constructed as a nonprofit entity and is primarily used as a vehicle for researchers. In a 2008 research paper, Berg and colleagues summarized the results of numerous research studies of the Iowa Electronic Market for a dozen years of election results (Berg, Forsythe, Nelson, & Rietz, 2008). Their results showed that the markets demonstrated outstanding accuracy and generally performed better than polls. In the case paper, Google reported similar performance.

Why Would an Organization Need a Prediction Market?

This question focuses on why an individual in the organization may not share their information through processes that are already in place: knowledge management systems, organized data gathering processes, task teams, etc. Researchers have identified a number of potential reasons why an employee may not share their information in these contexts.

- Individuals may feel their proprietary knowledge is a competitive advantage against their fellow employees (Gilmour, 2003). We will discuss this idea in greater depth in Chapter 5.
- They may fear loss of power or control, or fear ridicule or criticism (Schutte & Snyman, 2006).
- They may not feel the particular sharing transaction is fair (Sigmund, Fehr, & Nowak, 2002).
- There may be organizational culture issues that limit information sharing (De Long & Fahey, 2000).

Prediction markets have the potential to break through some of these issues. But, being able to overcome these obstacles will depend on the design of the market.

What Are Some of the Key Design Issues?

Research and the Google case have identified four key design issues.

- Ease of Use—If the market is difficult to use, then participation may be low.
- Incentives—Incentives are a key tool to overcome the issues with sharing mentioned above. However, there is an important tradeoff here: the incentives must be large enough to overcome objections to sharing via existing mechanisms, but not so large as to encourage counter-productive behavior (e.g., an employee sabotaging a project to delay it and thus winning in a prediction market). In the case of Google, payouts from winning were in the form of company T-shirts (at Google, logoed T-shirts are highly valued). At Intel (Hopman, 2007) employees win cash.
- Anonymity—This is a crucial consideration and addresses some of the obstacles to sharing mentioned above. Consider the following scenario:

  A strong, outspoken manager has called a meeting to work on the group's next demand forecast. The manager has already told his supervisor that he expects demand to grow. The manager has also let his group know that this is his expectation. A new employee to the group has some deep insight that contradicts the manager's viewpoint. When the manager asks for dissenting inputs, the new employee stays silent. However, in the anonymous prediction market this employee makes his bias known by virtue of how he trades.

- Accuracy versus Precision—Details of this tradeoff are discussed in Chapter 9. My research has shown that the design of the prediction market can tailor its accuracy versus precision (Jolly, 2011).

What Issues Might Limit Organizational Use?

The Google case does a good job of highlighting some issues that may limit the use of organizational prediction markets. First, some employees may fear that the prediction market could replace them. For example, members of a forecasting group may fear job loss if a prediction market performs well at the forecast their group is responsible for. Also, managers may not want the visibility into *their* programs that a prediction market may bring. For example, consider a prediction market that is running to predict the schedule of an internal project. If the prediction market suggests the project is well behind schedule, then the manager will need to explain to their supervisor why the market is wrong.

100

Synchronizing

The segregation example earlier in the chapter illustrated a grouping phenomenon where agents sorted themselves. Another class of model that creates grouping patterns is *synchronization*, also called *peer effect* or *threshold models*. Fads, riots, and uprisings may be due to this effect. In this type of phenomenon, the actions of others influence the individual's behavior. A key difference of synchronizing versus sorting is a change in the preference of the agents in synchronization.

Mark Granovetter (1978) wrote about a simple version of this class of model where participants have two choices and their choice is dependent on the choices of others in the group. He defined an individual's threshold as the minimum number of other people needed to make a similar choice for that person to make the same choice. For example, if your threshold is one, then one other person must act before you would act. If your threshold is zero, then you will act without any others acting. If your threshold is 20, then 20 other people must act for you to act. To illustrate, consider the situation of giving a standing ovation at a theater. Let's look at a group of five people as shown in Table 2. In this table, each column represents a different scenario to examine. In Scenario 1, person 1 has a threshold of 0. Person 2 has a threshold of 1, and so on. Will there be a standing ovation in Scenario 1? Since person 1 has a threshold of 0, they will stand. Person 2, seeing person 1 stand will also stand. But, what of person 3? With only two others standing, they will not stand since their threshold is 3. Nor will person 4 or 5. So, in this case, the ovation will not be fully adopted.

	Scenario 1	Scenario 2	Scenario 3	Scenario 4
Person 1	0	0	0	1
Person 2	1	1	1	2
Person 3	3	2	2	3
Person 4	3	2	3	4
Person 5	3	2	4	6
Average	2.0	1.4	2.0	3.2
Std. Dev.	1.4	0.9	1.6	1.9
Full Standing Ovation?	No	Yes	Yes	No

Table 2. Four Adoption Scenarios Illustrating Granovetter's Model

Now, consider scenario 2. Person 1 will again stand. Person 2 will also stand. Now persons 3, 4, and 5, seeing persons 1 and 2 standing, will join the ovation, and the ovation will be complete. If we compare scenario 1 and scenario 2, we see that in scenario 2 the average threshold was lower. Is that a key metric to predict full adoption? If we look at scenario 3, we see that there would be full adoption of the ovation. But here, the average is the same as scenario 1. Finally, look at scenario 4. Here the ovation is not adopted at all. It has the largest average and also the largest standard deviation.

What can be said about predicting full adoption? First, clearly, it is difficult to predict in the real world since we don't have access to each individual's threshold. Also, even if we have descriptive statistical data about the crowd, such as the average threshold or the standard deviation, it can still be problematic. In general, we see:

- There must be early adopters to initiate the movement;
- Generally, a lower average threshold increases the likelihood of adoption; and
- Generally, a higher standard deviation of thresholds increases the likelihood of adoption

These types of synchronization models are susceptible to long, thin tails on the distribution of thresholds. As an extreme example, consider the distribution of thresholds shown in Figure 45. There is one person with a threshold of 0. There is also just one person with a threshold of 1. Similarly, there is just one person with thresholds of 2, 3, 4, 5, 6, 7, 8, 9, 10, and 11. The masses have a threshold of 12. In this extreme case, the tail of 12 people can pull the mass into adoption.

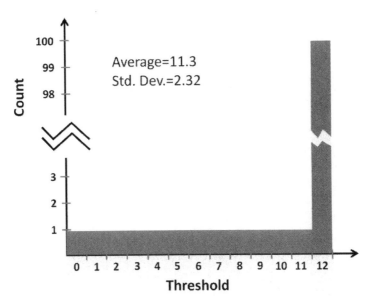

Figure 45. An Extreme Example of a Long Tail
That Can Sway a Large Group With a High Threshold

In summary, sorting effects occur when individuals rearrange themselves; synchronization or peer effects occur when individuals change their minds. In some cases, it may be difficult to identify if sorting or peer effects contributed to an emergent pattern. In the case of segregation, clearly people didn't change their ethnicity. However, in other cases, such as distribution of voting patterns (red versus blue states), there may be a mixture of effects present. To help with identification, it may be valuable to collect data over time, and particularly longitudinal data.

Interactions and the Sugarscape

One of the most important works in the area of ABM is *Growing Artificial Societies* by Joshua Epstein and Robert Axtell (1996). The book chronicles and explains Epstein and Axtell's efforts developing a social science simulation program called Sugarscape. For most classes in ABM, this book will be required reading. Chapter 4 in Eric Beinhocker's *The Origin of Wealth* (2006) gives a rich, but concise, summary of the Sugarscape work.

Epstein and Axtell look at many of the aspects of modern human society and explore the possibility of creating ABS for which the societal aspects will emerge. This is in the same manner that the previous simulations demonstrate emergent segregation and ant superhighways. Some of the Sugarscape simulation models are available in the NetLogo library.

Life on the Sugarscape revolves around sugar: Patches produce it and agents need it to survive. The most basic Sugarscape simulation features: Patches

- Are arranged in a grid, just as in the NetLogo simulations.
- Can grow and hold sugar. Sugar is the energy source for agents. Sugar is consumed and stored by the agents. When sugar is consumed from a patch, it will grow back at a predetermined rate. This rate of sugar regrowth varies from patch to patch. In the initial Sugarscape simulation, Epstein and Axtell created a landscape with two sugar mountains.

Agents

- Metabolism—Agents require a certain amount of sugar on each clock tick. The metabolism can vary from one agent to another (but is fixed at birth).
- Vision—Agents have the ability to sense conditions on nearby patches. Specifically they can see other agents and the amount of sugar on a patch. Agents can only see vertically or horizontally (not diagonally). The distance an agent can see varies across agents (but is also fixed at birth).
- Movement—Agents can (but are not required to) move on each clock tick. Agents will move to whatever vacant square they can see that holds the most sugar.
- Sugar Stores—If an agent collects more sugar from a patch than they require for their metabolism in that clock tick, they can store it for later use. Sugar store is a metric of agent wealth.
- Mortality—When created, each agent has a randomly determined maximum lifetime. Also, if the agent needs more sugar for their metabolism than is available on any given clock tick, they will die.

Figure 46 illustrates the stages of the simulation. As shown in the upper left image, when the simulation begins, a set number of agents are randomly distributed across the grid. Each agent has a randomly generated value for vision, metabolism, and maximum lifetime. The upper right image shows the simulation after the first clock tick. The agents now start to find the areas of higher sugar. Rings of agents are forming at the boundaries of the sugar mountain. The image on the bottom left shows the grid after a number of clock ticks. Notice that a number of agents have died, primarily due to lack of adequate sugar. Also notice a bit more definition to the ring pattern. In the final graphic in the bottom right, later in the simulation, the rings have stabilized around the sugar mountains. Also, notice in the final figure that a few more agents have died (some from lack of sugar but some from their lifespan).

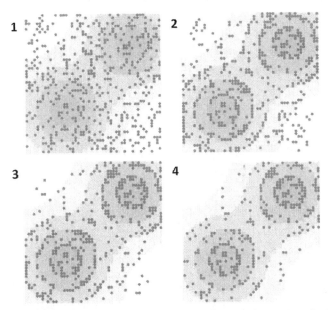

Figure 46. Sugarscape Simulation. Top Left: Random Population at Start; Top Right: After 1 Time Unit; Bottom Left: After a Few Time Units; Bottom Right: After Many Time Units. The Shade Difference Indicates the Agent's Vision (Darker Agents Can See Further)

Figure 47 shows the agent's wealth distribution (sugar stores) at the beginning and end of the simulation. The set of graphs on the left describe the situation at the beginning of the simulation. The graphs on the right are later in the simulation (after approximately 100 time units). The graph on the top is a histogram of the wealth in units of sugar across the population of agents. Notice two things at the start of the simulation: first, the distribution of wealth is relatively uniform; second, the range of values are between zero and 25 units of sugar. The graph below wealth is the Lorenz curve. The Lorenz curve is often used in economics and expresses the cumulative distribution function of the sugar stores. If there

105

were complete equality (each agent has exactly the same amount of sugar), then this curve would be a straight line sloping at 45% (the dark line shown). Since there is a random distribution of sugar at the beginning of the simulation, this curve bows slightly and indicates a degree of inequality. The Gini index, shown in the bottom curve, is a measure of this inequality metric over time. The higher the Gini index, the greater the inequality (or greater bowing of the Lorenz curve). Examining the changes in these metrics as the simulation has progressed, the top right chart shows that there are a few agents who have gained a great deal of wealth in terms of sugar, with some having nearly 150 units of sugar. The bulk of the agents, however, still have a range of 0 to 20 units of sugar. This inequality can be seen in the Lorenz curve with a greater bow towards the lower right corner. Finally, the evolution of this inequality is seen in the graph of the Gini index over the simulation timeframe. This is seen to consistently rise in and reach something of a plateau at the 0.5 level.

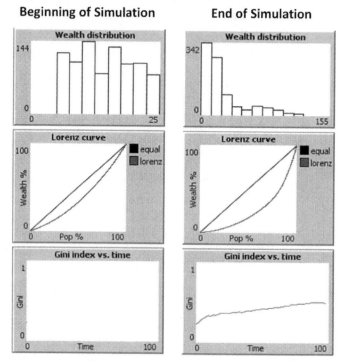

Figure 47. Agent's Wealth Distribution (in Sugar) at the Beginning and End of the Sugarscape Simulation

Economic inequality is currently an important social discussion, so it's worth examining how this effect manifested itself in the Sugarscape simulation. Since all parameters are randomly set at the beginning of the simulation, there are no inherent biases. Also, we know there is no governing body that can affect the results. The inequality is instead an emergent property of the interactions between agents and the environment. Since this effect comes about from aggregation of all the interactions, there is no simple cause. The rich are not exploiting the poor, nor are the poor less endowed. The result would indicate that efforts by a Sugarscape government to stamp out inequality would be quite challenging.

Epstein and Axtell go on to expand the capabilities of their simulation world to model multiple social phenomena. Below are some of the capabilities they added and the resulting emergent behaviors.

Sugarscape Feature: Seasons—A periodic change in the level of sugar on the patches.
New Emergent Effects: High-vision, high-metabolism agents develop migration patterns and low-vision, low-metabolism agents hibernate.

Sugarscape Feature: Reproduction—Agents can reproduce with the rate dependent on their wealth (store of sugar).
New Emergent Effects: Large oscillations in populations and potential for endogenous extinction events.

Sugarscape Feature: Trade—A commodity also necessary for the agent's metabolism, spice, was introduced. Agents were allowed to trade sugar for spice. The ratio of the trade negotiated between agents was considered the price.
New Emergent Effects: Prices did not reach equilibrium as predicted by classical economics. Instead, prices tended to move dynamically around attractor values resembling the action of chaotic systems. Also, in contradiction to the prediction of classical economics, the markets were locally efficient but globally inefficient, which was a result of the separation of transactions in time and space.

There are several more interesting simulations outlined in Epstein and Axtell's book, and they are definitely worth reviewing. Also, the simulations shown here are from NetLogo.

Diversity, Randomness, and Characteristics of Aggregation

In the synchronization models, we saw that variance plays an important role in the eventual adoption, or non-adoption, of a movement. In general, diversity plays an important role in systems where aggregation of interactions are important. The deepest examination of this topic has been done by Scott E. Page of the University of Michigan. His important book *The Difference* (2007) collects much of his work into one volume.

While it's not possible to cover all aspects of this book, a couple of important items will be highlighted. Page derives a couple of interesting theorems related to diversity. Page relies on a combination of axiomatic rigor and Monte Carlo simulations to support these. First, Page proposes the Diversity Prediction Theorem, which asserts that diversity and accuracy contribute equally to group performance. This says, in essence, that it is equally important to have a diverse group as to have an accurate group. So, for example, when you are selecting a task team for your project at work, don't just think about how accurate the work of a potential team member will be, but also consider how their unique expertise would add diversity to the team.

Another idea Page proposes is the Crowds Beat the Best Average law. This asserts that a group's collective performance is at least as good as the average performance of a crowd member. So, if you have chosen the most prominent expert to work on a problem, the performance of a diverse group containing that expert will outperform that expert on his own.

Page goes on to discuss what types of diversity are valuable. That is, diversity that is relevant. Page lists four types of relevant diversity:
- Diversity in perspectives: ways of representing.
- Diversity in interpretations: categorizing.
- Diversity in heuristics: problem solving.
- Diversity in models: inferring effects.

These are all diversities in problem-solving methods. These types of diversity cover the phases of the problem-solving process from interpretation, framing, model selection, and finally analysis of model results. Although Page does not address it directly, based on our earlier discussion on the wisdom of crowds, we should add for completeness:

- Diversity in information.

Many organizations require their managers to complete diversity training. Typically, these sessions have two main messages:
- It's not *nice* to discriminate.
- It's potentially against the law to discriminate.

If you are a manager at a large corporation, it is quite likely that you attended this type of training. But, what important message is typically missing from this training? The message that a diverse group should perform *better* than a group with less diversity. The bulk of this training usually focuses on ethnic and gender discrimination. These factors are not directly relevant diversities per Page's list. However, different ethnicities may have different social structures and cultural backgrounds. These differences may well lead to relevant differences in diversity (e.g., perspectives and heuristics). The message is important: A manager should seek out diversity. Of course, one also wants to be nice and stay out of legal issues. But, you should seek diversity because the performance of your team will be improved. And, not only in hiring, keep these ideas in mind as you build task teams across an organization.

In his excellent book *Turtles, Termites, and Traffic Jams* (1997), Mitchel Resnick outlines a list of five heuristics associated with the aggregation of interactions:
- Positive feedback isn't always negative.
- Randomness can help create order.
- A flock isn't a big bird.
- A traffic jam isn't just a collection of cars.
- The hills are alive (i.e., don't forget the environment).

Positive feedback isn't always negative: Positive feedback may bring to mind the screeching sound you hear when someone places a microphone too near a loudspeaker. Or, if you happen to be an engineer, it may bring to mind some runaway process, such as a nuclear reactor melting down. But, as Resnick reminds us, positive feedback isn't necessarily bad. In aggregation of interaction phenomena, it often plays an important role in creating the emergent patterns and structures. In the example of the foraging ants, it was positive feedback that created the ant superhighways and the efficient collection of the most nearby food sources.

Randomness can help create order: Some people view randomness as destructive, but in some cases it actually helps make systems more *orderly*. And, in some cases, randomness is crucial in the emergent effect. In the case of the foraging ant simulation, the random turning of the ants in the search for food was critical in the process of locating all food sources. In some cases, a seed of randomness may be necessary to disturb equilibrium and precipitate changes.

A flock isn't a big bird: It is important to not confuse levels in a system. Often, people confuse the behaviors of individuals and the behavior of groups. Just because an individual ant seems to wander around aimlessly, doesn't mean a colony of ants will behave this way. This is sometimes known as the *fallacy of composition*. We will see interesting examples of this in the next chapter on strategic behavior as well.

A traffic jam isn't just a collection of cars: This is, in a word, emergence. Aggregation of interactions can create emergent effects that are beyond simple collections of the objects.

The hills are alive: People often focus on the behaviors of individual agents and overlook the environment that surrounds the agents. In the foraging ants example, the ground plays an important role in that it holds the pheromone that the ants have dropped. Agent-based simulation models specifically model this with the patches, representing the environment, that can be influenced by agents and hold state.

Second Order Emergence

Recall the key idea illustration of emergence from aggregation of interactions in Figure 38. With more intelligent agents, like humans, the emergent effect is perceptible and can, in some cases, change the rules the agents are using. When a traffic jam occurs, drivers may hear about it on the radio and alter their driving rules to use side streets. This type of effect is called *second order emergence* and is illustrated in Figure 48 with a new arrow that feeds back from the emergent effect to the agents. This clearly makes the emergent behavior that much more difficult to understand and predict. An interesting example of this effect is George Soros' idea on reflexivity in markets (1987). Soros argues that as markets integrate information and move towards some type of equilibrium, the movement process influences the behavior of market participants, which pushes the market past equilibrium.

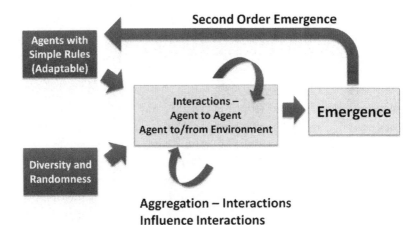

Aggregation – Interactions
Influence Interactions
Figure 48. Illustration of Second Order Emergence

Example: Bottom Up Impact—Intel

In this example, we will look at Intel's transition from a dynamic random-access memory (DRAM) company to a microprocessor company. The details come from Stanford University Professor Robert Burgelman's excellent book *Strategy Is Destiny* (2002). This example makes it clear that decentralized, bottom-up processes in business are not just about second or third order effects, but can shake the very core of an organization.

In the late 1970s and early 1980s, Intel was primarily a DRAM company. Intel had developed some of the first semiconductor DRAMs. Intel was the market share leader, and management had tailored the company to be the best in that market. But in the early 1980s, extreme competition emerged, particularly from the Japanese semiconductor producers. Due to the severe competition, Intel's margins were suffering. Previously, early in the 1970s, Intel had built the first microprocessors (the Intel 4004 was an example). At that time, the microprocessor was not an important product for the company. While the margins were good, it wasn't a high-volume product (being used primarily in some calculators). Consequently, microprocessors garnered little of management's mind share.

Intel was at what Andy Grove, CEO at the time, refers to as an inflection point. Intel's revenue growth was slowing, and Grove describes two options from this point. First, doing nothing would mean a continued slowing of growth until it reversed itself and revenues began to fall. Or, the company revitalized itself and started a new growth curve. In fact, from our dynamic systems discussion, this is well described as a system reaching its carrying capacity. The revitalization Grove referred to could be the exponential growth of a new system component (for example, a new market).

In the early 1980s, management was struggling with company direction. Management saw the revenues and margins flattening, and were trying to chart the course. Intel had developed immense competency at managing their fabrication plants (called fabs). Fabs are very capital intensive, and making certain they're running at full capacity is extremely important to the profitability of the company. At the time, DRAMs were using the majority of the fab capacity. The top-down management direction was that the first priority was to use the fabs to meet DRAM needs. Management felt that despite decreasing margins, it was very crucial to maintain market share so the fabs could remain completely utilized (keeping the fabs full reduced product costs and kept margins acceptable).

But, there was a problem. The DRAM customers were consistently not getting their orders filled. Microprocessors were taking an increasing share of the fab capacity and were limiting the DRAM shipments. After high-level management meetings, the directive was again made to make sure DRAM customers got their requests. But, even after these top-down directives, microprocessors continued to garner their share of the fab capacity.

While the management meetings were taking place, many layers down the organization chart, a group of employees called *planners* were hard at work. The planner's responsibility was fairly straight-forward: schedule the fab capacity. As blank silicon wafers were started in the fab, they were earmarked for which product they would become, since each product had a unique set of surface patterns. This allocation process was built on some preset conditions, and the planner followed a script to determine which product each new wafer would become. The problem was that the filtered down top management directives were in direct conflict with these preset conditions. The preset conditions were largely based on the profit margin of the individual products. At the very bottom of this chain, the planners were obviously working with their managers, trying to figure out how to interpret the top-down direction versus what their written rules were telling them to do. If you've ever played the children's game of telephone, where one person tells a story to another person who tells the story to the next person, you can imagine that this directive that came out of a meeting of senior managers had gotten somewhat filtered and distorted by the time it got down to the planners. This was creating quite a dilemma for the planners and, in effect, they were following their preset conditions, which were to maximize the profit margin of the company. And so they kept allocating microprocessors and shorting the allocation of the DRAMs.

Despite several top-down directives, microprocessors continued to earn more and more wafer starts. Eventually, top management started to notice the very positive impact on the company's bottom line. In effect, they started to see the growth in the revenue and margin that defines the emergence out of an inflection point. Finally, Andy Grove and Gordon Moore sanctioned the transition—after the planners had already started it! Intel managers had put a system in place in the factory that reacted to a change in the market conditions before it was specifically identified by the managers themselves. These bottom-up processes, planners following the specified rules, had driven the company in a new direction! Of course, management could have eventually halted the allocation of capacity to microprocessors. So Intel's management deserves the accolades they have received for making the hard decision to *officially* transition to microprocessors. But these bottom-up processes had initiated the new era of Intel, which subsequently built billions of dollars of shareholder's equity.

Summary and Action Plan

The key idea, as depicted in Figure 38 and Figure 48, is that agents with simple rules can interact, and these interactions can aggregate to create emergent phenomena. This effect can occur through time or space. These are decentralized and self-organized processes. They may rely on randomness and diversity. And, they may be very difficult to predict. In fact, since randomness is an important consideration, the emergent effect may not occur in each instance.

There are two critical considerations for business. First, emergent effects from aggregation of interactions may help clarify phenomena that we are having a difficult time explaining. Second, the phenomenon of aggregation of interactions may provide useful tools for business. We discussed prediction markets as a tool. Crowdsourcing is another excellent tool with examples such as Wikipedia and open-source software.

Are grouping patterns important in your business situation? Two aggregation mechanisms can create groupings: sorting and synchronizing. If people are changing their relative positions (e.g., clients moving), the mechanism may be sorting. If people are changing their minds (e.g., product or fad adoption), the mechanism may be synchronization. If sorting is reasonable, then strive to gain an understanding of the key metrics that are driving the changes (e.g., the similarity metric from the segregation example). If synchronization is probable, then attempt to understand the characteristics of the adoption threshold distribution.

Is recruitment at work in your business? For example, for an online seller, feedback may be a mechanism for recruiting customers. Attempt to understand the mechanisms at work in the recruitment. For the online seller, what methods could foster the submission of more positive feedback?

Is assimilation a factor in your project? For example, assimilation is important for an Information Technology (IT) group's efforts to maximize the benefits of their knowledge management system. If so, undertake efforts to understand the mechanisms at work in the two components of assimilation: collection and aggregation. To improve collection, efforts that foster participation may be useful. To improve aggregation, look for ways to improve analysis of ideas submitted by participants.

Finally, consider if creating an agent-based simulation of your business challenge may be helpful. This type of effort could give invaluable insight into the mechanisms at work. Agent-based simulations are also outstanding tools to communicate system effects to others in the organization.

Further Reading

An excellent summary of agent-based modeling is provided in Chapter 4 of Eric Beinhocker's *The Origin of Wealth* (2006).

Mitchel Resnick's excellent work *Turtles, Termites, and Traffic Jams* is easy to read and provides valuable insights (1997).

If you have more time, the important work *Growing Artificial Societies* by Joshua Epstein and Robert Axtell (1996) which, as mentioned, details the Sugarscape simulation is highly recommended.

James Surowiecki's *Wisdom of Crowds* (2005) provides an excellent introduction to this effect. Surowiecki is a writer at *The New Yorker* and delivers a very well researched and well written book.

Scott E. Page *The Difference* (2007) is an important work but may be a bit more of a challenging read.

Questions

1. Complexity scientists consider the economy as a *complex adaptive system* because people are adapting their behavior as conditions change. Should the weather be considered a complex adaptive system?

2. Systems thinkers are not concerned with how individuals operate, they only think about the whole. True or False? Discuss.

3. What are some reasons the suggestions (e.g., the probabilities as expressed by percentages) of a prediction market might be incorrect?

Discussion of Questions

1. The air and water particles do not adapt to changing conditions so the weather is not considered an adaptive system. However, it certainly is a complex system.

2. False. We need to understand how individuals make decisions to build system level models. In the ant simulation we build programs for each ant. In the beer game we build individual decision models. What systems thinkers do not believe in is reductionism. That is, that you can understand a system simply by understanding how individual components work.

3. There could be several. Here are some:
- Something like an information mirage may have created a bubble.
- Complex systems are simply difficult to predict, and even though the group is smart, they simply couldn't get it right.
- The group doesn't have any knowledge relevant to the question (that is, they were all just guessing).

5. Strategic Behavior

With dynamic behavior (Chapter 3) and aggregation of interactions (Chapter 4), the core of the systems thinking toolbox is complete. Now the focus will be to add a series of crucial layers around this core. First, we will look at the topic of strategic behavior. Game theory is used as the framework for this discussion, but the chapter will also rely heavily on behavioral aspects.

Introduction

The need to think strategically is common, and is often critical in business. There are many situations that crucially rely on what others will do. The marketing department is making decisions on pricing and advertising. The finance department is in negotiations with vendors and dealing with investors. Manufacturing is working with suppliers. Human resources is anticipating employee reaction to organizational changes. And you, the employee, are dealing with other employees.

Chess is a great reminder of strategic thinking since failure to consider what the other player might do will result in a very short game. So, a chess match is used as the key idea graphic for this chapter (Figure 49).

If I do this, he might do that.

Figure 49. Key Idea Graphic for Strategic Behavior

There are two facets, or vectors, of strategic behavior: conflict and coordination. In most business situations, there will be aspects of both present. The level of conflict or coordination present is largely a function of the structure of the situation. Game theory affords us a way to understand this structure.

The Prisoner's Dilemma—An Introduction

Game theory will be more fully described shortly, but let's just jump right in and talk about the most famous, and most important, game: the Prisoner's Dilemma[16] (PD). Even if you have some exposure to the PD, it is recommended you read through this section. Here's the scenario:

> Two individuals, Bonnie and Clyde, are arrested for suspicion of a major crime. The police are only able to gather limited evidence. Given this evidence, they estimate that they can only convict them of a much lesser crime (such as trespassing). However, if they can get one prisoner to testify against the other, then they feel they can get a conviction for the major crime. The police, wishing to convict at least one for the major crime, decide to take each prisoner, alone and independently, and make the following offer: "Rat out your accomplice and we will drop the lesser charge on you and throw the book at your partner!" The prisoner, mulling this over, asks, "What if I rat them out and they rat me out?" To which the police respond, "Well then, you'll both go to jail for the major crime. But we won't throw the book at them, or you, since you both helped us out."

Since both Bonnie and Clyde have two options, the possibilities cover a 2 x 2 matrix and are shown in Table 3.

---

[16] The formalism of the PD (that is, describing it in terms of the two prisoners) is generally attributed to Albert W. Tucker. Some, including Wikipedia as of this writing, attribute the initial framing to Flood and Dresher at RAND.

		Bonnie's Choices	
		Stay Silent	**Rat Out Clyde**
Clyde's Choices	**Stay Silent**	Clyde—1 year in prison Bonnie—1 year in prison	Clyde—3 years in prison Bonnie—Go free!
	Rat Out Bonnie	Clyde—Go free! Bonnie—3 years in prison	Clyde—2 years in prison Bonnie—2 years in prison

Table 3. A Tabulation of the Different Results From the Prisoner's Dilemma

The dilemma of the prisoner is whether to rat out their partner in the hopes of going free, or to stay silent and hope the other prisoner stays silent as well. But, as it turns out, there is a very clear best choice for each prisoner. Let's look at this from Clyde's perspective. First, what if Bonnie decides to stay silent? The payout chart of Table 3 reduces to just the left column (with title **Stay Silent**). Then, clearly it is better to rat her out since he'd rather walk free than spend a year in prison. Second, what if Bonnie rats him out? Well, looking at the right column, again it is clear that he should rat her out, because two years in prison is better than three! So, whatever Bonnie decides to do, it is better to rat her out. This analysis is the same for Bonnie, and her best choice is to also rat out Clyde (this is called a symmetric game). So one would expect the two prisoners to rat each other out and both spend the next two years in prison. This situation, that one choice is better independent of what the other person chooses, is called *dominance*. That is, the choice of ratting out the other prisoner dominates the choice of staying silent. Not every game will have a dominant solution, but this one does.

The PD, when viewed from the individual prisoner making their decision alone in the interrogation room, seems straightforward. One might wonder, why all the fuss about this game? Stepping back and looking at this game from the higher level provides the deep insights. By both defecting, Bonnie and Clyde each spent two years in prison. But, if they had both stayed silent, they both would have spent only one year in prison. Clearly, from the outside perspective, this is a much better solution for the group of prisoners. It was the dominance of the choice to rat out the other that drove the group to a deficient outcome. *The individuals were rational, but the group was irrational!* This is an example of the fallacy of composition, which was discussed in Chapter 4. Just because all individuals act in one fashion, we can't expect the group to act in the same way.

The PD also receives so much attention because it is ubiquitous in social interactions, business and otherwise. In Chapter 1, we saw that the common practice of 360 degree evaluations creates a PD for the employees. Later in the chapter, more organizational occurrences of the PD will be discussed.

Game Theory

We will use game theory as a way to study strategic behavior. That is, as a way to frame strategic behavior, study it, and make sense of it. A game, as seen for the Prisoner's Dilemma (PD), is a hypothetical situation where two or more parties will interact. There are a number of assumptions made about the situation.

- Perfect Information—Here it is meant that all players understand the rules and payouts of the game. In our example of the PD, it means Bonnie and Clyde both know what will happen in any scenario of choices (e.g., they know Table 3).
- No Communication—Unless otherwise specified, there is the assumption of no communication between parties prior to making their choices.
- Simultaneous Actions—All parties choose at the same time.
- Rational Actors—Rationality certainly has a meaning to each of you reading this. But in game theory, it has an explicit meaning. Specifically, it means the actors follow the four axioms of modern utility theory (completeness, transitivity, convexity, and independence).

The payouts in a game are expressed in terms of utility. Utility is the ultimate benefit of a game result to the player. This is an important idea and is often misunderstood by casual students of game theory. What is the utility of winning a vacation to Hawaii? It isn't the price of the trip. It is the personal value of the fun and relaxation of the trip. While the price of the trip is easily quantifiable in a unit of measure we all understand (dollars), the unit of measure of the fun and relaxation of the Hawaii vacation is not. Game theorists have an answer: utiles (pronounced *you-tills*). Using utiles as the payout of a game creates many interesting side effects. First, the same objective payout could have very different utility to different players. Winning a thousand dollar lottery would be a big deal to a student tired of macaroni and cheese for dinner. But, a thousand dollar lottery wouldn't even make the radar of the CEO of a large corporation[17]. Using utiles also means that the true payouts are not observable.

Let's now revisit the PD and transform the payout table into a more standard form. First, the *staying silent* option is called **Cooperate** to indicate that the prisoner is attempting to work with the other prisoner to get the best result. Second, the *rat out* option is called **Defect**, because *rat out* doesn't sound very academic. Finally, the years in prison payout must be converted into utiles. Clearly, it is hard to know what the different, ultimate, negative value of one, two, or three years in prison might be. One tactic game theorists use is to simply order them. So in this example, the possible outcomes are zero, one, two, or three years in prison. To any freedom loving criminal, three years has the lowest utility. So, one could transform the payouts as: zero years = four utiles; one year = three utiles; two years = two utiles; and three years = one utile. You might argue that years in prison should equate to negative utility. But, as it turns out, game theoretic analysis will not change with linear transformations of the payouts. In fact, in many cases, we could simply make the payouts zero years = Best; one year = Second Best; two years = Third Best; three years = Worst. The final convention is the way the utilities are shown in the table. By convention, the row player's payout is shown first followed by a comma, and then the column player's payout. The transformed payout matrix for the PD is shown in Table 4.

		Column Player's Choices	
Row Player's Choices		Cooperate	Defect
	Cooperate	3,3	1,4
	Defect	4,1	2,2

---

[17] Recall a famous golfer, who you probably all know, who won a very expensive car during a golf tournament. When asked what he did with the car, he answered, somewhat casually, that he just gave it to his caddy.

Table 4. The Prisoner's Dilemma Payout in Standard Form

A payoff matrix is not the only way to represent a game. In some cases, expressing the game as a decision tree may be useful. Figure 50 shows the PD in a decision tree format. This may help visualize the analysis as it separates the two choices of the other player. One downside of this analysis is that it masks the requirement of simultaneous choice. In business, this type of graphic may be useful in bargaining and negotiation situations.

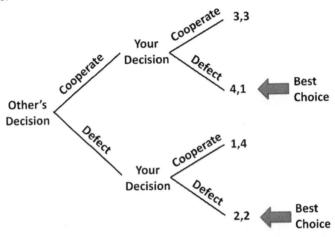

Figure 50. Decision Tree Format of Prisoner's Dilemma

Let's examine another game: the game of Chicken. The situation is as follows:

> Two teenagers meet on a deserted street to determine who is the bravest. While all their friends watch from the side of the road, they drive to opposite ends of the street. One of their friends stands between them with a flag, and upon dropping the flag, they speed towards each other. The one who swerves is the chicken.

The payoff matrix for this game is shown in Table 5. The obvious problem is that if neither swerve, they crash their cars and they potentially have serious injuries.

If they both swerve, the payoffs are 0, 0. Neither one is a chicken but neither one is the hero. If the row player does not swerve, but the column player swerves, the row player's payout is high, four utiles, because he's the hero and the column player is the chicken. This game is symmetric so there is a -4 utiles payoff if the row player swerves and the column player does not since he will be the chicken[18]. Now, if they both don't swerve, there's a very large negative payoff. One can make that -10 or -1000; if they get killed in the crash then perhaps it's minus infinity. The first order of business is to check for a dominant strategy. From the row player's perspective, what would he do if he knew the column player was going to swerve? Looking at the left column, then he would not swerve since a payout of four utiles is more than zero. What if he knew the column player was not going to swerve? Then, clearly, he would swerve. So, there is no dominant strategy in this game. While there is no dominant strategy, game theory still has something to say about this game. What if the stipulation of no communication is relaxed and a player is allowed to make an irrevocable commitment? Say, for example, as they are speeding towards each other, one player removes their steering wheel and tosses it out the window. Now, that player simply cannot swerve, even if they wanted to. This irrevocable commitment will affect the outcome since the other player must now swerve. This type of strategy can have applicability in business. In a game of Chicken with your business competitor making an irrevocable commitment, such as a large capital investment in a manufacturing plant, could cause your competitor to swerve!

		Column Player's Choices	
		Swerve	Don't Swerve
Row Player's Choices	Swerve	0,0	-4,4
	Don't Swerve	4,-4	-10,-10

Table 5. The Payout Matrix for the Game of Chicken

[18] There is another assumption made in game theory that is usually not discussed. That is, that both players share the same utility for the outcomes. This is not necessarily the case in a real-world game. For example, you would *not* want to get into a game of Chicken with someone who is suicidal.

Let's study another game; this one is usually called *Battle of the Sexes.* Here's the setup:

> A couple wants to go out for a date. The choices are a baseball game or the opera. One partner prefers the baseball game, and one partner prefers the opera. They both know the date is tonight, but they haven't agreed on a location. So, they must independently choose one event to attend[19].

The payout matrix is shown in Table 6. In this matrix, the row player prefers the ball game and the column player prefers the opera. Since it is a date, clearly they want to be together. So, when they make different choices, they both have negative utility[20]. When they are together, they both have positive utility. However, one partner has a bit more utility since they have a preference in the event. Like Chicken, this is a game without a dominant strategy. But, if we can relax the requirement of no communication, the partners could pretty easily get to a satisfactory solution.

		Column Player's Choices	
		Ball Game	Opera
Row Player's	Ball Game	2,1	-1,-1
Choices	Opera	-1,-1	1,2

Table 6. Payout Matrix for the Battle of the Sexes Game

Two facets of strategic behavior, conflict and coordination, were mentioned earlier. Now that we have examined three games we have seen varying degrees of each. Consider a 2 x 2 with cooperation and coordination ranked as low or high as shown in Table 7. The PD features

---

[19] Today, many set this game up without the dating, opera, and ball game descriptions. This is primarily because that description of the game could be considered sexist. Historically, the game is described as the man preferring the ball game and the woman the opera. The original description was kept to be consistent with most of the game theory texts. The funny thing is, when I grew up, it was my mother who deeply loved baseball while my dad didn't care for it.

[20] There is a slight variant to the payout matrix for this game that gives the utility of the row player choosing the opera and the column player choosing the ball game as -2,-1 and the row player choosing the ball game and the column player choosing the opera as -1,-2. Here, it acknowledges that while they are not together on the date, at least they are at their preferred event. This variant doesn't change the analysis.

elements of both competition and coordination. Chicken is high on the competition metric but low on cooperation. The Battle of the Sexes game is high on cooperation and low on competition.

		Cooperation	
		Low	High
Competition	Low		Battle of the Sexes
	High	Chicken	Prisoner's Dilemma

Table 7. Comparing Games on Their Level of Competition and Cooperation

In the PD, game theoretic analysis offered a recommendation for action since there was a dominant choice. What other types of recommendations for action can game theoretic analysis afford? In the case where there are more than two choices, the idea behind a dominant choice may be able to eliminate some of the options. This is most easily illustrated in a decision analysis context. In Table 8, the attributes of three choices are compared. When comparing three cars, we might be concerned about speed, energy use, and price as the three most important attributes. We want a faster car to help us merge onto the freeway safer, low energy use to control operation costs, and low purchase price. In this example, **Car 2** is better than **Car 3** in every attribute. This allows us to eliminate **Car 3** from consideration and simplify our decision.

	Speed	Energy Use	Purchase Price
Car 1	Fast	High	High
Car 2	Medium	Low	Low
Car 3	Slow	Medium	Medium

Table 8. Comparing the Attributes of Three Choices. Choice 2 Dominates Choice 3 in Every Attribute, Which Allows Choice 3 to be Removed From Consideration

Now consider a different game to examine another type of recommendation from game theory. Consider the common children's game of rock-paper-scissors with the payouts given in Table 9. First, this situation represents a class of game called *zero-sum*. That is, the sum of the payoffs in each square is zero[21]. As before, there is no dominant strategy. However, if you were to play this game more than once (as kids usually do) then game theory can help. When a game is played repeatedly, game theory recommends a mixed strategy. In a mixed strategy, you randomly choose between options based on a weighting. In this game, the weighting would be 1/3 for each option. So, you would randomly choose rock, paper, or scissors with a long-term average of choosing each one a third of the time. For example, you fill an urn with 100 red balls, 100 green balls, and 100 blue balls. You randomly draw one ball and play rock if the ball is red, paper if it is green, and scissors if it is blue. Some of the world's best poker players use random choice to determine when to bluff.

		Column Player		
		Rock	Paper	Scissors
Row Player	Rock	0,0	-1,1	1,-1
	Paper	1,-1	0,0	-1,1
	Scissors	-1,1	1,-1	0,0

Table 9. The Payoff Matrix for the Children's Game of Rock-Paper-Scissors

Finally, we will look at a strategy called *maxi-min,* or *the best of the worst.* Consider another zero-sum game, with payouts as shown in Table 10, where the row player has three options and the column player has four options. Should both the row and column players choose Option 1, the payout will be 12 utiles to the row player and -12 utiles to the column player. Notice that for each set of options, the sum of the payouts is always zero. To analyze a game with a maxi-min strategy, one wants to think defensively. If the row player takes Option 1, what is the worst thing that can happen? In this case, the worst situation is if the column player chooses Option 2 and the row player only gets three utiles. This value is recorded in the rightmost column[22]. Now, we look at Option 2. Here, the

---

[21] In game theory, we only need a common fixed sum for the payoffs to qualify as a zero sum game.

[22] Notice that the maxi-min analysis proceeds in the opposite manner than the search for dominance. When assessing dominance, the row player would assume the column player made a choice and would ascertain their best resulting choice. With maxi-min the row player considers one of their choices and ascertains what the column player might do if they knew that decision. This difference in methods often confuses students of game theory.

worst that can happen is four utiles. Finally with Option 3, the worst case scenario is zero utiles. Now we repeat this analysis for the column player. If they choose Option 1, the worst case scenario is that the row player chooses Option 1 and they get -12 utiles. This continues until the column player fills out his minimum payout. Now, the row player will choose the maximum of these minimums, which is Option 2. He can do no worse than four utiles with this strategy. Similarly, the column player, if using the same strategy, would also choose Option 2. This option will give him no worse than -4 utiles. So, both have chosen Option 2, and this set of choices is a stable solution. In game theory, it is called a *saddle point* or a *Nash equilibrium*. This idea was put forward by John Nash, the Nobel Prize winning game theorist and also the subject of the movie *A Beautiful Mind*. Note that not all zero-sum games have a saddle point like this one. But, the maxi-min strategy always offers the player a recommendation.

		Column Player's Choices				
		Option 1	Option 2	Option 3	Option 4	Row Min
Row Player's Choices	Option 1	12,-12	3,-3	9,-9	8,-8	3
	Option 2	5,-5	4,-4	6,-6	5,-5	4
	Option 3	3,-3	0,0	6,-6	7,-7	0
	Col Min	-12	-4	-9	-8	

Table 10. A Zero-Sum Game Payout Matrix and the Maxi-Min Analysis

Game theory, like any tool in our toolbox, has pros and cons. First, it gives a framework for thinking about strategic behavior. It may offer you a suggestion for actions; or it may offer you an idea about what the other party's actions might be. Game theory may shed light on important considerations such as irrevocable actions or communications. But, game theory is built on a pillar of assumptions around rational actions, and humans simply don't follow those all the time. We will explore this idea thoroughly a little later in the chapter.

The Prisoner's Dilemma In Depth

To continue the exploration of game theory, it is worth really digging into the Prisoner's Dilemma (PD). We have but scratched the surface of the analysis of this incredibly important game. The payoff structure, in utiles, was shown in Table 4. Anatol Rapoport, one of the key early researchers in game theory, had an interesting characterization of the payoff matrix, as shown in Table 11. Defecting and hoping the other player will cooperate to get the large four utiles payoff is a temptation, while cooperating with the misplaced hope of the other player also cooperating is being a sucker. Rapoport argued that from an emotional perspective, the greed of trying to get maximum payoff and fear of being a sucker pushes players to defect. The deficient outcome of both players defecting is the punishment. And finally, when both players can cooperate, they receive the reward of one extra utile.

	Cooperate	Defect
Cooperate	Reward	Sucker
Defect	Temptation	Punishment

Table 11. Rapoport's Characterization of the Prisoner's Dilemma Payoffs

There is no solution, per se, for the PD but there are frameworks from outside agencies that can help. Laws, set up by governments, help persuade individuals to cooperate. And some have argued that breaking PDs is the primary role for government. Integrative frameworks such as love and the family unit foster cooperation. Also, some cultural norms such as the Golden Rule, cultivate cooperation.

So far, we have discussed the PD in terms of playing just once. But, how do the dynamics change if the game is played more than once? This is the question Robert Axelrod asked when he studied the game. Axelrod, who is a professor at the University of Michigan, studied this question in detail with the results published in a landmark book *The Evolution of Cooperation* (1984). Axelrod sponsored a tournament of PD strategies to develop the base of data for his research. He invited researchers to submit PD stratagems that would be played against one another in a repeated PD arena. The stratagems submitted needed to be codified such that the games could be played automatically. Each stratagem could accumulate the utiles it won in each game. The winner was the stratagem that held the most utiles at the end of the tournament. To illustrate, consider Stratagem A whose rule is to alternate between defect (which it plays first) and cooperate. Stratagem A is playing Stratagem B whose rule is to alternate between cooperate (which it plays first) and defect. In the first game of the round, Stratagem A plays defect while Stratagem B plays cooperate. Stratagem A wins four utiles[23] and Stratagem B wins one utile. In the next game, Stratagem A cooperates while Stratagem B defects. So, in the second game, Stratagem A gets one utile. Stratagem A's total after the second game is now five utiles. The round would be played for a predetermined number of games or *iterations* (this is generally called the *Iterated Prisoner's Dilemma*). Axelrod set up the tournament as a round-robin with each stratagem playing each other stratagem. In addition, each stratagem would play a version of itself, as well as a stratagem that generated random choices between cooperate and defect. The stratagem could not identify the stratagem it was playing against at the time. But the stratagem could use the results of each game it had played with that opponent to adjust its own moves. Axelrod wanted to see what the impact of future games would be on the success of different strategies. If the future loomed large, would it encourage cooperation?

Axelrod's results were profound. The winning stratagem, submitted by Anatol Rapoport, whom we just spoke about, was called *Tit-For-Tat*. The very simple strategy is shown in Table 12. Tit-For-Tat has only three rules. First, in the initial game of the round, Tit-For-Tat cooperates. After the first game, the Tit-For-Tat's move depends on the action of the other stratagem in the last game. Tit-For-Tat used the other player's move in the last game as its move in the next game. Tit-For-Tat has four critical characteristics:

- Nice—Tit-For-Tat cooperates first. If the other stratagem cooperates, it will continue to cooperate.
- Provocable—While nice, Tit-For-Tat is no pushover. If the other stratagem defects, Tit-For-Tat will defect in the next game. One might consider this as punishment for bad behavior.
- Forgiving—If the other stratagem defected in the past but subsequently changes its move to cooperate, then Tit-For-Tat will forgive the previous bad behavior and cooperate again.
- Clear—Tit-For-Tat is very unambiguous. If the other stratagem is keeping track of Tit-For-Tat's moves it could understand Tit-For-Tat's strategy. This encourages the other stratagem to cooperate to collect the extra utiles.

[23] Axelrod didn't use the exact payouts shown in our table. He used: Cooperate/Cooperate, 3,3; Defect/Cooperate, 5,0; Cooperate/Defect, 0/5; and, Defect/Defect, 1,1. This doesn't affect the discussion.

Axelrod argued the tournament results demonstrated that the essence of cooperation is reciprocity and the value of the future. The finance idea of a discount rate can be used as an analogy. If the discount rate is relatively low, the future is more important and cooperation will be encouraged.

Situation	Tit-For-Tat Strategy
First game of round	Cooperate
Other player cooperated in previous game	Cooperate
Other player defected in previous game	Defect

Table 12. The *Tit-For-Tat* Strategy

Behavioral Aspects

In Chapter 2 we discussed the psychological biases that affect judgment and decision making. Here, on a related note, we study the actual reactions of humans in strategic situations. The game theoretic assumptions about rationality are similar and related to the assumptions of rationality in classical economics. Just as a field of behavioral economics has been developed to understand the impact of deviations from those assumptions in economics, a field of behavioral game theory has emerged. Colin Camerer of Cal Tech is a leader in this field. We will use his important book *Behavioral Game Theory* (2003) as a key reference for this section.

We begin with potentially the most important bias: Humans may not even acknowledge they are in a strategic situation. The psychological bias here is called *competition neglect*, and was initially identified by Camerer and Lovallo (1999). The bias is quite simply when people do not consider that the results from their decision depends on how others will act. In business, an example is a team looking at lowering the price of a product to increase volume and not considering that the competition could meet, or even further lower, their price and nullify any market share gains. In *Thinking, Fast and Slow,* Kahneman argues that competition neglect is an artifact of the System 1 mind processes. Specifically, as mentioned previously, System 1 has a *What You See Is All There Is* (WYSIATI) bias, which only considers factors that are readily apparent at the time. For early humans, this bias was valuable to make fast decisions to avoid large predators. For planners in a conference room, the risk from large, fast predators is rather small. Kahneman goes on to assert that competition neglect is related to the overconfidence bias.

Next, we revisit the all important Prisoner's Dilemma (PD). As we saw, game theoretic analysis has a recommendation for players: to defect. But what do humans actually do in this situation? Psychologists have recreated the conditions of the PD and found that 50% of people cooperate when they are in a one-time (no iteration) PD. There are only hypotheses as to why. But a leading theory is that cooperation is an evolutionary behavior. That is, even though the game is played just once, people may be subconsciously playing a Tit-For-Tat strategy expecting to receive cooperation from someone in the future[24].

Psychologists have also studied the impact of changing the value of the payoffs in the PD. They have found that changing the payoffs can increase the incidence of defection or cooperation as payouts are increased. For example, considering the payoffs of Table 4, if the payout for Defect/Cooperate is changed from 4 to 8, then the incidence of defection will increase. In other experiments, psychologists have found that pre-game communication will increase cooperation. That is, simple conversation that helps the players get to know one another, increases cooperation. Psychologists have also found that, as Rapoport would have predicted, punishment in earlier games can increase cooperation.

As mentioned, payoffs in game theory are shown as utiles. This has the advantage of allowing game theorists to abstract their work above the difficult details of dealing with the individual variances in value of real-world rewards and punishments. The downside is that these utiles are masked from observation and make it difficult for practitioners to effectively use game theory results. In fact, the relationship between rewards and punishment and utility can have nonsymmetrical and highly nonlinear behavior. This was demonstrated in the revolutionary work of Kahneman (the author of *Thinking, Fast and Slow*) and his late partner Tversky in their famous prospect theory (1979). While there are many aspects to this theory, notable for us here is the relationship they found between utility and gains versus losses, as shown in Figure 51. The chart was developed based on Kahneman and Tversky's direct research results, and so prospect theory represents a descriptive theory. In this figure, the

---

[24] We have all heard the aphorism "what goes around, comes around."

x axis is the real-world gain or loss (e.g., in dollars) and the y axis is the internally felt utility. The first, and most striking, observation is the extreme nonlinearity of the curve. For a fixed increase in gain (or decrease of loss), the magnitude of the effect on utility decreases. This makes intuitive sense. As your bonus increases from $1000 to $2000, you experience a lot of joy. But, as your bonus increases from $50,000 to $51,000, that increase in joy is much less. The non-symmetry of the curve, however, is not as intuitive. Specifically, notice that the curve is steeper for losses as opposed to gains. So, Kahneman and Tversky found that the average respondent felt more negative utility for a $200 loss than positive utility from a $200 gain. This infers that respondents are inherently loss averse: fear was stronger than greed. Prospect theory could be valuable in situations of bargaining and negotiation. For example, when one party makes a concession, their utility impact is higher than the other party who had a gain. Prospect theory also supports the framing bias. Here, framing an outcome in terms of avoiding a loss is more compelling than receiving a gain.

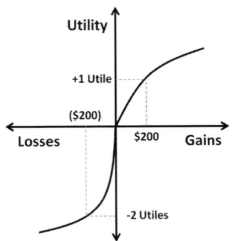

Figure 51. Utility Chart from Kahneman and Tversky's Prospect Theory

There are numerous other behavioral aspects, but we can only focus on a limited number. Learning by participants has been shown to be an important aspect of strategy. Learning in games has become an active topic in the academic research. The practical aspect here is to understand if the other party in your strategic situation has dealt with this type of circumstance before, as it will likely impact their strategic choices. Fairness is another extremely important aspect in strategic situations. This is elegantly illustrated in the Ultimatum Game. In the Ultimatum Game there is some amount of money that's to be shared. One player will propose the share for each player, and the second player can accept or reject that proposal. But, if the second player rejects the proposal, neither player gets any payout. For example, if there is $100 to be shared, the first player might suggest that they get $99 and the other player gets $1. With pure rational decision processes, the other second player would always accept this offer because $1 is better than nothing. However, experiments do not support this behavior. In fact, unless the offer is approximately a third of the total, the second player usually rejects the offer. Thinking back to Tit-For-Tat, this might be an attempt to punish the greedy behavior of the first player. Experiments have shown that offers in the range of 40% or more are rarely rejected. Offers below 20% are rejected about half the time. Whether the offer is accepted or rejected depends on knowing the other person, if the game has been repeated and various other conditions. Fairness should be considered in your strategic situation as it clearly impacts the other party's behavior.

Example: Agent-Based Simulation and Game Theory

In this example, we look at the use of agent-based simulation (ABS), discussed in Chapter 4, with strategic behavior, to study a common situation in organizations. This example comes from my research with Dr. Wayne Wakeland (Jolly & Wakeland, 2008, 2009). In this example, we take a systems thinking view on information sharing between colleagues in an organization.

In his *Harvard Business Review* article "How to Fix Knowledge Management" (2003), David Gilmour argued there was a fundamental flaw with the assumptions behind standard knowledge management programs. Gilmour argued that employees may not voluntarily share their valuable information without some type of direct payback, some "quid pro quo." Gilmour argued this "hoarding" of information was a direct result of organizational processes that rewarded employees who were more valuable to the organization. For those who have spent time in large organizations, Gilmour's argument may well bring recollections of some employees' behaviors.

Game theory provides an excellent framework to study the dynamics between employees that have the outlook expressed by Gilmour.

Consider the situation where two of these individuals meet and ask each other to share their personal information. For this exercise, let's call them *information hoarders*. Table 13 gives a possible payout table for this meeting. We first will walk through the payouts in the table to see how they come about. Consider the situation where both players refuse to share their information. The utiles are 2,2 which represents a status quo situation. That is, no information has been exchanged and the knowledge base of the group has not changed. In the case where both share, the relative knowledge of the two employees has not changed[25], but the sharing of information has increased the efficacy of the organization. That is, the organization can be more effective at its operations. If the organization is more effective, the employees benefit (e.g., either directly through profit-sharing or indirectly through job security). So, there are three utiles here. If one player shares and the other player does not, then the player who did not share has kept their own information to themselves *and* they have the other player's information. From their perspective, as expressed by Gilmour, that is the best outcome and has the highest utility: four utiles. The player who shared but did not receive any information in return gets the worst outcome, having given up their own private information to no benefit; they receive only one utile.

	Share	Don't Share
Share	3,3	1,4
Don't Share	4,1	2,2

Table 13. Game Theoretic Analysis of the Simultaneous Request to Share Information for Two Information Hoarders

As before, we first search for the presence of a dominant strategy. Consider the row player's options. First, if the column player shares, then it would be better for the row player to not share. In the case that the column player has not shared, then again it is to the row player's advantage to not share. So, this game does have a dominant strategy, and it is to not share. Since the game is symmetric, the column player has the same dominant strategy. In fact, this game has the same payout structure as the Prisoner's Dilemma (PD)! When these two information hoarders

---

[25] For example, prior to the game they both had one unit of information. After sharing, they both had two units of information. So, the amount of information they have relative to each other has not changed. This assumes they shared equally valuable information (likely valid if averaged over a number of occasions).

meet, they are locked in a PD where this local rationality drives them into the two utiles of benefit, when they could have exchanged information to realize three utiles of benefit. So, the emergent effect of local rationality leading to global irrationality is present.

Of course, not all people are alike. There are good arguments for other types of behaviors and value structures. For example, there may be individuals that gain utility from sharing. That could be because they like to help others, or perhaps they get some type of ego boost from sharing (for example, being viewed by others as knowledgeable or an expert in a field). Let's call this type of individual a *sharer*. Using similar game theoretic reasoning, the interaction between any two types of agents (hoarders and sharers) can be analyzed. An interaction between a hoarder and a sharer resembles Rapoport's Game #9[26] with a dominant strategy. An interaction between two sharers resembles the No Conflict game, which also has a dominant strategy. To summarize the results: Hoarders always hoard, and sharers always share.

An ABS model can be used to study how these tendencies in employees would impact themselves and their organizations. Two types of agents, sharers and hoarders, were randomly distributed on a NetLogo grid (called the InfoScape to pay homage to Sugarscape). The simulation follows the general model of Sugarscape except rather than sugar and spice growing, being harvested, and shared, the InfoScape simulation focuses on information. On each clock tick, new information becomes available on the grid. This *growth* of information represents new information from changes in the environment or information becoming available from information conduits (such as the internet, magazines, training classes, etc.). Agents harvest information and then look around for another agent to interact with. The simulation assumes that agents know whether their neighbors are information sharers or hoarders. This effect models the characterization from previous interactions. The simulation also models information evaporation (simulating the shelf life of information) and random movement on the grid (representing reorganizations and office moves). The simulation tracks average agent information as well as the total information accumulated by the organization.

---

[26] See (Rapoport & Guyer, 1978)

The simulation had some expected and some unpredictable results. First, as anticipated, organizations that were homogenously sharers versus homogenously hoarders generated much more net organizational information. Also, the simulation showed a nonlinear growth in organizational information as the synergy from sharing built up. However, the simulations also had a very unexpected result. In heterogeneous organizations (a mix of sharers and hoarders), sharers, on average, ended up with more information than hoarders! This seems to contradict the PD, which is one of the underpinnings of the simulation.

To see how this can happen, we must take a look at interactions over time. Figure 52 depicts six agents on the InfoScape. This is a balanced mix of agents, with three sharers and three hoarders. On the left is a sharer (**S**) next to a hoarder (**H**). In the middle are two sharers. On the right are two hoarders. The small circle with a **2** above each agent indicates they can collect two units of information on each clock cycle. The tables below each agent show that agent's information store after each phase of the simulation. For this illustration we neglect any information evaporation.

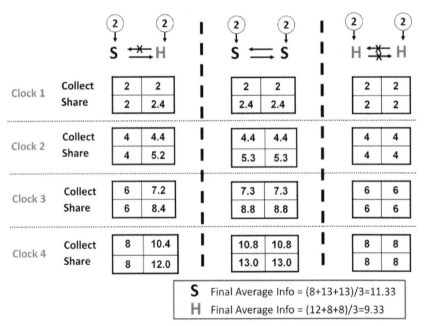

Figure 52. Illustration of Information Levels for
Three Pairs of Participants

In Phase 1 of the first clock cycle, each agent gathers two units of information. Each agent then requests sharing from their neighbor. For the first pair, the hoarder gets a fraction of the sharer's information but does not give away any of its own information. They conclude the first clock tick with **2** and **2.4** units of information respectively. This result agrees with our intuition: The hoarder is doing better than the sharer in terms of information held. The next pair are both sharers, so after collecting their two units of information, they share with their neighbor and each conclude the first clock cycle with 2.4 units of information. The final pair are hoarders and their information levels are two units at the conclusion of the clock cycle. After four clock cycles, we examine the information stores of the six agents. The average information for the sharers is larger than the average information of the hoarders! The synergy from the sharing of the middle pair has more than made up for the loss of the sharer in column 1.

The simulation was also used to study the effect of percent sharers and density. Density is an important factor because it can impact the opportunity to find a partner to share information. Consistent with the new-found intuition, the simulation found that information per agent generally increases with the percentage of sharers in the organization. The simulation also displayed a carrying capacity effect where increasing density created competition for the information being created in the environment. Unexpectedly, the simulation highlighted an interaction effect *between* these two emergent phenomena. While increasing density does create competition for the limited information of the environment, the increased density has a benefit for sharers as they are more likely to find another sharer to exchange information with. The maximum in information per agent occurs with 100% shares and an intermediate density.

There are practical recommendations here for both management and employees. Managers could cluster employees to increase information sharing. Google has studied this with their prediction markets and found evidence for better information flow for employees who were physically closer together (Cowgill et al., 2009). Also, some employers are now limiting the home office work time in order to bring employees together in the office. Managers should also use techniques to foster information sharing (such as fostering better relationships between employees) in order to increase overall organizational information. As an employee, you might consider the information sharing potential of an organization when choosing a new group. Also, when asked to share information with others, consider a strategy such as Tit-For-Tat.

Example: N-Player Games—Market Bubbles

So far, our analysis of games has focused on two players. However, games can be extended to any number of players, creatively called N-player games. Here we use a stock market example to explore a multi-player game.

In Chapter 4 we discussed bubbles and crashes in markets. But, given a bubble, when does the crash occur? In Chapter 2, we discussed the possibility of predicting the 2008 financial crisis. We identified a number of people who believed a crash was coming. Abreu and Brunnermeier (2003) propose an interesting theory on the continuity of bubbles. The researchers argue that even if investors recognize the market is in a bubble situation, these insightful investors cannot effectively end the bubble until a sufficient number of these investors simultaneously act. If the investors act on the bubble (e.g., sell or short the market) while a majority continue to pursue the bubble (e.g., buy or go long the market), the market will continue to rise and the investors that sold (went short) will lose money. Although Abreu and Brunnermeier pursue a mathematical analysis in their paper, we can also consider this a coordination game. Consider the payout matrix for the Stag Hunt game in Table 14. Let's assume there are only two investors in the market and they must act together to pop the bubble. If they both sell shares (short the market), then the market crashes and they both win big. If they both buy shares (stay long), the bubble continues and they also both win, but not as much. However, if one buys while the other sells, the trader buying will win as the bubble continues, while the investor selling will lose. Notice there is no dominant strategy for this game.

	Sell (C)	Buy (D)
Sell (Cooperate)	4,4	1,2
Buy (Defect)	2,1	2,2

Table 14. Payoff Table for Stag Hunt

The N-player payout graph of Stag Hunt is shown in Figure 53. If there are ten people participating in the market and eight buy while two sell, there are 20% cooperating (going short or selling). The payout for all the cooperators is the value of the dashed line at the 20% cooperate point. The payout for the defectors (those buying) is the solid line from the same *x* coordinate (20% cooperators). Notice that in this game, the dashed and solid lines cross. That means that after a certain percentage of the group cooperate, the cooperators have a higher payout. Where the two lines cross is an equilibrium point. For this game, the equilibrium point is unstable. That means if this were an iterated game, once the percent of cooperators pass the equilibrium value, then the percentage should start increasing since the payout for the cooperators just keeps increasing as the percentage of cooperators increases. However, if the initial percentage of cooperators is below the equilibrium value, then a set of iterated games should move the percentage of cooperators down, eventually to zero. So, according to this model, one could imagine a bubble market experiencing some number of drop and recovery cycles as a number of investors below the critical value are selling the market, then later see the market drop and continue dropping as the initial drop is precipitated by a percentage of investors greater than the critical value.

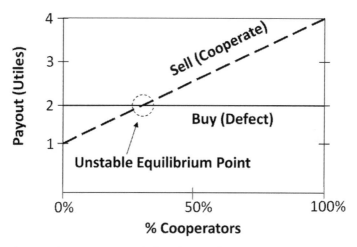

Figure 53. Payout Graph for the N-Player Stag Hunt Game

Summary and Action Plan

The key idea graphic for this chapter in Figure 49 highlights the strategic nature of many business situations. And, as we discussed, there is a human decision bias (competitor neglect) that may lead us to forget there is another out there who impacts the results of our decisions.

Let's use a common marketing problem to review the ideas of this chapter. A company is considering lowering the price of one of its products. Table 15 attempts to put the option of lowering a product's price in a game theoretic framework. Four potential responses by the competitor are shown in the figure[27]. Usually the financial analysis of a price decrease focuses on the situation where the competitor maintains their price. In this case, margin percentage will decrease, but the company would expect to sell more units from a combination of market share increase as well as potential market expansion from price elasticity of demand. But what if the competitor decides to match the price reduction? In this case, market share will remain about the same and the net effect will be a bottom and top line reduction from reduced revenue and lower margin percentages. What if, in response, the competitor actually reduces their prices below your new price? Now the tables have turned, and your company must react to the competitor's actions. This could lead to the Escalation archetype mentioned in Chapter 3 and potentially a price war.

		Competitor's Action			
		Raise Price	Maintain Price	Match Price	Reduce Further
Your Action	Lower Price	Share↑↑ Margin↓	Share↑ Margin↓	Share ~ Margin↓	Start Price War!

Table 15. Game Theoretic Analysis of Pricing Decision

It is worth revisiting the guidance that prediction is difficult in complex systems and extreme caution must be used when forecasting from models. In general, the decision frameworks used in models is quite simplistic. Consider the decision models used in the Beer Game simulation of Chapter 3. There, simple linear models were used that had no dependence on the actions of others (i.e., those models had competitor

---

[27] This is obviously a simplification since there are usually several competitors in a market. The response of all competitors should be evaluated.

neglect). Even so, the simple linear decision models were relatively difficult to implement. Reflecting back to the beer game simulation model, consider the effort required to add strategic behavior between retailers. Clearly, putting in this type of detail in simulation models can overwhelm the difficulty of the task very quickly.

The strategic decision checklist next can help you work through issues addressed in this chapter. Checklists are valuable tools and can help overcome Kahneman's proposed WYSIATI (What You See Is All There Is) bias of the System 1 mind. Download a copy of the checklist from RichJolly.com/STBdownload.

Strategic Decision Checklist

o **Does the result of this decision depend on another's actions?** First things first, avoid competitor neglect.

o **Is this coordination, competition, or a bit of both?** How does the situation fit in this classification? It may give you a clue for possible actions. For example, if it is purely competition, then an irrevocable commitment may be an option worth analyzing.

o **Can I quantify my options, their options, and the potential results?** This is reminding you to attempt to write out the options and the other party's potential responses. You can use a payoff matrix, decision tree, or another form if it helps.

o **Is this a Prisoner's Dilemma (PD)?** The PD is so common that your situation may well be one. If so, we have discussed a lot of ways to respond.

o **Is the other entity an individual, small group, or organization?** Who is making the decision on the other side, and what are their motivations? What are their utilities? We will get into this in some detail when we talk about the TOP (Technical, Organizational, Personal) multiple perspectives approach in Chapter 8.

o **What information is public, what is my private information, what private information might the other party have?** It is important to consider the information space. For example, in the case of negotiating a price, the seller may have much better information about the product (think about buying a used car).

o **Have I interacted with this entity in this situation before?** Is this some type of iterated game? Do you have any clues as to their strategy? Also consider if the other party has been in this situation before with another player. They may have learned something from those previous interactions.

o **What are the factors of utility to me and the other entity?** Think about both your own and the other party's motives. Attempt to translate the objective outcomes (e.g., dollars) into utility. Recall prospect theory and the nonlinearity and non-symmetry (loss aversion) of the curve.

o **Is there a sequencing to the decisions? Could first or last moves be critical?** Think about the sequence of decisions. In the game of Chicken, if the other player has already thrown their steering wheel out the window, then you have lost that option.

- o **Is it legal or beneficial to communicate?** The legal framework is obviously key here, but signaling may be a viable strategy. Communication can be valuable if there is some degree of coordination in the situation (versus purely competitive).
- o **Should I announce my strategy?** Announcing your strategy could be very valuable in a situation with a high degree of coordination.
- o **Does it seem there is no clear best strategy (warranting random choice)?** If there is no clear best strategy, and the game is iterated, then a random response may be the best option.

Further Reading

An excellent summary of game theory is provided in Chapter 10 of Eric Beinhocker's *The Origin of Wealth* (2006).

Axelrod's landmark book *The Evolution of Cooperation* (1984) is quite readable, not too long, and filled with insights.

Colin Camerer's important book *Behavioral Game Theory* (2003) is *the* text on that topic. But it is academically oriented and not the easiest read.

I haven't found a good, readable game theory text that I really like. I've used *Game Theory: A Nontechnical Introduction* by Morton Davis (1970), and it is pretty good.

Questions

1. Some say that the Prisoner's Dilemma (PD) game contradicts Adam Smith. Smith argued that each person, pursuing his or her own selfish goals, would lead to collective efficiency. However, in the PD, when each player pursues their own personal best option, the group ends up with less than they could have had if they had cooperated. A savvy game theorist would counter this argument with:

A. Price competition is a PD and leads to optimal prices for consumers. This competition is a form of collective efficiency.

B. The game theorist has no direct retort and will say simply that Smith was wrong.

C. The game theorist argues that in the PD, pursuing one's own goals (e.g., adopting the dominant strategy) does lead to collective efficiency because everyone gets the best option (since this game has a solution).

D. Research by behavioral game theorists has shown that humans only defect about 50% of the time. This heterogeneity of cooperation and defection across the population actually generates an emergent condition of efficiency.

2. In a real-life experiment, in which game would you expect a higher rate of defection?

Game A		
	Cooperate	Defect
Cooperate	3,3	1,4
Defect	4,1	2,2

Game B		
	Cooperate	Defect
Cooperate	3,3	1,8
Defect	8,1	2,2

3. Two Vulcans (who are known for their logic and strict adherence to the axioms of rationality) meet and must simultaneously choose between two options (Option A and Option B). Being Vulcans, they share the same utility of outcomes. From Vulcan 1's perspective:

- The best outcome occurs if he chooses Option B and Vulcan 2 chooses Option A.
- The second best outcome occurs if both choose Option B.
- The third best outcome occurs if both choose Option A.
- The worst outcome occurs if he chooses Option A and Vulcan 2 chooses Option B.

Note: A deficient outcome occurs when both parties could have been better off with another choice. Also, Vulcans are the race of beings from the planet Vulcan. They were created in the TV show *Star Trek*. Mr. Spock is the most famous of all Vulcans (even though he is only half Vulcan). Which of these statements are true?

A. There is a dominant strategy, but it leads to a deficient outcome.
B. There is a dominant strategy, and the outcome is not deficient.
C. There is no dominant strategy (which would really annoy Vulcans—if they had emotions that is).
D. There is insufficient information to determine if there is a dominant strategy.

Strategic Behavior

Discussion of Questions

1. The best answer here is A. For answer C, Defect/Defect does not lead to collective efficiency in the game. They could each have had a higher payout with Cooperate/Cooperate. There is no basis of support for the last option.

2. According to behavioral game theory research, increasing the incentive to defect from 4 to 8 utiles should result in a higher defection rate. So Game B is the best answer.

3. You must build the payout table for this. Note that since Vulcan's share the same utility, the game is symmetric. There is a dominant strategy to choose Option B. Unlike the PD, in this game the dominant strategy does not lead to a deficient outcome. This is the kind of game a Vulcan would love—if they had emotions that is.

Here are the Row Player's Payouts (note it is symmetric)

	Option A	Option B
Option A	Third	Worst
Option B	Best	Second

6. Ecosystems and Evolution

This chapter will delve into the analogies between business and biological systems. The origins of the term *business ecosystem* will be reviewed. Also, some industry structure frameworks will be studied. Next, the analogy of biological evolution as applied to business is examined. The discussion of evolution will center around the genetic algorithm—a change agent for systems. We will also revisit Nassim Nicholas Taleb and explore his provocative idea of *antifragility*.

Introduction

The expression *business ecosystem* has been coined and has built a good degree of credibility. We can use that credibility as a building block to help communicate our ideas about systems and business. Additionally, some of the prior business structure framing techniques are still very valuable in studying business ecosystems.

The chapter will also explore how systems change their structure. Thus far we have tacitly assumed that systems are stationary (with the exception of second order emergence discussed in Chapter 4). We now tackle that assumption head on. Martin Zwick, in his unpublished manuscript (2013), outlines two situations:

- Synchronics—The situation where the structure is constant.
- Diachronics—The situation where the structure is changing.

If a business system's structure does change over time, then how does it change? What models can be used to understand that change? We explore the idea that evolutionary processes that are present in biological ecosystems can be used as a model. The discussion on antifragility goes on to study some important characteristics of evolutionary systems.

The key idea graphic for this chapter is shown in Figure 54. First, entities in a business situation are interacting, as shown by the ovals and circular paths, and represent a business ecosystem. The large arrow and changing ovals illustrate that, over time, these relationships are themselves changing. The graphic alludes to an important idea which will be developed in the chapter—when trying to understand a system, looking at its past states can be valuable.

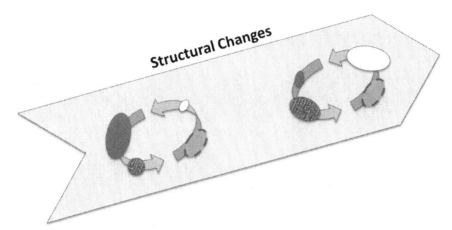

Structural Changes

Figure 54. Key Idea for Ecosystems and Evolution

Business Ecosystems

The literature around the analysis of collections of business entities has a long history. Here, we will not perform a complete review, but rather we will analyze a few carefully selected works. We begin with the effort of Harvard's Michael Porter and his well-known *five forces model* (1980). Porter's model considered the five rectangles in Figure 55. The center rectangle represents the direct competitors in the market. If the analysis was on the market for x86 processors, then Intel and AMD (Advanced Micro Devices, Inc.) would be the key competitors. The **New Entrants** square at the top of the figure represents companies that could enter the market. The rectangle below characterizes substitutes. For the x86 example, a substitute for the x86 processor would be the ARM processor. The use of a substitute by customers will require some type of effort and perhaps trade-off. For example, switching to an ARM processor would require a customer to change their software. There are inherent barriers for either new entrants (the cost of getting into the business) or substitutes (a cost to the customer to adapt). The rectangle on the right represents the customers. For the x86 processor example, this includes the original equipment manufacturers that build computers, such as Hewlett Packard and Dell. On the left are suppliers. In the x86 processor example, these include fabrication equipment suppliers, computer-aided design suppliers, and so on. The Porter model considers the balance of power between customer and supplier. In the x86 processor example, Intel has held dominant market share and wields considerable supplier power over the original equipment manufacturers. However, suppliers to

148

Intel, due to their larger numbers, have little power over Intel. The Porter five forces model was augmented by Andy Grove (1996), while CEO of Intel, with the addition of the two ovals shown in the figure: **Complementors** and **Government/Public**. These additions were a direct result of Grove's experiences at Intel. The key complementor for the x86 processor market has been Microsoft. Microsoft does not fit nicely into any of Porter's five boxes but is paramount to success in the x86 marketplace. Similarly, Intel has had situations where the public and the government have been important forces in business situations. These situations include Intel's lobbying of the United States government to impose sanctions on Japan for dynamic random access memory (DRAM) dumping and the public response to the Intel x86 floating-point math problem[28]. Of course, the modified Porter model is not exhaustive. Still, this model is useful for initiating a business ecosystem analysis. As a framework (a type of checklist), it helps overcome the WYSIATI (What You See Is All There Is) bias of the System 1 mind. Typically, I begin class case discussions using this framework. It has proven to be a good launching point into deeper systems analysis.

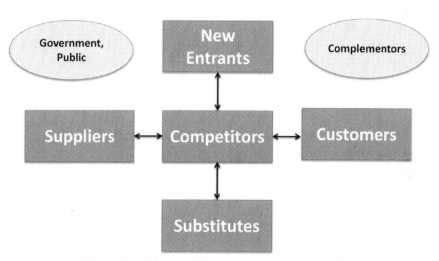

Figure 55. Modified Porter Five Forces Model

The term *business ecosystem* has earned a fair degree of brand equity. The term was coined by James F. Moore in his 1993 article in *Harvard Business Review*, "Predators and Prey: A New Ecology of Competition"

---

[28] http://en.wikipedia.org/wiki/Pentium_FDIV_bug

(1993). This article won the McKinsey Award and has been highly used in business school curriculums. One of the main points of the article is that there is a large amount of cooperation in the market in addition to direct competition. Moore does not directly discuss evolution but does refer to it in passing. The article is interesting and recommended for your reading list. In particular, since this article has such good credibility, it can be used as a launching board for your discussion of system effects with management.

Evolution: The Genetic Algorithm

Potentially the most useful model for the structural change of business systems is the evolution process of biological systems. Beinhocker explicitly makes that assertion and equates a company's business plans to the DNA structure of biological systems (2006). To deeply understand biological evolution, we will take a deep-dive examination of its core processes. The best way to accomplish this is to study the genetic algorithm. Specifically, we will study the implementation used for optimization in computer algorithms. This is an excellent representation of the biological process (since the algorithm has been expressly modeled after the biological process). A secondary benefit of learning the genetic algorithm is it can be used in your computer programs as an optimization routine. Even if you are particularly uncomfortable with math topics, keep reading this section. The description has been made intuitive and nontechnical.

Let's get the math part of the discussion out of the way. What is an optimization algorithm? An optimization algorithm finds the minimum or maximum of a function (an equation). Consider a simple equation:

$$y = x^2$$

What is the value of x that gives the minimum value of y? For this, we could do it by trial and error. That is just putting in different values of x and finding the minimum value of y (and perhaps plotting the results to see a pattern). Or, we could use mathematical techniques to find the minimum. However we proceed, we will find that for this simple case, a value of $x = 0$ gives the minimum value of y (which is also 0). But, when the equation gets very complicated, how do we proceed? This is a question that has launched considerable research, many books and even a field of mathematics (optimization theory). It turns out that the method to use depends quite a bit on *what* you are attempting to optimize. The *what* here is the characteristics of the equation's solution landscape. In very general terms, one can categorize equations as having either simple or complex solution landscapes. Here, a landscape is very simply the *n*-dimensional plot of the function. Figure 56 illustrates a simple and complex landscape. The simple landscape plot shown is just a three dimensional cousin of our friend from above, $y = x^2$. It has one maximum. The landscape on the right, the complex landscape, is an entirely different breed of cat. This function has two local maximums and one global maximum. The mathematical problem with the complex landscape is making sure you end up at the top of the largest peak and not the top of one of the smaller hills.

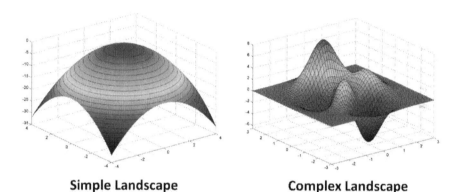

Simple Landscape   **Complex Landscape**

**Figure 56. Two Functions, *f(x,y)*: The Function on the Left
is Considered a Simple Landscape (One Single Maximum).
The Landscape on the Right is Considered a Complex Landscape
(Two Local Maximums and One Global Maximum)**

What might work to find the maximum of the simple landscape in Figure 56? A favorite algorithm is called *hill-climbing*. Here's how it works. First, randomly choose a value of *x* and *y*. Now calculate the value of the function at that point. In addition, calculate the slope in the *x* and *y* directions at the current point. (In math, the derivative gives us the slope. Or, one could simply evaluate the slope with arithmetic by looking at the value of the function at *x* plus some delta and *x* minus some delta). If either of the slopes are different than zero, just take a walk up the hill; that is, change your coordinate in the direction of increasing value of the slope. Continue this process until your evaluation point arrives at the top of the hill (where all slopes are zero).

What if we use the hill-climbing algorithm on the complex landscape on the right in Figure 56? Whether the algorithm will find the maximum depends on the starting point. This landscape has both local and global maximums. If the initial point is near either of the two local maximums, it will likely climb those small hills and stop at the local maximum. The algorithm has no way to know about the global maximum via slope. In fact, complex landscapes, like the one shown, cause problems for many optimization algorithms. The genetic algorithm (GA) is one optimization method that can find global maximums in complex landscapes.

Rather than starting at one point and moving towards the maximum, like the hill-climbing algorithm, the GA utilizes a *population* of points scouring the landscape for the maximum. Amazingly, the GA manages this search using just a few, very simple rules.

There are two requirements to use the GA. First, it must be possible to represent a data point as an array of bits (ones and zeros). Second, there must be a mechanism (a formula) that can take this string of bits and evaluate it into a single number representing the value of those bits. These requirements are represented in Figure 57. In biological organisms, the array of bits are the DNA strands. The DNA quantizes the characteristics of an organism. And in biological systems, the evaluation algorithm—the fitness function—is the ability of the organism to produce offspring and propagate its DNA.

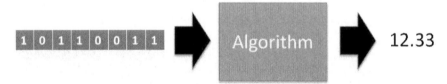

Figure 57. Illustration of a Fitness Function. A GA Needs a Sequence of Ones and Zeros to Produce a Single Value. In Biological Systems, the Fitness Function Takes Individuals (a Sequence of DNA) and Produces a Result of Offspring or No Offspring

Given these two requirements are met, then the GA is quite simple. With a population of data points, the GA executes the following sequence of steps over and over.

1. Assign a value of the fitness level to each member of the population (e.g., using the fitness function of Figure 57[29]).
2. Rank the population in terms of this fitness level.
3. Generate a new population based on the most fit members of the population.

For a math problem, the initial population is easily created by compiling random collections of ones and zeros.

The magic of the GA comes in Step 3, the process by which it creates a new generation. That process, while also simple, is elegant and effective. The components of Step 3 above are:

1. Select two parents from the set with high fitness.
2. Exchange their bit strings with a process called crossover.
3. Randomly mutate the resulting bit strings (by flipping a few bits).

Figure 58 illustrates the process. Two bit strings with high fitness are selected. In a biological system, this selection process has been the parent's survival in the environment. The bit streams are cut, and one of the pieces from parent one is combined with one of the pieces from parent two. Two children have thus been created with these components from each parent. In biological organisms, this process is the splitting and then recombination of the DNA sequence. Finally, a few bits are flipped to mutate the children. In biological organisms this is a byproduct of the splitting and recombination process, which is not quite as neat as the mathematical cutting and swapping of bit strings.

---

[29] Some readers may be a bit confused here as Figure 56 showed fitness functions in terms of rational numbers and the GA requires fitness functions of binary numbers (as shown in Figure 57). For mathematical problems, the solution is to simply quantize the rational number and represent the values as collections of bit strings.

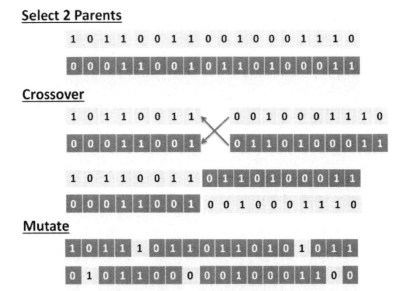

Select 2 Parents

Crossover

Mutate

Figure 58. Illustration of the Steps in the Genetic Algorithm Selection, Crossover, and Mutation

At this point, you may well be wondering how this apparently simple sequence of steps can be so powerful in finding global maximums in complex landscapes. By following the process as it searches for a maximum on a complex landscape, we can gain deep insight into the mechanism. Figure 59 shows the complex landscape of Figure 56. To begin the GA, we create a population. Here, simply using a random number generator can create any number of bit strings. The generated data points are shown as dots on the figure. The GA loop can now begin. The first step is to sort the dots by fitness, that is, their value on the z (up) axis. The dots with the highest fitness have dashed circles around them. These circled points, with high fitness level, will be the parents of the next generation. The parents are paired off, and the crossover and mutation procedures (Figure 58) are executed. This generates a new population, and the old population is now removed. The change is subtle but crucial. The population will have started to move closer to the three maximums. No one member of the population is key—increasing the average fitness of the population is the GA's mechanism to zero in on the global maximum.

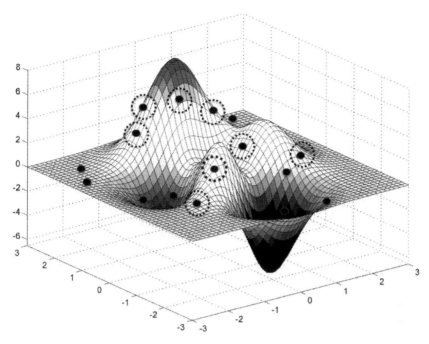

Figure 59. Fitness Landscape and Initial Random Population (the Dots). The Selection Process Chooses the Members With Higher Fitness (These Are Circled With Dashes)

Figure 60 shows the results of the GA after several generations. The bulk of the population is now clustered around the global maximum. Using these simple steps, repeated over and over, the global maximum has been located. But, there is more to learn from Figure 60. Notice there are a few population members near the peaks of the local maximums and a couple out in the flatlands. It would be easy to dismiss these as unimportant or mistakes. But they demonstrate a subtle, but crucially important, characteristic of the GA: The GA can adapt to *changes* in the fitness landscape! If suddenly one of the local maximums grows and becomes the global maximum, or a global maximum suddenly appears in the flatlands, then the GA will eventually find it! How could the landscape suddenly change? Imagine that the solar cycle changes and the earth slowly moves into an ice age. The GA would allow organisms to adapt to the new environment.

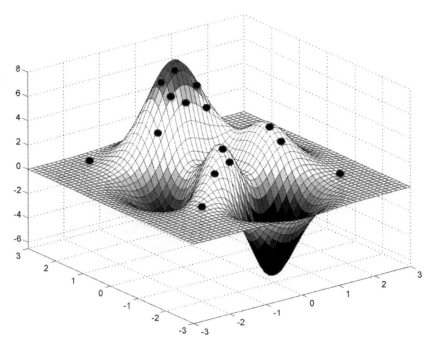

Figure 60. After Several Iterations, the GA Produces a Population Concentrated Around the Maximums and Still Randomly Produces Population Members Across the Landscape

There are some important characteristics of the GA:

- Simple—The GA works through simple processes.
- Effective Use of Randomness and Diversity—In biological systems, the random mutations that occur when real DNA splits and recombines are a crucial part of the process. Diversity, an inherent result of the GA process, is needed in the population for the crossover mechanism to work effectively.
- Robust—The GA is extremely robust in finding minimums or maximums in complex landscapes. But it is not infallible, as there are landscapes that a given GA (that is defined by population size, crossover pattern, and mutation rates, etc.) may not be able to find the maximum.
- Adaptable—As the landscape changes, the GA is able to find the new maximums.
- Remembers—The genome is an embodiment of all past generations. This exemplifies the aggregation of interaction processes we saw in the agent-based systems of Chapter 4.

It is interesting to think about the parallels of the GA and some of the processes we have already discussed. For example, the GA shares some interesting characteristics with the strategy of Tit-For-Tat that we discussed in Chapter 5. Specifically, they are both effective, simple, robust, and adaptable.

While businesses may not have DNA per se, the processes and lessons of the GA are important. The GA teaches business:

- The Power of Trial and Error—The GA has no objectives when it performs the crossover and mutation steps. It needs individuals to scour the fitness landscape to find the peaks. We will examine this much more in the next section when we discuss antifragility.
- Effectively Use Randomness and Diversity—These are two themes we have been repeating throughout this discussion. In Chapter 4 we saw examples where randomness is beneficial, and one of Resnick's heuristics is *randomness can help create order* . Also, in Chapter 4 we discussed the value of diversity with the notable work of Scott Page. The GA exemplifies these traits. Businesses should intelligently embrace randomness and diversity.

The GA computer algorithm can be quite useful. The GA can be used to solve optimization problems, or it can be included in systems simulations to add a degree of structural change to the analysis. If one is versed in a programming language, the GA programming technique is surprisingly simple.

Do businesses and business ecosystems evolve from GA type processes? As mentioned, Beinhocker makes this argument in *The Origin of Wealth*. It is a question worthy of debate and discussion. The structural components of business and ecosystems—company culture, business plans, products, processes, governmental laws, etc.—can play the role of DNA. However, the debate proceeds there is little doubt that studying the GA is extremely valuable for business leaders.

Antifragility

This section will introduce the fascinating topic of *antifragility*. This idea comes from Nassim Nicholas Taleb in his book *Antifragile: Things That Gain From Disorder* (2012). Taleb is also author of *The Black Swan* and one of the great critical thinkers of our day.

First, a definition. Consider something that is fragile. Taleb likes to use a wine glass as an example of a fragile object. Fragility is defined as a susceptibility to variation. As one starts shaking a wine glass, it may fall to the ground and break. Then, what is the opposite of fragile? A rock may come to mind. Nothing happens to a shaken rock. This could be termed *robust*. But is a rock antifragile? By its morphology, an antifragile object should be the opposite of a fragile object. So, something that is antifragile should gain, or get better in some way, from variations. Figure 61 illustrates this triad. It is an interesting idea, but is there anything that is truly antifragile? If so, what are the applications of antifragility?

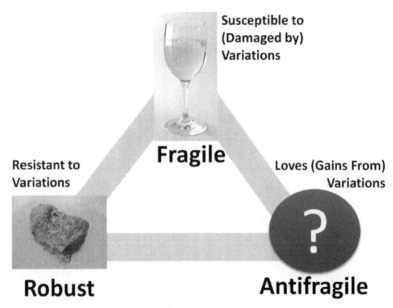

Figure 61. Fragile, Robust, and Antifragile

Consider a stock option. There are two basic types of options: calls and puts. A call option is the right, but not the requirement, to purchase a specified quantity of stock by a given date at a given price. To illustrate, consider that it is June and you have just purchased a call option, the right to purchase 100 shares of Intel stock at $25 by December. If the stock has gone up to $40 by December, you could exercise the option and purchase the 100 shares for $25, then sell those shares in the market for $40 netting a profit of $15 per share. However, if Intel stock has declined to $20 at that time, then you won't exercise the option and it will expire (worthless). Over the time from June to December, the price of the option will change as the price of Intel stock changes and as the expiration time approaches. In fact, finding a value for a stock option is an exceedingly difficult task. Fischer Black and Myron Scholes first derived a closed form formula for the price of an option in 1973[30].

Figure 62 shows the plot of a stock's price over time. Continuing the example above, consider this to be the stock price of Intel. On June 1, we purchase the aforementioned call option for Intel. This option gives us the opportunity to purchase Intel shares at $25 (the strike) anytime before December. We pay $1 for this option, for this opportunity. We notice that the Intel stock price has been moving up and down around this $20 mark prior to our purchase. The day after we purchase the option, the characteristics of the stock price dynamics change. From June 1 to July 1, Intel stock continues to move up and down, but the moves up and down are now much larger than they were in the time preceding our purchase. On July 1, Intel stock closes again at $20, but the option price has doubled to $2. The increase in variation in stock price has made the option *more* valuable. A stock option meets the definition of antifragile.

Figure 62. A Stock Price Change Over Time.

---

[30] This work helped Scholes win the Nobel Prize. Haug (2007) argues that floor traders were using an empirically derived version of the formula well before the Black-Scholes paper. Still, this does not diminish the brilliance of the solution method.

Figure 63 is a graph of the profit and loss structure of our Intel option at expiration. If Intel stock closes at $25 in December when the option expires, we will not exercise the option. So, we will have lost the $1 we paid for the option and have a loss. In fact, if Intel closes anywhere below $25, then we will not exercise the option and we will have a loss of the purchase price. If Intel price appreciates above $25, then we can exercise the option. At $26, we will break even. That is, our profit from buying at $25 and selling at $26 will exactly offset the cost of the option. If Intel stock rises above $26, we will see a profit. The increase is linear from that point with a slope of $1 profit per each $1 increase in Intel stock. While the curve is linear from $25 and above, the capped loss at $1 below $25 makes the overall shape of the curve nonlinear. The general shape of this curve is described as *convex*. Antifragile entities have a convex return curve. There is much more to be gained from upside surprises than to be lost from downside surprises. The option can benefit greatly by positive Black Swan events, but its loss from downside Black Swan events is limited.

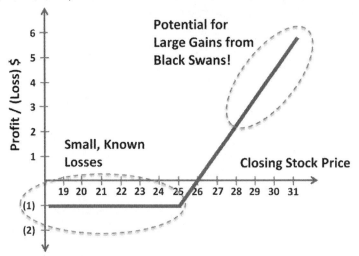

Figure 63. Stock Option Profit/Loss Chart

The profit and loss chart of Figure 63 doesn't tell the entire story. Consider that we are buying many options on many different stocks. To understand this situation, we need to look at the distribution of profit and loss across this portfolio. To simplify, let's say each option resembles the example just described; that is they each cost $1. Figure 64 illustrates a possible histogram (distribution) of returns. There will be many situations where the stock fails to rise or it falls, resulting in a loss of $1. There will also be many situations where the stock closes slightly above the strike price and we get a small profit. But, there will be a few situations where the stock closes much higher than the strike price. In these cases, we will make a nice profit. For the portfolio to make money overall, these few bigger wins must compensate for a lot of small losses. The time-dependent value of our portfolio while executing this strategy would have the shape as in Figure 65. The portfolio value would sit relatively flat, or decline slightly, until one of those rare event winners came about. Then the portfolio value would suddenly rise from the profits.

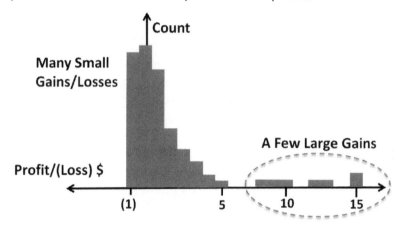

Figure 64. Distribution of Returns From Options

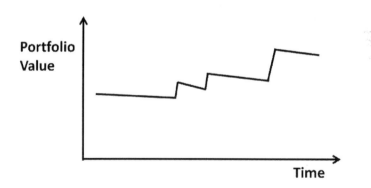

Figure 65. A Potential Option Portfolio Value Over Time

Note: The preceding discussion is by no means a suggestion to purchase or trade options. This was used to illustrate antifragility concepts only. Many have lost money trading options.

Now, let's revisit the genetic algorithm. Look again at Figure 60 and recall the few population members in the flatlands. Given the current landscape, these population members, the result of DNA mutations, will perish. This is a negative cost to the population as a whole. But, if the fitness landscape were to change, and the mutated population member happens to end up near the new global maximum, then the population as a whole can reap a huge reward. Consider how evolution works. Fish characteristics are stable for long periods as they are living in the ocean. Then, a mutation produces a fish that can exist out of the water. This new type of fish can reap the rewards of plentiful resources on land that the other fish could not. A plot of evolution will look something like that of the option portfolio shown in Figure 65 with long periods of no change and then a sudden leap to a new level. Evolution is antifragile! While individuals in the population are fragile, the population as a whole is antifragile.

There are a number of important takeaways from antifragility.

Seek Out Convexity; Look for *Free* (or Cheap) Options—Look for opportunities to build optionality into your strategies. Can you add a clause to the contract for returns? Before hiring the employee, begin with a probationary period. In many cases, valuable options can be added with little or no cost. Look for convexity! As Taleb says in the book *Antifragility*, be long volatility—be long gamma[31].

There Is Value in Trial and Error—Sponsor trial and error in your organization—viva la entrepreneur. Take the example of Google. Google allows employees to use a percentage of their work time on projects of their choice. Google Maps and Google Prediction Markets are excellent outcomes from this policy. A difficult part of this policy is to reward (or at

---

[31] When traders own a stock, they say they are long in that stock. In options, Gamma is the second derivative of the change in the option price with respect to the underlying stock. Gamma is a measure of the option's price change with volatility of the underlying. Buyers (owners) of options are long volatility–long gamma. That is, option owners benefit from volatility.

least not punish) failure in risk taking. With the idea of convexity, one expects some failures, but a small number of big successes.

Things That Have Been Around for a While, Tend to Be Around for a While Longer—In an evolutionary environment, populations residing around a maximum on the fitness landscape are likely to persist. Taleb likes to use the chair as an example. It has been used for a long time in human history and will be used for a long time to come. How about a smart phone? Taleb suggests, as a very general rule of thumb, one could expect a technology to persist going forward for at least the amount of time it has been in existence.

Randomness Cannot Be Eliminated. There Are Limits and Risks to Masking Its Effect—Environments have inherent sources of randomness. Entities in that environment have evolved to deal with this inherent randomness (and as mentioned in Chapter 4, randomness may be beneficial to systems). Efforts to limit, or mask, this inherent randomness may work for a while, but could backfire in the end. Long-Term Capital Management, a hedge fund management company, held a highly leveraged portfolio that blew up spectacularly (nearly taking the U.S. economy with it) from efforts to mask risks from fat tails in return distributions (Lowenstein, 2001).

Sudden Changes

In the last section, we discussed evolutionary systems and noted that they can remain stable for long periods and suddenly change as a random mutation hits the evolutionary jackpot. This phenomenon of sudden changes can occur from a number of other mechanisms. In this section, we will review some of these mechanisms.

Not all equilibriums are alike. An egg carefully balanced on end is in equilibrium. An egg resting in an egg carton is also in equilibrium. Clearly, there are significant differences between these two types of equilibrium. In your house, you have a thermostat set at 70 degrees that switches a furnace and air conditioner off and on. As long as your furnace and air conditioner have fuel, one can expect the temperature to remain close to 70 degrees. However, the outside air temperature has been 70 degrees for a few hours. In fact, we can't expect that equilibrium to be maintained. Ecosystem equilibrium can be equally unstable. Consider a predator and prey relationship between fishermen and salmon. The population level of salmon may remain reasonably in equilibrium over long periods, and then suddenly decrease with a relatively small change in the number of fishermen. These types of systems frequently exhibit basins of attractions; that is, a predisposition to reach equilibrium at certain levels. A descriptive (but not accurate) analogy is shaking an egg carton and having an egg move from one location in the carton to another. These unstable equilibrium, or *punctuated equilibrium* as they are sometimes called, are common in all types of evolutionary systems. Lindgren (1991) noted this type of behavior in systems of computer generated strategies in his simulation of the Iterated Prisoner's Dilemma tournament. Here, certain strategies would emerge, become dominant and stable for long periods, and then suddenly become extinct. A slow, almost imperceptible, decline was masking the exponential process underneath it.

Another proposed mechanism leading to sudden changes is *self-organized criticality*. This idea was developed by P. Bak and colleagues (Bak & Chen, 1991). It is best illustrated with the idea of a pile of sand. Consider a machine dropping sand, one grain at a time, right on the top of the sand pile. Drop after drop falls with no effect. Then, one drop falls, and an avalanche of sand commences. Can one say that last grain of sand *caused* the avalanche? Bak argues no. Instead, the avalanche was a result of the sand pile being in a super-critical state. That one grain of sand was just the final straw, a catalyst, for the avalanche. Bak opened up the idea that many real-world sudden changes are related to self-organized criticality, ranging from forest fires to market crashes.

The key message here is crucial; if your business ecosystem seems stable, don't be lulled into a potentially false sense of security. Big changes can happen very quickly. Don't confuse low volatility with low risk. Andy Grove, former Intel CEO, was fond of saying "Only the paranoid survive." These are wise words. Models used in business often do very well in periods of stability, but fail miserably in times of sudden changes. They work well when you don't need them and fail when you need them the most.

Example: Evolution of Ecosystems—Computers

Perhaps you have heard the old story about the father who, upset about his kid's trivial complaints, tells his kids he had to walk miles to school through snow several feet deep. Well, I can remember a time when the computing power of the phone you hold in your hand required an entire air conditioned room, and this story is true!

Flash back to the late 1970s and the Digital Equipment Corporation (DEC) introduces the VAX minicomputer. This system was a breakthrough in the evolution of computing, offering a complete hardware system (computer, storage, print, etc.), full software stack (operating system, business applications, etc.), and at the most affordable price to date. To deliver this technology, DEC used what is today called a *vertical ecosystem* (or what might be sometimes called a *walled garden*). That is, DEC developed (or at least controlled) and sold every major component of the system. DEC made the computer systems, sourced and resold peripherals, and developed the major software components. The VAX architecture propelled DEC to an immensely profitable decade.

However, as discussed in the example of Chapter 4, a small outlier was flickering in the world of computing. Intel's microprocessors were digging a foothold in consumer electronic items such as calculators. Meanwhile, a tiny company, Microsoft, was developing a primitive (by DEC standards) operating system for this microprocessor (DOS). In an incredibly serendipitous, and unpredictable, catalytic event, IBM chose the Intel microprocessor and Microsoft DOS operating system for its business experiment (trial and error) into the market for personal computers.

As a short aside, let's examine the view of personal computers at this time (approximately 1980). Perhaps you are wondering why the IBM personal computer is described as a business experiment. You probably think this project was an obvious winner for IBM and was well funded with extensive visibility at top levels of IBM management, but that would be a narrative fallacy. In fact, this was a nascent market, and many believed the market for personal computers would never develop. Ken Olsen, the founder of DEC, famously quoted "There is no reason anyone would want a computer in their home."

Of course, now we know the Windows/Intel Black Swan grew to dominate the market for computers[32]. The ecosystem that grew to support this new architecture was radically different than the vertical ecosystem of DEC. Intel and Microsoft were small and could not support all the components of a full computer platform. Also, IBM wanted to enlist more partners for their small project. A horizontal ecosystem developed where multiple third parties could develop components for the platform. After a long and profitable era, this horizontal ecosystem eventually proved to be the undoing of IBM's personal computer business. With the architecture open, other computer original equipment manufacturers, such as Dell and Compaq, could compete directly with IBM.

Example: Building an Ecosystem—SAP[33]

The Harvard Business School case *SAP AG: Orchestrating the Ecosystem* provides an excellent recounting of SAP's efforts in the mid-2000s to construct a Windows/Intel like ecosystem around their Enterprise Resource Planning (ERP) software[34]. There are a number of interesting aspects to this case, but two will be discussed here.

First, a platform ecosystem has many inter-related components. The case write up does a great job giving the high level overview of these pieces. The complexity of these pieces is enough to get the reader's head spinning. There's no need to recount it here; the point is there are many details and considerable resources will be required to develop and manage this kind of program.

Second, and most importantly for our discussion, building an ecosystem represents a sort of *unnatural* act. In the case of the Intel and Microsoft ecosystem, the components all developed as the market developed. Some components and participants developed and subsequently left the ecosystem. The relationships between entities all developed naturally, over the course of time. SAP was attempting to put the ecosystem in place themselves in a short period of time. Consider the following analogy:

---

[32] DEC was eventually sold to Compaq, who later merged with HP. In a bit of irony, much of the remaining DEC facilities and staff in Massachusetts were sold to Intel!

[33] SAP is a German multinational software corporation.

[34] For our purposes here, just think of ERP as an operating system for servers, the big computers that reside in data centers.

> Scientists find an island in the Pacific Ocean that has absolutely no life on it, plant or animal. The scientists decide to construct a biological ecosystem that is a complete food chain. They import plants, animals, insects, etc., and populate the island. What do you think will happen?

When I pose this question in class, students immediately and instinctively exclaim, "everything will die" or, " the island will turn into a weed patch." Constructing an ecosystem is hard, but not impossible. SAP has had success. But be prepared to spend substantial resources to nurture it.

Summary and Action Plan

The key idea from this chapter, as illustrated in Figure 54, is that structural changes are always at work in the business ecosystem. The system tools described in the previous chapters have all assumed a degree of stability in the system structure (synchronics), which was a necessary assumption to complete the analysis. But, we must always keep in mind that our models are not reality (remember George Box). The reality is that the structure is constantly evolving.

We did a very brief and selective review of the academic literature on business ecosystems. The Grove/Porter seven forces model is a valuable tool to start our thinking about a business ecosystem. This tool can help us to consider which tools from the systems thinking toolbox to focus on. The outstanding work of James Moore (who coined the term business ecosystem) can help add credibility to our systems thinking ideas when presenting to management.

The biological evolution process can be used as a model of business ecosystem evolution. The genetic algorithm has provided many valuable insights into the evolutionary processes. The idea of antifragility, for which evolution is the most important example, gives us tremendous guidance:

- Seek out low-cost options in your business and look for convex payouts.
- Embrace trial and error processes, and foster entrepreneurship.
- Embrace randomness, and be aware that attempts to mask or limit its effects may seem to work in the short run but could have big consequences in the future.
- Value diversity; it is important in evolutionary processes.

Finally, we reviewed unpredictable changes in systems. Don't be lulled into complacency. Grove's "Only the paranoid survive" are words to live by.

Further Reading

An excellent summary is provided in Chapter 9 of Eric Beinhocker's *The Origin of Wealth* (2006).

Nassim Nicholas Taleb's book *Antifragile: Things That Gain From Disorder* (2012) is highly recommended. As mentioned before, Taleb's writings can be a bit edgy, but the critical thinking is superb.

Questions

1. You are constructing an ecosystem map of your company's industry. You are having some difficulty really seeing how all the pieces fit together. What might be a good next step?

2. Question 5 in Chapter 3 related to Intel's Itanium program. Now that we have learned a bit more, which course of action is best for Intel in this situation?
A. Continue with the Itanium direction as described.
B. Use a genetic algorithm inspired strategy of starting two smaller projects to fully explore both options. One project would be an exploration of the Itanium as described. The second project would be an exploration of extending the current x86 architecture to 64 bits.
C. Drop out of the microprocessor business and look for a new inflection point. After all, only the paranoid survive, according to Grove.

3. Which of the options below have a convex payoff (small known losses and potentially large gains)?
A. Taking antibiotics for a non-life-threatening virus in order to avoid losing a few days of work.
B. Cheating on an exam.
C. Picking up nickels right in front of a moving steamroller (where the operator cannot see you).
D. Purchasing the oil rights from a wheat farmer for his land.

4. The genetic algorithm (GA) could be considered a tool to answer a question. Here, the question needs to be parsed in a way that its solution can be expressed by a fitness function. For example, for optimization, the question being answered is "What's the largest?" Which other process that we have discussed is analogous to the GA in that it can answer questions, is relatively simple, effectively uses diversity, exhibits robustness and adaptability, and fundamentally uses a population in the solution process?

5. You have generated several generations of populations using a genetic algorithm (GA) on a complex landscape (e.g., several local maximums and one global maximum), and the GA hasn't found the maximum value in the landscape. What is the best next step?
A.   Try a hill-climbing (gradient ascent) algorithm.
B.   Run the GA for more generations (more iterations).
C.   Remove the crossover portion of the algorithm to improve its accuracy.
D.   Remove the mutation portion of the algorithm to improve its scalability.

6. Discuss some ways to add optionality to a business deal.

7. As mentioned in Chapter 3, when building a simulation model, two steps are needed to determine the model's correctness—verification and validation. Validation is the process of assessing how well the model matches the real-world system. The most common method of validation is to break the real system data that you have acquired into two sets: a training set and a test set. The training set is used to determine the parameters of the model. Then, the completed model's behavior is compared to the test set data to assess validity. For example, if Ben Bernanke's team were building a model of the economy, they might use the economic data from 2012 to determine the model's parameters, and then test the model with data from the first half of 2013. Which ideas from this chapter are fundamentally at odds with this ubiquitous validation practice?

Discussion of Questions

1. Reviewing the history could be quite valuable. The odd relationships you are having difficulty understanding may be due to past circumstances and the path of industry evolution.

2. B makes the most sense. Start with two small projects and use the option to cancel one later.

3. The best answer here is D.

	Upside	Downside
Taking antibiotics for a non-life-threatening virus in order to avoid losing a few days of work.	You get a couple of extra days of work.	When you have a serious illness and really need the antibiotic then it may not work.
Cheating on an exam.	You improve your score on that exam, which is only a part of the grade of one class.	You are kicked out of school.
Picking up nickels right in front of a moving steamroller (where the operator cannot see you).	A few nickels.	Being flattened by the steamroller.
Purchasing the oil rights from a wheat farmer for his land.	You strike oil!	Your rights are worthless.

4. A prediction market has these characteristics.

5. Gradient ascent will be very initial-condition dependent with this type of landscape (it may run up one of the local maximums and get stuck there). Removing crossover or mutation will ruin the GA mechanism. Just run more generations, and the GA will probably work fine. Besides, that's also the easiest thing to try (computer cycles are cheap these days)!

6. Here are a few:
- A business loan that has a clause to allow penalty-free early payoff.
- Purchasing a corporate bond that may be converted to a quantity of stock.
- Hiring an employee on a 6-month retainer before putting them on permanent employment.
- Purchasing the mineral rights from a property owner.

7. If evolutionary processes have fundamentally changed the structure of the real system between the times of the train and test set, then the fundamental assumption of stationarity of the process is not valid.

7. Networks

In this chapter we will discuss networks. Just a few short years ago, in the days before LinkedIn and Facebook, very few thought about nor took notice of networks. Back in those *old days*, an instructor in this field had to work hard to introduce and motivate the discussion. But now, networks are in the forefront of most people's thinking. The chapter begins with a very short review of network science. This will lead into a discussion of network dynamics and network management.

Network Science and Real-World Networks

Figure 66 shows the basic components of a network: nodes and edges (or links). In our cases, nodes will represent some type of entity such as a person, a company, etc. An edge will represent a relationship between the two entities. On a map of Facebook connections, these edges represent Facebook friendships. A challenging issue with network analysis is ascribing characteristics to the relationship (the edge). For example, look at your Facebook network. Now consider that network as if you need to borrow $1,000. Are all links alike?

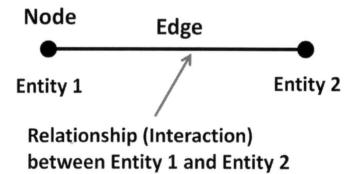

Figure 66. Definitions in a Network Graph

Much of the basis for network science today comes from the field of mathematics called *graph theory*. Graph theory has a rich history and its beginnings are typically attributed to Euler. Of particular interest for our efforts, graph theory gives us some descriptive metrics to evaluate a network.

A measure of how connected the network is:

$$Average\ Degree\ of\ Connectivity = \frac{Number\ of\ Edges}{Number\ of\ Nodes}$$

A measure of how large the network is:

$$Average\ Path\ Length = \frac{\sum All\ Path\ Lengths}{Number\ of\ Paths}$$

Some common network types have descriptive names: star, ring, bus, tree, line, and so on. Finally, the histogram of the number of connections per node will become a key descriptive metric for understanding real-world networks.

Many people have had the occasion to meet someone at random and then find out that they both had a friend in common. This *small-world* effect has received a plethora of discussion in the recent past. *Six degrees of separation* argues that any two people can be linked with six or fewer connections. The six degrees of Kevin Bacon finds the shortest number of connections between any actor or actress and Kevin Bacon (oracleofbacon.org). This idea traces back to psychologist Stanley Milgram and an experiment he performed in 1950. Milgram enlisted a group of people from Nebraska and Kansas via a newspaper ad. Each participant was given the name of a stockbroker in Boston and told to get a letter to this stockbroker. Their instructions were that they could only pass the letter to someone they personally knew. The letter would also record the path it took to arrive. Milgram found the median number of intermediate links was five, thus spawning the *six degrees* phrase.

Surprisingly, the research into the characteristics of real-world networks received relatively little attention after Milgram's work, but in the late 1990s that would change. At that time, separate research groups of Duncan Watts/Steven Strogatz and Albert-Laszlo Barabasi/Reka Albert were making key discoveries (for an excellent overview, see (Barabasi & Bonabeau, 2003). One of the key insights was an understanding of how real-world networks were different than random networks[35]. Small-world,

---

[35] A random network is constructed by first creating a set of nodes and then using a random number generator (RNG) to randomly add edges between nodes.

real-world networks have unique characteristics in terms of combinations of path length and degree of connectivity. A crucial breakthrough came when the researchers plotted histograms of the number of connections to each node. A network that is randomly created should have a random histogram of the degree of connectivity as in Figure 67.

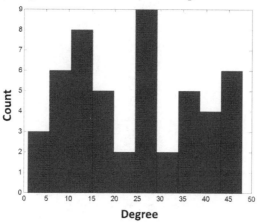

Figure 67. Histogram of Degree of Connection for a Random Graph

What did the researchers see when they plotted the histogram of real-world networks? To illustrate, the *Preferential Attachment* model from the NetLogo library will be used. This NetLogo model will allow you to run the model yourself and explore the relationships as the model constructs real-world-like networks and extracts their connectivity histograms. We will discuss how this model works shortly. Figure 68 shows the output of this model after 340 nodes and their connections have been constructed. The graph in the middle left plots the degree (number of connections) of a node versus the number of occurrences. Of the 340 nodes, approximately 210 of them have only one connection. Approximately 50 have two connections, but a few nodes have many connections. The graph directly below has the same information, but is plotted on a log/log scale. Notice that on the log/log scale, the relationship is approximately linear for a large range of degrees. Contrast this relationship to a random generated graph of Figure 67. Very clearly, real-world networks have special characteristics.

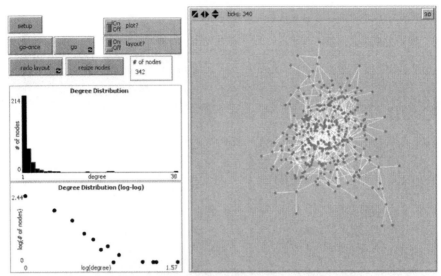

Figure 68. Screen Capture of the NetLogo Library Model Preferential Attachment Demonstrating the Power Law Relationship of Number of Nodes to Degree of Connection

Researchers have studied numerous real-world networks from social interactions through the URL page links of the internet. These networks have consistently demonstrated a linear relationship of degree versus probability when plotted on a log/log scale. As illustrated in Figure 69, the probability can be described by the power law equation with slope of alpha. This is sometimes called the networking coefficient, and usually ranges between two and a bit over three in real-world networks.

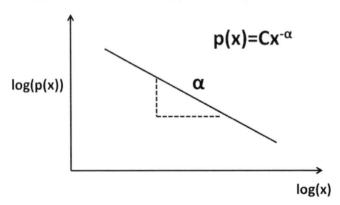

Figure 69. Plot of the Count (or Probability) Versus the Number of Connections to a Node in a Small-World Type Network

Real-world networks exhibit clustering that also departs from random network characteristics. For example, airline network maps exhibit clustering with hub cities like Chicago, Denver, or Atlanta having many more flights than the average city. These networks are designed in this manner to optimize the air carrier's objectives. However, characteristics similar to this are seen in evolved networks such as friendship networks. Figure 70 illustrates a network of friends. Consider the group of five on the top left with yourself and four friends. A message within this group can *rattle around* as it goes between friends. This is sometimes called an *echo chamber* effect. Information only flows into or out of this chamber from the friend on the right, labeled here as a *broker*. These brokers are critically important in creating the small-world effect.

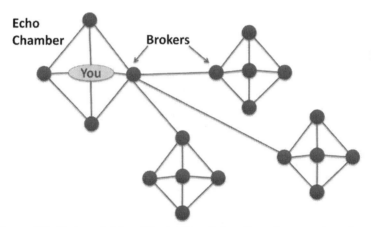

Figure 70. Network Map Illustrating Echo Chambers and Brokers

Figure 71 is a network analysis of political blogs developed by network science researcher Lada Adamic at the University of Michigan. The lighter nodes are the conservative blogs and the darker nodes are the liberal blogs. Most of the connections are between nodes of the same type. Only a few connections exist between conservative and liberal blogs (the lightest lines in the gap between the two clusters), illustrating a pronounced echo chamber effect and the relative scarcity of brokers.

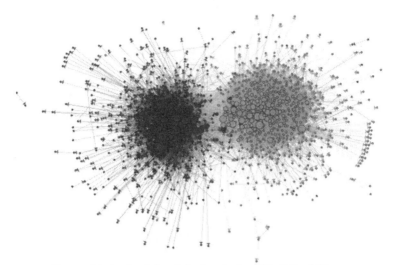

Figure 71. Lada Adamic's Analysis of Political Blogs

The clustering and hub characteristic of real-world networks have important implications on risk. In general, these types of networks are robust to a random failure because there are generally many paths around a node that fails. This was a primary consideration in the Defense Department's construction of the original internet: survivability from attacks. But small-world networks are vulnerable to targeted attacks at the hubs. As I write this paragraph on September 26, 2014, airlines are suffering large flight cancellations and delays due to a fire set by a disgruntled employee in the air traffic controller station in Chicago, a key airline hub city. Real-world networks are also susceptible to cascading failures. The large Northeast power outage of 2003 began with an outage in Ohio and cascaded across the Northeast U.S. and Canada, eventually impacting over 50 million people.

What is the mechanism at work that creates small-world networks instead of random networks? Revisiting the NetLogo simulation Preferential Attachment (Figure 68) gives us a hypothesis. The simulation progresses by adding one node at a time, and the newest node is given one link to another node. The node linked to is chosen by a semi-random method, and this algorithm has a bias that is based on the number of connections a node already has: the rich getting richer. This makes intuitive sense for a human network; as a new person comes into a group they naturally are drawn towards the person with the most connections. This mechanism will also be familiar from dynamic interactions in Chapter 3. This is the Success to the Successful archetype at work!

Figure 72, the key idea graphic for this chapter, contains a real-world network topology, shown along with the power law characteristic. Finally, the key idea graphic includes the Success to the Successful system diagram.

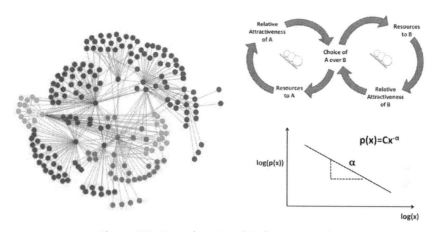

Figure 72. Key Idea Graphic for Networks

Network Dynamics

Two aspects of network dynamics are considered: synchronics and diachronics. First, assuming the network is not changing, the flow of items, primarily information, across the network is studied. Then, the nature of a network's structural change over time is examined.

Networks can be considered a topology upon which any of the system mechanisms we have discussed can flow across. Feedback loops can form across networks, as anyone who has heard a piece of information from a colleague that originated from themselves can attest. Aggregated interactions can flow across a network. For example, a fad moving across a network following Granovetter's model. Probabilistic diffusion and percolation models are often used to study flow across networks. Perhaps the most common models used to study flow across networks are those related to the spread of disease. These models include the Susceptible-Infected (SI) model and the Susceptible-Infected-Recovered (SIR) model. These models are wonderfully explained in Sterman's classic textbook

Business Dynamics (2000). To get some feel for these processes, we will once again call upon NetLogo. Lada Adamic has created a NetLogo model that simulates flow across a network with the SI process. Figure 73 shows the interface of the model with a 300 node small-world network simulated. An initial infection (or source of information) is shown with the bull's-eye and marked with the arrow.

After a few time steps, the infection has moved out from the source, moving across the connections of the network as seen in Figure 73. Notice that in this particular simulation, a node far from the initial source has been infected while many nodes directly adjacent to the source remain uninfected.

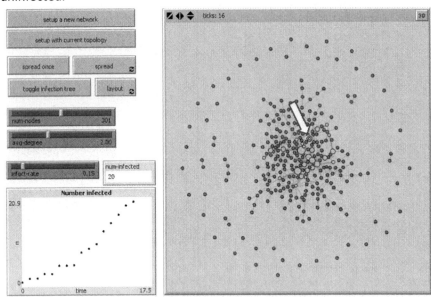

Figure 73. The Infection, Which Began at the Bull's-Eye (Arrow), Has Spread Across Network Links

After a number of time steps, the entire core echo chamber has been infected. Figure 74 shows a plot of the number infected over time with the characteristic S-shape that is indicative of the SI process. The NetLogo model provides a means to test the effects of network size, degree of connectivity, and infection rates. One can verify, as intuitively expected, that infections or information flow faster across networks with a higher degree of connection.

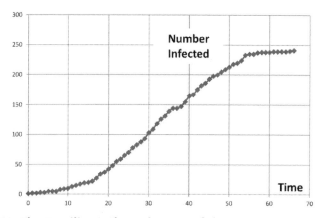

Figure 74. The Familiar S-Shaped Curve of the SI Process. Exponential Growth to a Limit Is Seen in the Number Infected Over Time

Flow across networks depends on the type of network structure. Most evolved real-world structures have the clustering effects. However, in business, some structures are constructed, not naturally evolved. A most notable example is the organization structure that is almost always built as a hierarchy. In a hierarchy, information can flow down and up relatively effectively. However, information flow across branches of the network have inherent limits; namely, the nodes near the top of the hierarchy. To compensate for this issue, organizations sponsor various mechanisms to foster cross-organization communication ranging from formal knowledge management systems to informal social events. This example also illustrates that, in any given situation, there are usually multiple networks layered on a set of nodes. For example, with employees in a business there is the formal command and control organizational hierarchy: less formal networks of common skills (e.g., an engineering council), very informal social networks based on interests outside of work (e.g., a hikers club), informal networks based on community circumstances (that manager's son and my daughter are in the same class at school), and many more.

Another important part of the systems thinking toolbox is an understanding of how the structure of networks changes over time. As mentioned in the last section, the most strongly supported hypothesis is a Success to the Successful process. When thinking about networks of relationships, this makes intuitive sense. We are all familiar with people who really enjoy interacting with people and love to keep in contact with their acquaintances. They enjoy the process of making new contacts and building relationships. It makes sense that they serve as information hubs and are the link between various echo chambers.

An extremely important effect of networks is the way they impact growth of new business or new technology. Consider the growth of new technology such as the telephone. How does the value of this device change as adoption increases? A heuristic has been developed, usually referred to as Metcalfe's Law[36], to describe this effect:

$$Value\ of\ Device\ =\ Number\ of\ People\ Using\ It^2$$

Economists often refer to this as the *networking effect*. Of course, we wish they had been a little more specific, since the impact and implications of networks are much broader than just this value effect. However, this term has developed a fair degree of usage and name recognition. Of course, this is just a heuristic, but it does highlight the nonlinear nature of technology value with adoption. This nonlinear nature is something we have come to expect in our exploration of systems, but again is counter to the human tendency to make linear extrapolation. The telephone is the example used most often to illustrate this effect. One telephone has essentially zero value, but when most of your friends also have a phone, then there is great value in the device. The networking effect is prevalent in many, many business situations. As Facebook gained in popularity, new users were more likely to choose it because that's where their friends tended to be. This creates a particularly powerful reinforcing feedback loop. With the value increasing, according to Metcalfe, as square of the number using it, the probability of the next person choosing it increases as the square. When there are competing alternatives, the nonlinear change in value can lead to pronounced tipping points. Consider the case of two competing smartphone applications such as a chat application. As more of your friends gravitate to one option versus the other, the relative value changes dramatically (a Success to the Successful example).

---

[36] Metcalfe's law is attributed to Roger Metcalfe and was first discussed in terms of computer networks (specifically Ethernet).

Managing Networks

To improve a group's, or their own, performance, a manager needs to actively manage the networks around them. In this section, we build upon the understanding of real-world networks and examine what actions and tools are available to managers.

First, how can a manager understand the networks in their organizations? Various network records—fingerprints—may be available. Huberman and Adamic (2004) describe a study at Hewlett Packard Labs where network maps were created using email and phone logs. Of course, in larger organizations, this capability would need to be implemented by a concerted effort between the group to be studied, the information technology (IT) department, and human resources. Knowledge management systems also contain the raw material to build network maps. Given that some types of records are available, there are excellent tools for network topology analysis. Gephi is one such tool, and their short YouTube video titled *Introducing Gephi 0.7* gives a nice overview of the capabilities of this class of tool.

Figure 70 illustrated that brokers are key links in a network. They are critical mechanisms for information to flow between groups. In some cases, organizations have designated individuals to fulfill this role—e.g., a liaison between marketing and design. But, Figure 70 illustrates a potential issue. Here, the brokers are the single point of contact between groups, and that can lead to problems. First, these brokers are a bottleneck in the information flow. Second, and more importantly, if they leave the organization, then the echo chambers become isolated. To mitigate these problems, as illustrated in Figure 75, a manager may work to increase the linkages between groups to improve information flow and to make the network more robust. Organizations can use many mechanisms to create additional linkages in the general organization. These range from Friday afternoon picnics to organized company conferences.

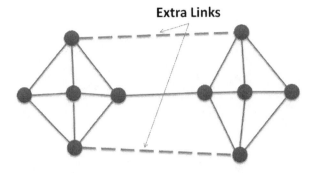

Group 1 (e.g., Design)   Group 2 (e.g., Marketing)

Figure 75. Adding Extra Links Between Echo Chambers Increases Information Flow and Reduces Risk of Losing the Connection if a Hub Leaves the Network

As a professional, you need to manage your own personal network. The idea of maintaining and nurturing a personal network of business contacts is discussed in any number of books, so these topics will not be covered here. It is recommended to use the best tools at your disposal in the personal network management task. As I write this in 2014, the best tool is LinkedIn. LinkedIn's Search, and particularly Advanced Search, are powerful tools. In terms of finding a new job, LinkedIn may be the most important tool at your disposal. Although LinkedIn won't display network topologies, you can search for someone out of your personal network, and LinkedIn will show you the most direct relationship path. In terms of maintenance, there is value in keeping in touch with the members of your direct LinkedIn network. To that end, the general recommendation is to only add members to your personal network that you know well. If they would not be willing to relay a message, then it is not recommended to add them to your network.

Example: Networks—LinkedIn

The Harvard Business School case *LinkedIn Corp., 2008* highlights two important points from this chapter.

First, this case illustrates the rise in importance, and the changing role, of professional networks. In the early days of LinkedIn, having a profile was an indicator that one was not happy in their current job and was looking for a new position. So having a profile was not something one wanted to have known by their current employer. Today, that has changed, and most professionals are members of LinkedIn. Many employers encourage its use to support employee growth. In fact, employers have started using LinkedIn as a way to recruit talent that is not yet actively looking for new positions.

Second, the growth of LinkedIn illustrates the networking effect. When just a few people had profiles on LinkedIn, LinkedIn's value was limited. Today, with so many professionals having profiles, the LinkedIn search engine becomes an incredibly valuable tool to find industry contacts. Metcalfe's law would argue the value of LinkedIn has grown by N^2, and the nonlinear growth rate in number of users in Figure 76 would agree.

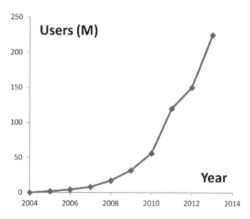

Figure 76. Number of LinkedIn Users by Year (Source: Company Website)

Summary and Action Plan

Awareness of networks in business is important. For human resource groups implementing policies, or IT groups implementing knowledge management tools, the informal networks of employees may be crucial to successful deployment. For a marketing group, understanding how information can spread, perhaps in a viral manner, may be critical. The key idea graphic, Figure 72, reminds us of some of the key characteristics of networks. Most real-world networks have some degree of hub-and-spoke nature, with echo chambers and brokers who move information between chambers. Most real-world networks have a small-world nature; there are a small number of connections between any two nodes. A log/log plot of a histogram of the number of connections per node will be approximately linear indicating a power law relationship. The graphic

185

reminds us that the most likely mechanism creating these characteristics is the Success to the Successful archetype.

If possible, it may be highly valuable to gain some insight into the topology of your networks. Email or phone logs, knowledge management, system access records, etc., can be used, and a tool like Gephi can provide powerful visualization of the network. In particular, critical hubs can be identified and extra links between subgroups can be added to improve resilience and information flow. If your network has some type of mission-critical nature (like the electrical subsystem), then understanding where failures could cascade may be crucial.

Networks are constantly changing. Many business technologies will be subject to what economists call the *networking effect*. Metcalfe's law, a heuristic, argues that the value of a technology grows as the square of the number of people using it. If there are multiple technologies developing at the same time, the network effect can lead to powerful tipping points between the two technologies (Success to the Successful on steroids).

Further Reading

An excellent summary of the topics in this chapter is provided in Chapter 7 of Eric Beinhocker's *The Origin of Wealth* (2006).

Melanie Mitchell's outstanding book on complexity science, *Complexity: A Guided Tour* (2009), has an excellent discussion of networks in Chapters 15 and 16.

Duncan Watts' excellent book, *Six Degrees: The Science of a Connected Age* (2003), provides an insightful discussion and also has an entertaining recounting of the history of the scientific work.

Questions

1. Consider the network of friends shown. Assume the only contact is between friends as identified in the network. If the numbers in the circles represent that person's adoption threshold for some new fad, then according to Granovetter's law as discussed in Chapter 4, will Joe adopt the fad?

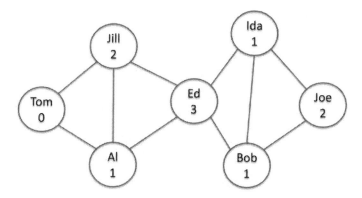

2. Metcalfe's Law suggests that the value of a technology grows as a power law function of number of users. Could the mechanism of this value growth be an example of the Success to the Successful archetype?

Discussion of Questions

1. No, the fad will stop at Ed. Note that without considering the network effect, we would expect Joe to adopt.

2. Strictly speaking, no. Success to the Successful requires two alternatives and the choice of one over the other. The nonlinear growth in value in Metcalfe's law is due to a single reinforcing feedback loop.

8. Multiple Perspectives

In this chapter, we explore the idea of multiple perspectives. The version described here was codified by Harold Linstone, Professor Emeritus of systems science at Portland State University. The ideas are discussed in his excellent, but perhaps difficult to find, journal article in *Systems Practice* (1989) as well as Dr. Linstone's book *Decision Making for the Technology Executive* (1999) which, as of this writing, is still available. If you aspire to higher levels of management, this is a chapter you will not want to skip.

Inquiry Systems

Before proceeding to multiple perspectives, it will be valuable to discuss inquiry systems, which can also be thought of as modeling methodologies. At first blush, this may seem academic with little practical value, but understanding this taxonomy is very valuable in understanding how models are interpreted. The taxonomy presented here is largely based on the work of Ian Mitroff and Murray Turoff (1973). Most of the tools in the systems thinking toolbox are modeling methods, so understanding as much as possible about models is crucial for their effective use. The organizing principal for this taxonomy is the validation process of the model.

Let's begin with the modeling methodology used extensively in mathematics, which Mitroff and Turoff refer to as the *Leibnizian inquiry system* where models are built based on a formal system of logic. For example, theorems are built on axioms through step-by-step logical arguments. The validity of these models is based on the internal consistency and formal completeness.

Next, the *Lockean inquiry system* is used extensively by empirical sciences. Consider, for example, the economists of the Federal Reserve Board. The economists have enormous amounts of data including years of job reports, trade balances, economic activity, inflation, and on and on. Advanced statistical methods and time series modeling (econometrics) is used to build models of the economy. Since the models are fit to data, validity is assessed via agreement among the relevant community of experts. This validation method was a driver for the now prevalent peer review process for journals. The Lockean inquiry system is intimately linked to the inductive reasoning process discussed in Chapter 2.

Next is the *Kantean inquiry system*. Consider a psychologist, say Daniel Kahneman, and an experiment he might use to test his ideas. Kahneman is interested in a particular human decision bias, so he recruits a group of subjects and randomly assigns them to one of two groups. One group is exposed to one condition, and the other group is exposed to another condition. The results are recorded and subjected to statistical tests to determine if any differences observed are beyond random variation. Unlike the economist, Kahneman is able to control the environment of the test and isolate the conditions of interest. This process is the backbone of the scientific method: the experimental method. The validation method is this feedback process. The Kantean inquiry system is based on deductive reasoning.

Mitroff and Turoff next describe what they call the *Hegelian inquiry system*. The primary user of this system is the judicial system. Here, the problems are very complex, and parties may be withholding or altering data. Dialectic inquiry is a key technique used. The validation is by due process, which is a set sequence of steps outlined by laws that seek to arrive at the best conclusion possible given the circumstances.

Finally, Mitroff and Turoff describe the *Singerian inquiry system*. This inquiry system accepts the imperfection of models and seeks to constantly revise itself as new information becomes available. Linstone's TOP (Technical, Organizational, Personal), which will be described next, is an example. Also, the methods put forth in this book constitute a Singerian inquiry system. Table 16 summarizes the five inquiry systems.

Inquiry System	Method	Validation Process	Example
Leibnizian	Logical	Internal Consistency and Formal Completeness	Mathematics
Lockean	Empirical	Agreement Among Relevant Community	Empirical Science (e.g., Economics)
Kantean	Experimental	Feedback	Scientific Method
Hegelian	Dialectic	Due Process	Judicial
Singerian	Iterative	Constant Revision	Linstone's TOP—Multiple Perspectives

Table 16. Summary of the Inquiry Systems Described by Mitroff and Turoff

Besides framing TOP and the philosophy of this book, it is important to understand the differences in inquiry systems. Much of the modeling work done for business falls in the Lockean category. Businesses often uses existing historical data and make projections. It is important to realize there is limited control of variables as in the Kantean inquiry system. The limits on inference are paramount to interpretation. Understanding how to correctly build statistical studies, with proper control of variables, is essential in these types of analysis. For an entertaining and readable guide to statistics in a Lockean framework, see the excellent book *Freakonomics* (Levitt & Dubner, 2005).

TOP (Technical, Organizational, Personal)

We've put men on the moon, why can't we ____?

Many of you have heard this utterance at some point. The blank is often filled with something like "get our economy moving." In many ways, this saying sums up TOP. First, the question itself represents *T* thinking. Second, the answer to the question is usually TOP. TOP is an acronym for Technical, Organizational, and Personal. These are perspectives, ways of looking at a system. TOP argues that real-world problems that involve other humans require a multiple perspective view to understanding.

To begin, consider the quest to understand nature. Physicists strive to understand the physical laws and nature of the world. Engineers strive to build structures by understanding, and adapting to, the laws of physical forces. These can be immensely difficult problems, but nature has no agenda, and nature will not exhibit strategic behavior. There are very fundamental differences between solving a problem in physics and a problem in the business world. Consider these assumptions:

- Problems can be solved.
- Problems have a best solution.
- To understand a complicated problem, we must break it apart into simpler components that can be understood.
- Data should drive the solution.
- Building models leads to an understanding of the problem.
- Quantitative analysis is more valuable that qualitative analysis.
- As I observe this problem, I am objective.
- The problem is independent of the observer (me).

These are good assumptions for the physicist tackling a problem in particle theory, but perhaps not always for the business manager. These assumptions characterize the *T* perspective, which is grounded in the scientific method and is intensely rational. In modern, Western society, the relentless success of science has made the *T* perspective the de facto paradigm for problem solving. But for solving problems that include groups of people, is it enough? Linstone argues no, and that other perspectives must be also used.

> You never really understand a person until you consider things from his point of view... Until you climb inside of his skin and walk around in it.
> — Harper Lee, *To Kill a Mockingbird*

The *O* and *P* perspectives challenge many of the assumptions of the *T* perspective. The problem may be highly dependent on the observer. Consider a toddler painting on the wall, is this a big mess or a fun creative experience? The *O* perspective examines issues from the view of organizations, and for any given issue, there will be multiple organizations to consider. A business thinker may need to consider the business as an entity, the groups within the business, other businesses, unions, governments, lobby groups, groups of consumers, and on and on. The *P* perspective examines issues from the perspective of the individual. For any complex business issue, there are many individuals to consider. The key decision makers are usually the most important to consider, but the perspectives of other individuals may be important to consider depending on the situation.

> I can't understand this company policy. It doesn't make any sense.
>> New employee
> It's just the way we do things around here; it's our culture.
>> Seasoned coworker

The O perspective views the issue through the lens of the organization. In our systems thinking viewpoint, an organization, a collection of individuals, has an emergent behavior unique from those of the individuals. An organization seeks its own stability (its own continuation) and its own goals, and an organization will put processes in place to achieve these goals. The organizational hierarchy, organization culture, and organization goal statements are all important processes by which the organization moves towards its objectives.

The P perspective focuses on the individual. What are the goals of the individuals involved? For senior executives, these may focus on power and influence, whereas for some, fairness and ethical behavior may be key. These goals will vary greatly across human societies and cultures. Many Asian cultures are deeply committed to collective good, and Western societies may have a bias towards entrepreneurship. Within these cultural norms there are, of course, great variations in individuals. In the P perspective, emotions can be crucial, especially in situations of high tension or crisis.

TOP is not an idealistic theory; it is practical advice for the real world. TOP urges the decision maker to consider all three perspectives. For most, the T perspective is the natural, and to some extent, default approach. Usually, it is the O and P perspectives that must be systematically considered.

There is no formula for reconciling between the three perspectives. They must all be considered and weighed against one another. As a very general heuristic, the O and P perspectives increase in importance as the decision moves higher in the management hierarchy. TOP is a Singerian inquiry system, and it is pragmatic. Directions that result from TOP analysis must always be revisited to ascertain if the analysis was complete enough, or to determine if conditions may have changed. There may not be a right or best answer.

There are a number of common failure modes. First, as one might expect, there is an overconfidence and over-reliance in the T perspective. Some analysts may attempt to use T thinking to capture O and P perspectives (for example, using only statistical survey data to characterize O and P perspectives, without support of qualitative research). Also common is a lack of considering interactions between perspectives and, in particular, not considering interactions between O and P perspectives. For example, an individual may feel tension when their own P perspective is at odds with the O perspective of the organization of which they are a member. Crisis situations frequently result in not adequately considering the O and P perspectives. An organization may have latent, but crucial, processes that surface when the crisis hits (reminiscent of latent feedback loops). Also, a crisis may elicit strong emotions that powerfully influence the P perspective. In some cases, the T perspective may be clouded by the P perspective. A prime example here is a failure to anticipate low likelihood and severe consequence outcomes because of human decision biases (P perspective).

It is insightful to think about repeatability in TOP. The T perspective presumes repeatability, since its base is scientific processes and the Lockean and Kantean inquiry systems. The O and P perspectives, on the other hand, presume a greater degree of variability. Consider the executive who had a wonderful morning with their spouse and children one day, or who may have had a fender bender on the drive to work the next day. These different experiences may change the decisions that executive will make in a given day. Table 17 very briefly summarizes some of the key aspects of each perspective.

T - Technology	O - Organizational	P - Personal
Rational	Process	Emotions, Behaviors
Problem solving	Culture	Mental Models
Models	Bureaucracy	Power

Table 17. Key Characteristics of the Three Perspectives Analysis

Example: TOP—Wide-Body Jets

Not only does this example illustrate TOP, it also touches upon ecosystems, game theory, and many aspects of the book's discussions. As our final example, it provides an excellent capstone. Much of this example draws upon dialogue in Linstone's book *Decision Making for Technology Executives*. However, there is quite a bit of additional information available on this topic, including cases from Harvard Business School.

In the late 1960s, a need was becoming evident for a wide-body commercial jet smaller than the Boeing 747. American Airlines sent initial ideas for the specifications to the leading aircraft manufacturers: Boeing, Douglas, and Lockheed. Boeing would win the contract for a supersonic jet (a win that would nearly bankrupt them) and so would not participate in the market. Douglas and Lockheed, however, were deeply interested. The deep, inherent problem was that the market size was not large enough to support two vendors given the huge airplane development costs. A dramatic game of Chicken ensued between the two contenders: the Lockheed L-1011 and the McDonnell-Douglas DC-10.

A Porter five forces model analysis is a great way get the big picture view of the ecosystem (Figure 77). The two competitors were Lockheed and a newly merged McDonnell-Douglas group. Although unlikely, Boeing was a potential new entrant to this market. Customers exerted considerable power to the aircraft manufacturers. The *Big Four* of American, United, TWA, and Eastern wielded the bulk of this customer power. However, other customers would emerge to play keys rolls in this drama. Suppliers provide the raw materials and design tools for the planes, and engine manufacturers are particularly important suppliers. Some airlines have preferences on engines, and this would play an important role in the proceedings. Finally, other aircraft are potential substitutes. Obviously, they are filling the role at the current time.

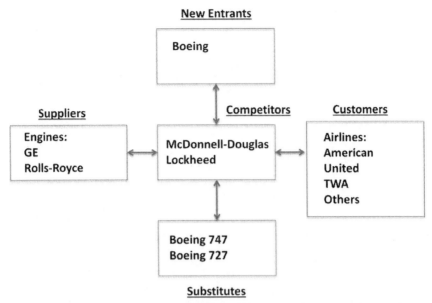

New Entrants

Boeing

Suppliers   **Competitors**   **Customers**

Engines:
GE
Rolls-Royce

McDonnell-Douglas
Lockheed

Airlines:
American
United
TWA
Others

Boeing 747
Boeing 727

Substitutes

Figure 77. Porter Five Forces Model of the Wide-body Tri-Jet Market

Key *T* Perspective Items:
- All major participants were aware that profits from virtually 100% of the estimated market size would be necessary to make an acceptable profit on the development costs of a new airplane. If two vendors entered the market, at least one of them would never make an adequate return on the development costs.
- The technical details of the planes were quite similar. However, the DC-10 had been designed to be able to use either General Electric or Rolls-Royce engines.

Key *O* Perspective Items:
- Lockheed's management was under extreme pressure to diversify away from their dependence on the defense business.
- Airlines weighed prior positive deals with aircraft vendors very high. American and United had a preference for Douglas based on a long relationship. TWA had a long relationship with Lockheed.

Key *P* Perspective Items:

- In what he considered one of his biggest mistakes, the Lockheed CEO Dan Haughton didn't pursue a merger with McDonnell Corp., and this was a merger that Douglas was able to accomplish. As Haughton later stated, "I didn't pursue it aggressively enough. We could have put the money together." (Newhouse, 1982)
- Mr. Smith, president of American Airlines, had a history of negative relations with James McDonnell. It was speculated this could tip American's order to Lockheed. But, shortly before the contracts were to be announced, Mr. Smith became Secretary of Commerce for Lyndon Johnson. His replacement did not harbor the same ill will.
- United contacted Dan Haughton, Lockheed CEO, and asked if an L-1011 with General Electric engines was possible. In what Haughton himself considers another big personal mistake, Lockheed declined to do the design changes to use the other engine.

From the game theory perspective, there are several key issues involved. Lockheed and McDonnell-Douglas decided to enter the market knowing that both could not survive. This dynamic has the payout structure of a game of Chicken: only if one left the market (swerved) could the other make a profit. If they both stayed in the market and split the market share, then both would never repay the development costs. However, from the customer's perspective, having two vendors is desirable. If only one vendor was available, that vendor would have monopolistic pricing control. Clearly, that's not what the airlines would want. But, on the other hand, if both airlines stayed in the market and split market share, then the health of the airline makers could have been impacted. If they both went bankrupt, then the airlines would need to rely on Boeing for most of their aircraft. Finally, the airlines would also consider what their competitor's actions were to determine if they could get a strategic advantage against their competitors, depending on how the market developed.

Table 18 shows how the order process transpired. American, who had written the initial specification, made the first order for DC-10s. Perhaps they hoped that their first move would sway the other airlines to follow suit and also order the DC-10. However, TWA and Eastern ordered the L-1011 next. Then, British Air and Delta, not part of the then Big Four came in with large orders of 74 L-1011s. The final card was in United's hand. They could end McDonnell Douglas' efforts with an L-1011 order. This would also strike a blow to American since they were lined up for the DC-

10s. Instead they went with the DC-10, giving McDonnell-Douglas enough orders to keep the development going. This sealed the fate for both vendors, and they both ultimately lost money on the aircraft development and sales.

	American	TWA Eastern	British Air	Delta	United
DC-10	25				60
Cumulative	25				85
L-1011		94	50	24	
Cumulative		94	144	168	

Table 18. Jet Orders in Chronological Order

Further Reading

Dr. Linstone's *Systems Practice* article (1989) is an excellent summary of TOP. However, this article can be difficult to find.

Dr. Linstone's book, *Decision Making for the Technology Executive* (Linstone, 1999) which, as of this writing, is still available, is a valuable resource. One of the great strengths of this book is the vast collection of examples.

Questions

1. In his book, *Decision Making for Technology Executives*, Linstone likens the TOP integration process to the prosecuting or defense attorney's narrative in a trial. Discuss this analogy.

2. In management training programs, decisiveness is often taught as an important characteristic of successful leaders. Discuss how this relates to the constant feedback and revision in a Singerian inquiry system.

Multiple Perspectives

Discussion of Questions

1. The attorneys are using the information from the trial (evidence, witness testimony, depositions, etc.) to build a coherent synthesis of the events. While the conclusions of the defense and prosecution will be diametrically opposed, both arguments will be logically complete and supported by portions of the available information (assuming they are competent lawyers). TOP integration is similarly a process of constructing a logical argument from the available information. There's no guarantee of uniqueness, or correctness of the conclusions.

2. Decisiveness in an executive is valuable. Decisiveness gives the team confidence and can create self-fulfilling results. However, if situations evolve or new information becomes available, and the direction is no longer valid, change is warranted. This example illustrates yet another yin-yang relationship that frequently confronts the systems thinker.

9. Pulling It All Together

Finally, we have completed our systems thinking toolbox and framework (Figure 78). Chapter 1 argued that these tools from systems science—or complexity science as some may say—have the potential to bring new and significant insights to your business problems. However, like any tool, they bear the burden of potential misuse. The argument built through the book is that a different philosophy, or mindset, of problem solving was needed. Now, after the lessons of Chapter 8, we can label this different way of thinking as a different inquiry system. In this final chapter, we will pull together this new way of thinking.

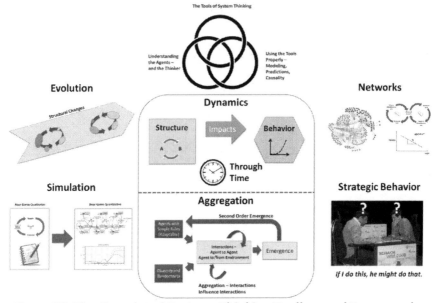

Figure 78. The Completed Systems Thinking Toolbox and Framework

Understanding Reality Using Models

The systems thinking toolbox is a collection of models. In many cases, these may be new types of models for you. For the most part, the sections describing these models have focused on the details of the models and their construction. But an important part of the message of this book is that proper use and avoidance of pitfalls of models is crucial. Just as a screwdriver can remove a screw if used properly, improper use can strip the threads of the screw. In this section, we discuss the proper use of models.

Modeling was defined in Chapter 2 as:

> Modeling—a *process* to develop a *representation* of reality to understand, communicate, or predict.

A key point of this book has been that modeling is a process. Building the model can be as valuable as running the model. We have focused on the point that models are only representations of reality, and in many cases, models are wrongly built only for prediction purposes. It has been stressed that prediction is very difficult in complex systems and using a model to predict is a double-edged sword. We need to keep in mind the other uses of models. The process of modeling was depicted in Figure 12, also from Chapter 2, and is repeated in Figure 79. The graphic focuses on the filtering and transformation process that takes a facet of reality and presents it for us to examine and derive insights. George Box summed it up with "All models are wrong, but some are useful."

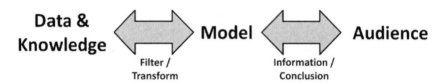

Figure 79. Graphical Representation of the Modeling Process

It is worthwhile to think of models in terms of various perspectives. To illustrate this, consider a sphere as depicted in Figure 80. In three dimensions, we see the spherical shape; in two dimensions, a circle; and in one dimension, a line. Each may have something to offer the examiner. If interested in the diameter of the sphere, then the one dimensional model is valuable. If the topic is the circumference, then the two-dimensional model is helpful. Of course, one can also look in four dimensions and see the sphere moving in time, giving the modeler an idea of the dynamic behavior.

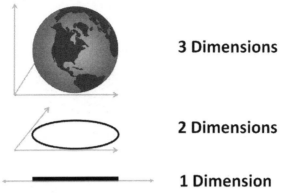

3 Dimensions

2 Dimensions

1 Dimension

Figure 80. Representation of a Sphere in 1, 2, and 3 Dimensions

Consider an analyst who is interested in the stock market. Here, we have one of the great examples of a complex system. Traders, institutions, exchanges, governments, and more are all parts of this system. Figure 81 depicts layers of models as perspectives on the market. All of these models are illustrating different aspects of the underlying reality: the market. In Chapter 3, we described a system dynamic model illustrating feedback loops and delays in this complex system. In Chapter 4, we described a model that focuses on the information of the agents and how that information was assimilated. In Chapter 5, we discussed a model that uses game theory to describe a potential mechanism to pop bubbles, and various ecosystems and networks can be overlaid on the market structure. None of these models *are* the market, but any one of them, or even using multiple models, may give the analyst crucial insights into the market and perspective on their specific question. To paraphrase Lao Tzu, *The market that can be told is not the eternal market.*

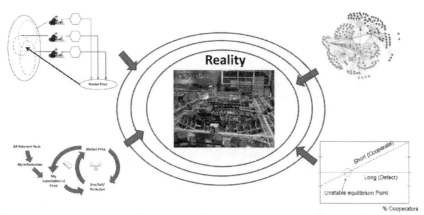

Figure 81. Different System Models of a Market

Model use presents something of a dilemma—a yin-yang relationship. On the one hand, not using models will prevent the analyst from the insights they can bring. On the other hand, overusing models, or thinking the models represent reality, can lead to misuse and problems. The analyst must strike some balance between the two extremes in using models where the utility of modeling is the greatest. At this optimum point, the analyst must be aware of the human psychological biases that may entice the modeler onto the slippery slope of model overuse.

Business Forecasting

This section summarizes and very directly addresses the use of models for prediction. If your group is chartered to generate forecasts, you are residing right between the horns of the model use dilemma just mentioned. For many in your organization, models may equate to prediction tools, but we have learned that utmost care must be used when using models for prediction. Here, we will examine this caution in deep detail and set a framework for the use of models for prediction.

In each chapter the potential issues with prediction using any particular model have been described, and Table 19 gives a sampling. Of course, any model is just one aspect of reality, as noted in Figure 81. But within a given model type, all important factors must be added for validity. For example, if building a dynamic model, have all the feedback loops been included? Some may be present, but they could be dormant and very difficult to identify. If the dynamic model has representations of human decisions, how well do these represent reality? In the beer game dynamic model of Chapter 3, ordering decisions were based on simple linear combinations of factors. This simple decision model, which captures none of the nonlinearity of typical human decision processes, was still a challenge to implement in the Vensim model. Once the elements of the model are put together, the parameters of the model must be set. This brings in issues including model fit (overfit or underfit), as discussed in Chapter 3. At the risk of repeating too much of the book, the discussion will stop here. But consider all the concerns listed, and the hundreds more that are not listed, as you assess the predictive strength of your model.

Have all feedback loops that are actually present been modeled? Some may be dormant.	Have you modeled all aspects of strategic behavior?
How well do decision models represent reality?	Have you modeled evolutionary effects?
How sensitive are results to parameter selection?	Is there a possibility of punctuated equilibrium?
Has the model been overfit? How much real (RBP) data do you have to test this?	Have the networks been mapped onto the model?
What about diversity? And randomness?	Have all three perspectives (TOP) been considered?
What about an exogenous shock?	and so on ...

Table 19. 1001 Reasons Your Model May Not Predict Correctly

How does a model's predictive ability change with system complexity and the time frame of the prediction? System complexity doesn't have an absolute metric, but several factors clearly contribute to higher complexity. In Melanie Mitchell's excellent text on complexity science, *Complexity: A Guided Tour* (2009), she devotes Chapter 7 to *Defining and Measuring Complexity*. Metrics can be degree of connectivity, entropy, depth, fractal dimension, and so on. Time frame is the period over which the model's outputs are being evaluated (e.g., days, months, years, etc.). Figure 82 attempts to very qualitatively describe the relationship. The curves are intended to be points of equal probability of accurate predictions. As the system complexity or time frame of the prediction decrease, then the model's probability of making accurate predictions will increase. Attempting to predict the U.S. economy many years in the future represents a point in the top right of the chart, and so the probability of accurate predictions are quite small.

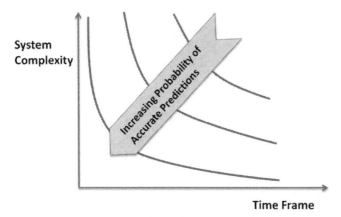

Figure 82. Qualitative Description of a Model's Predictive Ability When Used for a Complex System

It is worthwhile to recall the lessons of Chapter 6. Complex systems can appear quite stable for extended periods, and this stability could lull the model builder into assuming the system is less complex than it truly is. During this period of stability, your models may be giving accurate predictions. This success may encourage the model builder to put more faith into their models. But, if a sudden change occurs, then the modeler may be caught off guard. It can result in the case where the model works well until it is needed the most. We are reminded of Taleb's story of the turkeys on the farm. Their model of human benevolence worked perfectly until they needed it the most, the day before Thanksgiving. Or, for a more concrete example, consider the Federal Reserve's prediction of U.S. GDP growth for 2008. They predicted a growth between 1.8 and 2.5 percent when the actual GDP change was a contraction of 0.4%.

When considering the predictions of a model, one must evaluate two aspects: accuracy and precision. Figure 83 illustrates accuracy versus precision in terms of a marksman's shot pattern. For a marksman aiming at the center of the bull's-eye, the top left target shows a result that is accurate but not precise, as the geometric mean of the shots are at the center of the target but the dispersion is great. The marksman on the top right is quite precise since all their shots are in a small cluster, but there is a bias that have all shots away from the center of the bulls-eye. The marksman in the bottom right is neither accurate nor precise. Finally, the pattern in the bottom left indicates both accuracy and precision. Human decision biases can easily confuse the two.

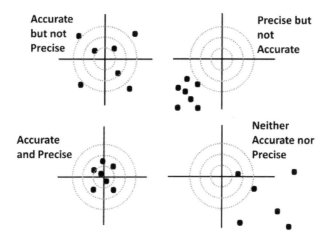

Figure 83. The Marksman's Results When Aiming for the Center of the Circles

Certain models and processes can be tailored to favor accuracy or precision. For example, research has shown that the design of a prediction market may influence accuracy versus precision (Jolly, 2011). One possible framework for assessing the relative importance of accuracy and precision focuses on the project's mission criticality versus exploratory nature and the strength of the signal one is attempting to ascertain. A mission-critical nature warrants accuracy as the cost of an incorrect prediction is greater than in the case of an exploratory project. And, in general, as the signal weakens, the need for precision increases to rein in the inherent variance.

Can Black Swan events be forecasted? Despite the suggestion of narrative fallacies, many past Black Swan events were not predictable. However, methods are available to expand the scope of the forecaster to raise awareness of some potential Black Swan events, for example, convene sessions to brainstorm risk factors that are currently not on your threat list. In these sessions, consider inviting a diverse group of organizational members to spur fresh thinking. Also, consider inviting your forecast customer to bring their perspective. Set up processes to monitor the environment for potential warning signs of change. Review your system models and identify areas of high leverage. Put special brainstorming emphasis on these high impact areas.

Finally, in preparing your forecast for delivery, consider these items. First, it is crucial to think deeply about who will use your forecast and how it will be used. Use the TOP methods from Chapter 8 as you assess the forecast customer's usage. Consider if the users of the data are in a mission-critical task. Think about the complexity of the system and the time frame of the prediction, and make certain that the audience understands the limitations of the model. Couch forecasts in terms of possibilities and probabilities, and point out potential blind spots in the model. Encourage *good* uses of model predictions. For example, in scenario planning, a model prediction can be used to consider possible steps by a competitor or another member of the ecosystem; or an entrepreneur may use the model predictions to start an exploratory project.

Managing the Unpredictable

The difficulty in predicting complex systems has been highlighted. Given this, what can be done to manage this unpredictability? In this section, the insights of systems thinking into this problem is discussed.

As a first step, examine the taxonomy of uncertainty developed by Andrew Lo and Mark Mueller (2010), as shown in Table 20. The taxonomy begins with Level 1 uncertainty, which Lo and Mueller call **Complete Certainty**. There is no uncertainty here, and examples may be in the domain of mathematics (e.g., two plus two equals four with zero uncertainty). Level 2 uncertainty is called **Risk Without Uncertainty**, with an example being the flip of a fair coin. Here, one knows the exact probability of the outcomes. Level 3 uncertainty is called **Fully Reducible Uncertainty.** This means that, with enough experiments, one can collect the data necessary to build the complete probability distributions. For example, to assess the distribution of height of adult human males, it is possible to collect enough data to build this distribution. Level 4 uncertainty is characterized as **Partially Reducible Uncertainty**. Here, no matter how many experiments are run and how much data is collected, the true probability distributions cannot be known. Finally, in Level 5, the uncertainty is completely irreducible. For these situations, any level of experiments or data provides no information. Examples of Level 5 uncertainty are questions of religion or deep philosophy.

Level 1	Complete Certainty
Level 2	Risk Without Uncertainty
Level 3	Fully Reducible Uncertainty
Level 4	Partially Reducible Uncertainty
Level 5	Irreducible Uncertainty

Table 20. Levels of Uncertainty

Think about the character of the risk in the area under analysis. Is the analysis concerning a natural system, or a human society system? If the risk is concerning the natural world, then event distributions will tend to follow normal, or Gaussian, distributions. If the risk is with human society systems, then the event distributions will tend to be non-Gaussian with long tails. That is, natural world systems tend to be Level 3 uncertain while human society systems tend to be Level 4 uncertain, per Lo's taxonomy. The non-Gaussian distributions are much more difficult to characterize. The characteristics of these long-tail distributions is inherently more difficult to describe since rare events are fewer in number (smaller samples) and inherently non-parametric. For example, consider an airline evaluating risks. When evaluating risks from nature (snow storms, hurricanes, volcanic ash, and so on), the past can be used to build models and design mitigations. The airline may not know if a debilitating snow storm will occur this month, but they do have a good idea of the probability. On the other hand, the airline may have very little understanding of the probability that an act of terrorism will occur.

Uncertainty leads to risk in business. The discipline of risk management and insurance provides guidance and frameworks to assess risk and minimize potential impacts. A reference used in the development of this section is George Rejda's excellent textbook *Principles of Risk Management and Insurance* (2001). The first step in managing the risk is to understand its nature, and a categorization can be valuable here. One common categorization considers business risk is in one of four categories: hazard, operational, financial, and business. Within a category, a better focus can be gained on where uncertainty manifests and where that uncertainty would rank on the Lo and Mueller scale. The important point is to increase the understanding around the risk and where the uncertainty lies.

There are five basic means to deal with risk: avoidance, loss control, retention, noninsurance transfer, and insurance. Avoidance is choosing not to participate. If you are concerned about risks of doing business in a certain country, then simply do not participate in that market. In loss control, one attempts to reduce the probability that the negative event will occur. There are two general methods of loss control: prevention and reduction. For example, if you are concerned about the loss of intellectual property from employees' laptop computers, then implement policies that limit the number of employees who can have laptop computers (prevention) and encrypt the data in the event of a loss (reduction). With retention, the risks are accepted and the business practice continued. Retention can be active or passive. Active retention means that there is an awareness of the risk and a decision to continue. Passive retention means that there isn't awareness of the risk. Finally, the risk can be transferred to another party, and this can be either through the usual purchase of insurance or through a noninsurance transfer. Examples of noninsurance transfer include extended warranties on equipment or hedging in a financial market.

Figure 84 shows one framework for deciding which risk control method to use. The framework considers the impact of a loss and the likelihood. For very high likelihood and high impact risk, avoidance may be dictated. If the impact is high but likelihood low, or impact low with high likelihood, then loss control may make sense. For low impact, low likelihood events, active retention may be appropriate. For cases with moderate impact and likelihood, insurance may be the best approach. Of course, this framework only provides guidelines and each situation must be studied and assessed individually.

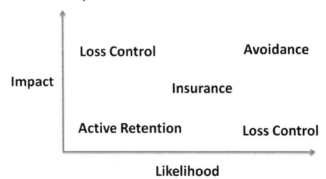

Figure 84. Risk Strategy Framework

An important objective of pre-loss risk management is finding the most economical preparation. There is a tradeoff to be made between risk and risk control. If a business never took on any risk, there would be no opportunity for profit. Figure 85 describes a method to evaluate the effectiveness of risk control methods. Consider a total cost as described by the equation:

$$Total\ Cost = Risk\ Control\ Costs + Cost\ of\ Losses$$

In the graph, there are three curves: the expected loss, the cost of risk control, and the total cost, which is simply the sum of the two. The curve for expected loss is monotonically decreasing as more risk control measures are instituted. Of course, as more and more risk control measures are implemented, the cost of these measures increases. This leads to a characteristic that the curve for total expected loss has a minimum, which indicates that there is an optimal amount of risk control to be applied. Of course, with this type of analysis, while the cost of risk control may be well understood, the cost of losses can only be estimated.

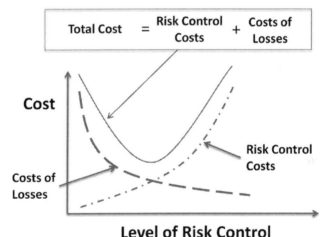

Level of Risk Control

Figure 85. Analysis of Cost With Different Levels of Risk Control

As risk events become more uncertain, that is, risks of Black Swans, the likelihood and to some extent impacts become nebulous. To deal with these risks, look for ways to make the system more robust or, if possible, antifragile. For example, adding redundancy trades off costs for robustness. In *The Black Swan*, Taleb describes the barbell strategy to increase antifragility. Here, most of the resources are moved to areas of very low risk, and a few of the resources are moved to areas of high risk and high reward. An investing example would be to move the bulk of the portfolio into government bonds, and put a small portion into a very high-risk and high-reward instrument such as options. This type of strategy reduces the Black Swan risk on the bulk of the resources while creating opportunity from positive Black Swans. For a business, entrepreneurs could play the role of these high-risk and high-reward instruments.

Focusing on Results

The book has spent a lot of time discussing models that systems science offers and that can help in the understanding of complex systems. But a model's behavior and the impact of that behavior on the topic that precipitated the modeling effort must be differentiated. This might be thought of as keeping clear between *what* and *so what*. Excessive focus on the details of a model may obscure an appreciation of the implications.

In *Antifragile,* Taleb (2012) suggests the idea of conflation of events and exposure to events. To illustrate, the last section discussed the risk of data loss from employees' laptops, but the real concern is not the data loss but what can happen as a *result* of that data loss. Or consider the investor who is weighing the purchase of a stock. They may think that the company is well managed and the products are good, but is that a reason to invest in the stock? Compare this investor with one who does a detailed discounted cash flow analysis of expected earnings taking into account competitors, business risks, governmental issues, etc., and has decided the current stock price is discounted versus its expected value. One action is to build effects into models as much as possible. This will keep the *so what* at the top of mind and also help to gain an understanding of the nonlinearities that exist between the model phenomenon and the phenomenon's impact.

> In theory, there is no difference between theory and practice. But in practice there is.
>
> Yogi Berra

This quote almost always elicits some good chuckles. However, this quote contains deep and important insights. Yogi Berra was a baseball player and manager, which are both occupations not typically associated with deep thinkers. But managing a baseball team is not the easiest of undertakings, and having a TOP multiple-perspective outlook is very valuable for a baseball manager. *T* thinking includes which athletes to play across a long schedule, game strategy, player development and training, and so on. The *O* perspective is needed to get the team working together, and working within the business organization of the general manager (as illustrated in the movie *Money Ball*). The *P* perspective is needed to deal with players with rather large egos. Perhaps a baseball manager is a good resource for business wisdom.

Table 21 uses Berra's quote and compares the **Theoretician** and **Practitioner**. The **Theoretician** focuses on the *T* perspective. The **Practitioner** uses the multiple perspectives of TOP. The **Theoretician** chuckled at Yogi's quote, but doesn't really understand its implications, whereas the **Practitioner** lives the quote. The **Theoretician** is overly dependent on models and may have difficulty distinguishing between models and reality, but the **Practitioner** uses models effectively, perhaps to understand scenarios or where to direct an entrepreneurial team. The **Theoretician** may build elaborate models to predict the probability of rare events, and the **Practitioner** may simply buy insurance. The **Theoretician** may look extensively for causes of events in complex systems, e.g., "What triggered the market's 2% market decline today?" The **Practitioner** seeks to understand relationships. The **Theoretician** has a tendency to focus on the *what*, while the **Practitioner** keeps their eye on the *so what*. With all these taken together, the **Theoretician** is fragile, and the **Practitioner** is antifragile.

Theoretician	Practitioner
T perspective	TOP perspective
Doesn't 'get' Berra's quote	Lives Berra's quote
Difficulty distinguishing between models and reality	Uses models to help understand where to tinker and build optionality
Attempts to predict probability of rare events	Buys insurance
Looks for causes	Understands relationships
Focuses on *what*	Focuses on *so what*
Fragile	Antifragile

Table 21. Comparing the Theoretician and Practitioner

Final Action Plan

This section pulls together the ideas from the book and presents the final action plan. The primary message of the book is that the ideas of systems science can augment your standard business skills. The insights of systems thinking can be particularly valuable at critical inflection points in business directions and your career. This is because emergent effects from system interactions are commonly at work at these critical junctures. Following standard business principles in situations with systems driven emergent phenomenon could lead to unexpected, potentially detrimental results. Also, without systems thinking, unanticipated solutions, based on non-intuitive leverage points, may be obscured.

Specifically, there are two goals. The first goal is to develop an intuition that will allow you to spot system effects quickly. This first goal is then to develop a new way of seeing, as expressed in Figure 5. The analogy used was the chess grandmaster playing many simultaneous games (Figure 4). As a business example, consider the busy executive that must monitor many projects. The executive must attend a meeting and quickly assess the situation. Frequently, these executives identify critical issues that the team had overlooked. These insights come from the executive's deep experience. Systems thinking intuition was explicitly defined as the training of your System 1 mind to recognize system mechanisms at work. Training your System 1 mind to identify system effects will take practice on your part. Systems thinking is as much a skill as it is a knowledge set. In my class, we take time each week for students to describe the system effects that they have seen during the week in their work or personal lives: feedback loops, strategic behavior, networks, etc. This goes slowly at the beginning of the term but, by the end of the term, this section of the class is dynamic and a high learning experience. Spend time thinking about current business events. Consider where system effects may be present and influencing behavior. Think about alternative explanations other than those suggested by journalists. Since systems thinking flies in the face of so many human judgment and decision biases, learning may be slow. And unfortunately, you may have times where you slip back from systems thinking to a *T* perspective.

The second goal is, once a system effect is recognized, to use the methods presented in the book to analyze and act. Consider the chess grandmaster moving from opponent to opponent in the simultaneous game exhibition and suddenly realizing one of his opponents was another chess grandmaster. The chess grandmaster's mode of operation would shift to one of deeper analysis of the game situation. A structured methodology to address this situation will be described next.

Figure 86 is a graphic illustrating the systems analysis framework. The main component of the framework is a funnel with three phases: problem definition, model construction, and analysis and recommendation. The funnel is used to indicate a narrowing of focus as the analysis progresses. Another important component of the framework is the presence of feedback loops reminding us of the inherent constant revision mechanisms of a Singerian inquiry system. Above the funnel are the symbols of the all-seeing eye and yin-yang relationship. The all-seeing eye reminds us to consider our own biases and limitations. The yin-yang symbol reminds us to constantly consider the inherent tradeoffs.

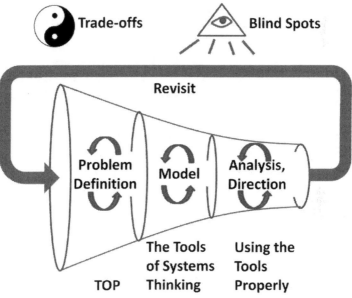

Figure 86. Systems Analysis Framework

The problem definition phase is the crucial first step in the process. An important result of the problem definition phase is to provide clear guidance for the modeling effort that follows. The modeling phase must be directed in order to achieve valuable and actionable outcomes. In the problem definition phase, the need for a multiple perspective TOP view is crucial.

- Within the *O* (organizational) perspective, be certain to consider all functions within the organization (marketing, engineering, manufacturing, sales, legal, and so on), and external to the organization (government, industry organizations, press, social media, and so on).
- In the *P* (personal) perspective, consider key decision makers and the ultimate customer of the analysis.
- In terms of scope, consider the different phases of a project (planning, design, production, and eventual retirement).

As indicated by the wide mouth of the funnel, think broadly in this phase.

In the model construction, use the elements of the systems thinking toolbox as described throughout the book. When a specific system mechanism is warranted in the model, review the chapter specifics to encompass all aspects of the model development. Also, review the guidance from this chapter's section Understanding Reality Using Models.

In the analysis and direction phase, use the ideas from the systems thinking framework (Figure 8) and specifically the ideas around using the tools properly. When presenting conclusions, consider using the method of Completed Staff Work. Completed Staff Work, often attributed to Napoleon Bonaparte, asserts the analyst should provide a set of possible actions and a recommendation to the decision maker. Consider:

- If forecasting is involved, consider the guidance in this chapter's discussion Business Forecasting.
- Refrain from, or carefully qualify, any assertions of simple causality.
- Carefully inspect the environment for possible Black Swans.
- When structuring recommendations, consider the inherent uncertainty and use the suggestions from the section Managing the Unpredictable.
- Remember that apparently stable systems can change rapidly and unexpectedly, as described in Chapter 6.
- Carefully inspect the models, and recommend checkpoints to identify potential unexpected and costly side effects.
- Inspect the models for sensitivity and embrace the points of high leverage in your recommendations.
- Search out convex payoffs and present ideas for optionality.

- Use established ideas, such as Moore's business ecosystem, as credibility building blocks for systems thinking.
- Consider using interactive system simulation tools as aids to communicate your insights.

In dealing with the complex systems that we find in the business world, we need to accept the inherent gaps in our information set and evolution of the system under analysis. System evolution appears to be an inherent condition. According to Zwick's *Ontology of Problems* (1995), the very mechanisms that bind sub-systems into a system (as opposed to a non-interacting collection or heap) also sows the seeds for system evolution and change. A Singerian inquiry system is most appropriate for analysis of these evolving business situations. This inquiry system urges the user to constantly consider the ramifications of new information and monitor the system for structural changes. The feedback loops on the diagram remind us of this process.

The all-seeing eye reminds us, as system analysts, that we must consider our own limitations. The System 1/System 2 related judgment and decision biases have been highlighted throughout the book. These same mechanisms can impact our ability to see system mechanisms. We must constantly be on guard for assumptions of simple causality, constructing narrative fallacies, making inference errors, and so on.

> The myriad beings carry the yin on their backs
> and embrace the yang.
> In the central hollow the breaths get harmonized.
> Lao Tzu, Verse 42 of *Tao Te Ching*

Systems thinking exposes many yin-yang relationships. Actions must be carefully considered as they may have unintended side effects or create unexpected changes through unrecognized feedback loops. Executives must strike a balance between model overuse and underuse. Model design needs to strike a balance between complexity (overfit) and simplicity (underfit). Business decision makers must strike a balance between decisiveness and consideration of new data or system evolution. Systems thinkers must find a harmony between theory and practice.

Skills That Support Applied Systems Thinking

Three key components of the systems thinking framework as shown in Figure 7 have been discussed, and there are skills that can reinforce systems thinking to support this framework. Four skills are presented here to support effective systems thinking, illustrated in Figure 87 as a pyramid to imply they build upon one another.

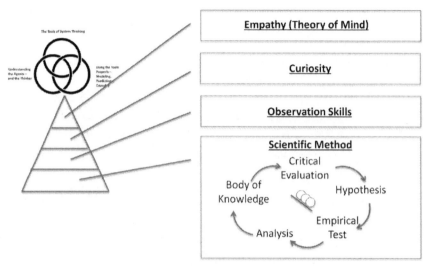

Figure 87. Key Skills That Support Applied Systems Thinking

The scientific method is a fundamental skill and reminds us that a level of rigor must be applied to our analysis. The scientific method is represented as a reinforcing feedback loop. First, a critical evaluation of the situation is conducted. We recall the famous quote of Isaac Newton who said, "If I have seen further, it is by standing on the shoulders of giants." Use the existing body of knowledge to your avail. But, remember, when evaluating that available information, always keep a bit of skepticism (essentially embedding a balancing loop). In an academic research project, this phase is the literature review. For business, the research material includes published reports, raw data, interviews with decision makers, and so on. From this evaluation, the analyst makes a hypothesis of some type. Perhaps suggesting a certain type of systems effect (e.g., a feedback loop, a type of strategic behavior, etc.) is impacting the situation. In academic work, this hypothesis should be stated in a way that it can be critically evaluated, preferably with tools from statistics. We recall also the lessons of inferential science, that hypotheses can only be supported or disproved,

218

but never proven. After the analysis is complete, the work moves into the body of knowledge on the topic. The feedback loop completes as this new knowledge is used as part of the next evaluation phase. When done correctly, this is a reinforcing feedback loop with the body of knowledge growing.

The next skill listed is the power of observation. The example par excellence for this skill is the great Leonardo da Vinci, and I invite you to practice this skill by learning right from this master. There are many excellent books that talk about da Vinci's observation techniques, but one option is to examine his work directly. Jean Paul Richter has meticulously gone through da Vinci's notebooks and published reasonably priced transcriptions with copies of the original drawings. These notebooks are highly recommended. As a wonderful exercise to test your observational skills, try this experiment: Take a picture from a book or magazine that you would normally have difficulty drawing, perhaps a picture of someone's face. Now, first try to draw this picture. If you are like most, you will be disappointed and the picture will look somewhat cartoonish. Now, turn the picture to be copied upside down. Repeat the drawing experiment (drawing your picture upside down just as you see it). Many find that this upside down method produces pictures that are vastly better representations of the original. This exercise sheds light on the inherent psychological model-building processes at work in the human mind and how we must strive to really see past the mental models our mind uses to make sense of reality.

Next in the pyramid is the skill of curiosity. If you have young children, watch them; they are ambassadors of curiosity. Tony Robbins describes curiosity as "asking high quality questions" (1991). Continually asking questions and digging deeper is crucial in systems thinking.

The final skill listed is empathy. Scientific research has provided interesting insights into this area, which is technically called *theory of mind*. Only a few members of the animal species have the capability to understand that other members of the species have their own unique thoughts. The excellent Nova series mentioned earlier, *Inside Animal Minds*, demonstrated some excellent experiments in this space. Interestingly, this ability is not present in young humans, and only develops around the age of four. Clearly, this skill is crucial in assessing strategic behavior, and it is also valuable in many aspects of systems analysis.

The End ... The Beginning

We can't solve problems by using the same kind of thinking we used when we created them.

Albert Einstein

I'll conclude the book with a request. As Einstein said, it will take a different way of thinking to solve some of the world's big problems. And the world seems to have no shortage of huge problems: global warming, extreme poverty, spread of infectious diseases, economic collapses, etc. I firmly believe systems thinking can offer help with these problems that the traditional perspective alone cannot. If you have read this far, I suspect you may agree. Let's work together to spread the ideas of systems thinking.

A thousand mile journey begins with the ground under your feet.

Lao Tzu, Verse 64 of *Tao Te Ching*

While the book has ended, your journey to becoming a systems thinker has only begun. I invite you to stay in contact as you develop your skills. Please visit me at RichJolly.com and sign up for my newsletter, or follow me on social media (Facebook, Twitter, etc.). I'll be providing a wealth of additional resources and information available from these sources. Best of luck on your transformation!

Questions

1. In *Antifragile*, Taleb discusses the application of *Via Negativa*. The origins of Via Negativa are theological. God cannot be described by what He is, but rather by what He is not. The concept can be applied more broadly to knowledge and actions. Amassing negative knowledge can be powerful, for example, what we can exclude from consideration. Similarly, Negativa actions, for example eating less sugar, could be just as effective as additive actions such as using drugs to control blood sugar levels. Discuss how this concept relates to systems thinking for business.

2. The difficulty in predicting complex systems has been discussed throughout the book. Discuss how decisions by a single individual can affect business forecasting.

3. The company CDE had built a complex system dynamic model of their business. Unfortunately, their model lacked a powerful dormant feedback loop that suddenly activated. Due to this oversight, their model was woefully deficient in predicting an important market change. However, CDE had only used the model to understand possible dynamics and had not *bet the company* on its predictions. Further, CDE had considered potential changes such as this (using other systems thinking mechanisms), and they had options in place to actually benefit from the change in the marketplace.

CDE's competitor was XYZ. XYZ had been virtually a twin of CDE. They were nearly the same size, had served the same markets, etc. XYZ had independently built nearly the same system dynamic model. They, too, had not included the powerful dormant feedback loop that had suddenly activated. However, XYZ had built their entire company process around the model's predictions. When the sudden and unpredicted market change occurred, XYZ was suddenly awash in extra inventory. They had insufficient reserves and, with the inventory buildup and drop in demand, were unable to secure emergency credit. They eventually filed for bankruptcy protection. Which best describes this situation?
A.   The unpredicted market change was a Black Swan to both companies.
B.   The unpredicted market change was a Black Swan to CDE but not to XYZ.
C.   The unpredicted market change was a Black Swan to XYZ but not to CDE.
D.   The unpredicted market change was not a Black Swan to either company.

Discussion of Questions

1. In terms of knowledge, subtractive knowledge is more robust than additive knowledge. In fact, this is a fundamental underpinning of empirical science. As mentioned in Chapter 2, you can only definitively disprove a hypothesis. Otherwise, you are providing support. Seeing more white swans may strengthen the hypothesis that all swans are white, but seeing a black swan can disprove it. The confirmation bias, the search for data that confirms existing beliefs (versus alternatives), makes this effect even more counterintuitive.

In terms of actions, negative measures may be similarly overlooked. Consider the linked reinforcing and balancing loops of the Limits to Growth archetype producing an S-shaped curve dynamic. As the balancing feedback loop begins to assert itself and growth slows, the natural tendency is to focus on the reinforcing loop and attempt to *increase* growth (e.g., adding sales force, advertising budgets, etc.). However, as Senge mentions, there is more leverage in focusing on the balancing loop and attempting to *reduce* the resistance. One example would be removing features from a product to make it simpler and cheaper, and thus appealing to a new market segment. As another example, for a robust system, the best action may be no action. In the example of Intel's transition from DRAM to microprocessors in Chapter 4, the system that the Intel managers had put in place was robust, and through the planners' decisions, Intel made the transformation to a microprocessor company— without action from the upper managers.

2. It is especially difficult to predict an individual's decision in any given situation. Situations in other parts of their life, which you may have no information about, could impact their business decisions on any given day. To really bring this point home, consider Vasili Arkhipov. Arkhipov was second in command on a nuclear-armed Soviet submarine off Cuba during the Cuban Missile Crisis. Arkhipov's submarine was being harassed by U.S. Navy destroyers in an attempt to force the submarine to the surface. The submarine's captain and political officer had agreed to use the nuclear weapon, as they felt the submarine was under attack. The U.S. and Soviet nations were under extreme tension at that time, and it is very possible that the submarine's use of a nuclear weapon off the U.S. coastline could have initiated a nuclear war. However, Soviet rules required three officers to unanimously agree before the nuclear weapon could be used. Arkhipov

refused to agree, and the weapon was not deployed. One single individual, a single linchpin, may have prevented a nuclear catastrophe. Keep in mind the potential impact of a single influential individual as you make your assessments about the future.

3. XYZ was caught by surprise from the market change and it ruined the company. CDE had considered the possible market change and actually benefited. So it was only a Black Swan to XYZ.

Remember the turkey farm example? The pre-Thanksgiving surprise was only a Black Swan to the turkeys, not the turkey farmer. Moral: don't be a turkey!

Postface

My Background and Motivations

I advise managers and anyone receiving recommendations to consider two important questions when evaluating advice:

- What are the qualifications of the person (or group) giving the advice?
- What are the motivations of the person (or group) giving the advice?

This book recommends that you apply *systems thinking* in your business endeavors, so you should be asking those two questions about me.

First, allow me to address my qualifications for writing this work. My coursework for achieving a PhD in systems science covered all of the topics discussed in this book. Part of the PhD process was to successfully complete comprehensive exams that verified my competency in these topics, and my dissertation focused on the inner workings of markets using a systems thinking lens[37]. I have kept active in the field of systems science, including adjunct teaching at Portland State University (where I teach a class on this topic), as well as actively exploring the use of systems ideas in markets. In addition to the systems science PhD, I have an MBA degree and a BS and MS in electrical engineering and computer sciences from UC Berkeley. This deep academic background is offset with extensive practical experience working as a senior executive at Intel. I've held roles in engineering, technical marketing, product marketing, and business strategy.

My prime motivation to complete this book is to bring the ideas of systems science from academia to practice. As I mentioned in Chapter 1, systems thinking has the potential to provide deep insights into mankind's most difficult problems. However, the current literature on systems science (or complexity science) is biased toward the theory over the practice. Many systems scientists like to consider their field to be *stuff free*, meaning that the ideas can apply across any number of contexts. For

---

[37] My PhD dissertation is available on the web. Just Google "Richard Jolly The Role Of Feedback in the Assimilation of Information in Prediction Markets"

example, game theory applies to individuals, groups of individuals, organizations, nations, even amoeba. Game theory can be applied to economics, business, psychology, family relations, and just about any other human endeavor. The tendency has been for systems scientists to write about the theory and let the practitioner figure out the application themselves. The downside of this practice is that the practitioner may never hear about systems science and not realize its practical value to their specific problems. This book is my attempt to reverse this course. So first and foremost, I'm hoping to inch the field of systems science into the public eye and increase its usage. Of course, I also have some personal goals here. Even though I do have a practical bias, I deeply enjoy the field of academia, and writing this book and teaching the associated class keeps me in contact with the university and academic studies.

To Learn More—The Big Picture

If you are a manager, you have found that one particularly unpleasant aspect of your job is to make difficult prioritizations. There are so many great resources to learn more about this field that it is hard for me to prioritize them for you. Of course, everyone of you has a slightly different background and different level of interests, so you will likely wish to reprioritize the list yourself.

First, I recommend reading something by Nassim Nicholas Taleb. The ideas are remarkable, and being exposed to his way of thinking is very valuable to systems thinking. *Antifragile: Things That Gain From Disorder* (2012) is recommended as a first priority.

Next, Part I and Part II along with Appendix 2 of Peter Senge's *The Fifth Discipline* (1990) is recommended. Even though this book was written over 20 years ago, the lessons on dynamics in human systems are just as valid today as then.

Third, Daniel Kahneman's important work *Thinking, Fast & Slow* (2011) is recommended. If you are pressed for time focus on Parts I, II, and IV.

Fourth, Taleb's (assuming you weren't too put off by the first read) *The Black Swan* (2007) is recommended.

In this reading list, it is assumed you have received a good overview of the systems science field by reading this book. If you are looking for some more reading that outlines the entire field, then I would highly recommend either *The Origin of Wealth* by Eric D. Beinhocker (2006), (with a focus on the chapters I mentioned at the end of each chapter) or Melanie Mitchell's outstanding book on complexity science, *Complexity a Guided Tour* (2009). Beinhocker's book focuses on the use of systems ideas in economics. Mitchell's work is broadly focused.

If you have specific interest in a given topic, see the reading list for that topic at the end of the chapter. Also, it is noted that systems science is a young field. Go to YouTube and search on any of the scientists or authors mentioned. It is always valuable to put a face to a name and hear about these ideas right from the researcher.

There are several active research centers working in the area. In particular, Santa Fe Institute (www.santafe.edu) and the New England Complex Systems Institute (NECSI at www.necsi.edu) are worth investigating.

Acknowledgments

Just as many phenomena in complex systems are emergent, this work is the result of countless interactions and relationships over the last several years.

First, I would like to thank the faculty at Portland State University for imparting the powerful ideas of Systems Science. In particular I'd like to thank Professor Wayne Wakeland, the Systems Science Program Chair and my dissertation committee chair, for all the knowledge and support. Systems Science Professor Martin Zwick deserves special thanks for deep insights and valuable counsel. Thanks to Melanie Mitchell, a pioneer in Complexity, for her perspective on the theories. I also appreciate the teaching of George Lendaris and Tad Shannon.

My Portland State University acknowledgments must also include other parts of the organization. Barry Anderson, Professor Emeritus in the department of psychology, introduced me to the ideas of the psychology of judgment and decision biases. I also thank the faculty and staff in the School of Business Administration (SBA). In particular, I'd like to acknowledge the ideas and guidance of SBA Dean Scott Dawson and Professor John Settle.

I've had numerous discussions with the experts and practitioners in systems science. I appreciate deep discussions with Professor Charles Plott of the California Institute of Technology (Caltech) on his research in prediction markets. I also acknowledge generous discussions with Jay Hopman who runs Intel's prediction markets. I appreciate and acknowledge the Santa Fe Institute (SFI) for hosting me in a visit and facilitating numerous discussions with the researchers in residence. In particular, discussions with Professor J. Doyne Farmer on agent-based models were very helpful.

As noted in the dedication, I do appreciate all the hard work of the countless researchers whose body of work has formed the ideas presented. I acknowledge all the discussions with students that helped me assimilate these ideas.

In terms of the manuscript, I must foremost acknowledge the Portland State University Systems Science Program and School of Business Administration for their support in the development of my MBA class *Systems Thinking for Business*. This class is the foundation for the book. The students in my classes have been active participants in the fine-tuning of the delivery—thanks! I appreciate the work of my reviewers. In particular, I'd like to thank Brett Schneider for many helpful suggestions. I acknowledge the many artists who have contributed graphics on the creative commons. Finally, I would like to thank my editor Renee Ergazos.

Last, but certainly not least, no manuscript can be completed without the support of the author's family. I thank my wife and children for supporting this effort.

Attributions

Cover & Figure 5	Can Stock Photo, Inc.
Figure 4	Grandmaster Vlastimil Hort , Stefan64. GNU Free Documentation License,File:Vlastimil_hort.JPG
Figure 7	Borromean Rings; Wikimedia Commons. Public Domain image. File:Borromean-rings-BW.svg
Figure 11	Koche Snowflake; Wikimedia Commons. Public Domain image. File:

	Flocke.PNG
Figure 14	Images courtesy pixabay under CC0 Public Domain License
Figure 28	Notepad courtesy pixabay under CC0 Public Domain License
Figure 39	Wikimedia Commons. File:Race and ethnicity New York City.png. Author: Eric Fischer. Creative Commons Attribution-Share Alike 2.0 Generic
Figure 41	NetLogo Segregation Model - Creative Commons Attribution-NonCommercial-ShareAlike 3.0 License - Copyright 1997 Uri Wilensky
Figure 43	NetLogo Ants Model - Creative Commons Attribution-NonCommercial-ShareAlike 3.0 License - Copyright 1997 Uri Wilensky
Figure 46	NetLogo Sugarscape 1 Immediate Growback - Creative Commons Attribution-NonCommercial-ShareAlike 3.0 License - Copyright 1997 Uri Wilensky
Figure 44	Man thinking courtesy pixabay under CC0 Public Domain License
Figure 49	World Chess Championship 2008. Anand – Kramnik. Wikimedia Commons. Author: Ygrek. File:SchachWM2008.jpg. Creative Commons Attribution 3.0 Unported license
Figure 61	Rock image: Wikimedia Commons; File:Hardened water eroded Igneous rock, Tenneti park, Visakhapatnam.JPG; Author-Adityamadhav83; Creative Commons Attribution-Share Alike 3.0 Unported license.
Figure 61	Wine Glass: Wikimedia Commons; File:White Wine Glas.jpg; Author-André Karwath aka Aka; Creative Commons Attribution-Share Alike 2.5 Generic license.
Figure 71	Political blog map courtesy Lada Adamic.
Figure 72	Network graphic- Wikimedia Commons. ; Author: Daniel Tenerife; GNU Free Documentation License, Version 1.2; File:Social Red.jpg
Figure 73 Figure 74	NetLogo Copyright 2008 Uri Wilensky. Modified by Lada Adamic 2009. Creative Commons Attribution-NonCommercial-ShareAlike 3.0 License
Figure 80	Earth courtesy pixabay under CC0 Public Domain License
Figure 81	Center photo - Chicago Board Options Exchange (CBOE) trading floor; credit: Richard Jolly

References

Abramowicz, M. (2007). *Predictocracy: Market Mechanisms for Public and Private Decision Making*: Yale University Press.

Abreu, D., & Brunnermeier, M. K. (2003). Bubbles and Crashes. *Econometrica, 71*(1), 173-204.

Axelrod, R. (1984). *The Evolution of Cooperation*. New York: Basic Books.

Bak, P., & Chen, K. (1991). Self-Organized Criticality. *Scientific American*, 46-53.

Banerjee, A. (1992). A Simple Model of Herd Behavior. *The Quarterly Journal of Economics, 107*(3), 797-817.

Barabasi, A., & Bonabeau, E. (2003). Scale-Free Networks. *Scientific American, 5*, 60-69.

Beinhocker, E. D. (2006). *The Origin of Wealth: The Radical Remaking of Economics and What It Means for Business and Society*: Harvard Business School Press.

Berg, J., Forsythe, R., Nelson, F., & Rietz, T. (2008). Results from a Dozen Years of Election Futures Markets Research. In C. R. Plott & V. L. Smith (Eds.), *Handbook of Experimental Economics Results* (pp. 742-751): Elsevier.

Bikhchandani, S., Hirshleifer, D., & Welch, I. (1992). A Theory of Fads, Fashion, Custom, and Cultural Change as Informational Cascades. *Journal of Political Economy, 100*(5), 992-1026.

Box, G. E. P., & Draper, N. R. (1987). *Empirical Model Building and Response Surfaces*. New York, NY: John Wiley & Sons.

Burgelman, R. (2002). *Strategy Is Destiny: How Strategy-Making Shapes a Company's Future*. New York: The Free Press.

Camerer, C. (2003). *Behavioral Game Theory: Experiments in Strategic Interaction*: Russel Sage Foundation/Princeton University Press.

Camerer, C., & Lovallo, D. (1999). Overconfidence and Excess Entry: An Experimental Approach. *The American Economic Review, 89*(1), 306-318.

Chabris, C., & Simons, D. (2009). *The Invisible Gorilla: How Our Intentions Deceive Us*. New York: Crown Publishers.

Colwell, R. P. (2006). *The Pentium Chronicles: The People, Passion and Politics Behind Intel's Landmark Chips*: John Wiley & Sons.

Cowgill, B., Wolfers, J., & Zitzewitz, E. (2009). Using Prediction Markets to Track Information Flows: Evidence from Google. In Das, Ostrovsky,

References

Pennock & Szymanksi (Eds.), *Auctions, Market Mechanisms and Their Applications*. New York: Springer.

Davis, M. D. (1970). *Game Theory: A Nontechnical Introduction*: Dover Publications.

De Long, D., & Fahey, L. (2000). Diagnosing Cultural Barriers to Knowledge Management. *Academy of Management Executive, 14*(4), 113-127.

Einhorn, H., & Hogarth, R. (1986). Judging Probable Cause. *Psychological Bulletin, 99*(1), 3-19.

Emery, N., & Clayton, N. (2004). The Mentality of Crows: Convergent Evolution of Intelligence in Corvids and Apes. *Science, 306*(5703), 1903-1907.

Epstein, J. M., & Axtell, R. (1996). *Growing Artificial Societies: Social Science from the Bottom Up*: Brookings Institute Press, The MIT Press.

Evans, L. (2011). *New Ideas in Chess*. Las Vegas: Cardoza Books.

Gilmour, D. (2003). How to Fix Knowledge Management. *Harvard Business Review, 81*(10), 17-18.

Granovetter, M. (1978). Threshold Models of Collective Behavior. *The American Journal of Sociology, 83*(6), 1420-1443.

Grove, A. (1996). *Only the Paranoid Survive*. New York: Knopf-Doubleday.

Hahn, R. W., & Tetlock, P. C. (Eds.). (2006). *Information Markets: A New Way of Making Decisions*: The AEI Press.

Haug, E. G. (2007). *Derivatives: Models on Models*: Wiley.

Hong, L., & Page, S. E. (2004). Groups of Diverse Problem Solvers Can Outperform Groups of High-Ability Problem Solvers. *Proceedings of the National Academy of Sciences of the United States of America, 101*(46), 16385-16389.

Hopman, J. W. (2007). Using Forecast Markets to Manage Demand Risk. *Intel Technology Journal, 11*(2), 127-136.

Huberman, B. A., & Adamic, L. A. (2004). Information Dynamics in the Networked World. *Lect. Notes Phys.*, 371-398.

Jolly, R. (2011). *The Role of Feedback in the Assimilation of Information in Prediction Markets.* Doctoral dissertation, Portland State University.

Jolly, R., & Wakeland, W. (2008). *Using Agent Based Simulation and Game Theory Analysis to Study Information Sharing in Organizations – The InfoScape.* Paper presented at the 41st Hawaii International Conference on System Sciences, Hawaii.

Jolly, R., & Wakeland, W. (2009). Using Agent Based Simulation and Game Theory Analysis to Study Knowledge Flow in Organizations: The

KMscape. *International Journal of Knowledge Management, 5*(1), 17-28.

Jolly, R., Zwick, M., Wakeland, W., & Woods, J. (2015). The mechanisms of information integration in experimental prediction markets. *Int. J. Economics and Business Research, 9*(1), 100-129.

Kahneman, D. (2011). *Thinking, Fast and Slow*: Farrar, Strauss and Giroux.

Kahneman, D., & Tversky, A. (1979). Prospect Theory: An Analysis of Decision under Risk. *Econometrica, 47* (2), 263-291.

Levitt, S. D., & Dubner, S. J. (2005). *Freakonomics: A Rogue Economist Explores the Hidden Side of Everything*: Harper Perennial.

Lewis, M. (2010). *The Big Short: Inside the Doomsday Machine*: W. W. Norton & Company, Inc.

Lindgren, K. (1991). Evolutionary Phenomena in Simple Dynamics. In C. G. Langston, C. Taylor, J. D. Farmer & S. Rasmussen (Eds.), *Artificial Life II, Santa Fe Studies in the Sciences of Complexity, vol. X*: Addison-Wesley.

Linstone, H. A. (1989). Multiple Perspectives: Concept, Applications and User Guidelines. *Systems Practice, 2*(3), 307.

Linstone, H. A. (1999). *Decision Making for Technology Executives: Using Multiple Perspectives to Improve Performance*: Artech House.

Lo, A. W., & Mueller, M. T. (2010). WARNING: Physics Envy May Be Hazardous To Your Wealth. *Journal of Investment Management, 9*, 13-63.

Lowenstein, R. (2001). *When Geinus Failed*. New York: Random House.

Mackay, C. (1841). *Extraordinary Popular Delusions & the Madness of Crowds*. London: Richard Bentley.

Maloney, M. T., & Mulherin, J. H. (2003). The Complexity of Price Discovery in an Efficient Market: The Stock Market Reaction to the *Challenger* Crash. *Journal of Corporate Finance 9*, 453- 479.

Mitchell, M. (2009). *Complexity: A Guided Tour*: Oxford University Press.

Mitroff, I., & Turoff, M. (1973). Technological Forecasting and Assessment: Science and/or Mythology. *Technological Forecasting and Social Change, 5*, 113-134.

Moore, J. F. (1993). Predators and Prey: A New Ecology of Competition. *Harvard Business Review, 71*(3), 75-86.

Newhouse, J. (1982). *The Sporty Game*: A. A. Knopf.

Nickerson, R. S. (1998). Confirmation Bias: A Ubiquitous Phenomenon in Many Guises. *Review of General Psychology, 2*(2), 175-220.

References

Page, S. E. (2007). *The Difference: How the Power of Diversity Creates Better Groups, Firms, Schools, and Societies* Princeton University Press.

Porter, M. E. (1980). *Competitive Strategy : Techniques for Analyzing Industries and Competitors*
New York: The Free Press

Rapoport, A., & Guyer, M. (1978). A Taxonomy of 2x2 Games. *General Systems, XXIII*, 125-136.

Rejda, G. (2001). *Principles of Risk Management and Insurance* (7 ed.). Boston: Addison Wesley.

Resnick, M. (1997). *Turtles, Termites, and Traffic Jams: Explorations in Massively Parallel Microworlds*. Cambridge, Massachusetts: The MIT Press.

Robbins, A. (1991). *Awaken the Giant Within: How to Take Immediate Control of Your Mental, Emotional, Physical and Financial Destiny*. New York: The Free Press.

Russell, G. (Writer). (2014). Inside Animal Minds: Bird Genius, *Nova*: PBS.

Sabbadini, S. (2013). Tao Te Ching: A Guide to the Interpretation of the Foundational Book of Taoism: Augusto Sabbadini.

Schelling, T. C. (1971). Dynamic Models of Segregation. *Journal of Mathematical Sociology, 1*, 143-186.

Schutte, M., & Snyman, M. (2006). Knowledge Flow Elements Within a Context: A Model. *South African Journal of Information Management, 8*(2).

Senge, P. (1990). *The Fifth Discipline: The Art & Practice of the Learning Organization*. New York: Doubleday.

Sigmund, K., Fehr, E., & Nowak, M. A. (2002). The Economics of Fair Play. *Scientific American, 286*(1).

Skinner, B. F. (1948). Superstition in the Pigeon. *Journal of Experimental Psychology, 38*, 168-172.

Soros, G. (1987). *The Alchemy of Finance*: John Wiley & Sons, Inc.

Sterman, J. D. (2000). *Business Dynamics: Systems Thinking and Modeling for a Complex World*. Boston: Irwin.

Sterman, J. D. (2001). System Dynamics Modeling: Tools for Learning in a Complex World. *California Managment Review, 43*(4).

Sunstein, C. R. (2006). *Infotopia: How Many Minds Produce Knowledge*: Oxford University Press, Inc.

Surowiecki, J. (2005). *The Wisdom of Crowds*: Anchor Books.

Taleb, N. N. (2007). *The Black Swan: The Impact of the Highly Improbable*: Random House.

Taleb, N. N. (2012). *Antifragile: Things That Gain From Disorder*: Random House.

Tversky, A., & Kahneman, D. (1973). Availability: A heuristic for judging frequency and probability. *Cognitive Psychology 5*(1), 207-233.

Tversky, A., & Kahneman, D. (1974). Judgment under uncertainty: Heuristics and biases. *Science, 185*, 1124-1130.

Watts, D. J. (2003). *Six Degrees: The Science of a Connected Age*. New York: W. W. Norton & Company.

Young, G. O. (2008). Prediction Markets: Wisdom of the Crowd Comes to the Enterprise. Cambridge, MA: Forrester Research.

Zwick, M. (1995). Towards an Ontology of Problems. *Advances in Systems Science and Applications*(1), 37-42.

Zwick, M. (2013). *Elements and Relations*. Unpublished Manuscript.

Glossary

Agent-Based Simulation (ABS)	A type of systems simulation that can reproduce emergent effects that result from aggregated interactions.
Agents	Entities that act in systems analysis.
Antifragile	Something that benefits from variations. The opposite of fragile. Not to be confused with robust (which is resistant to variations). The term is from Taleb's incredible book *Antifragile* (2012). A stock option is an example of something that is antifragile.
Balancing Feedback Loop	A type of feedback loop where a perturbation at the input of the system will decrease as it travels around the loop, so the values will eventually settle.
Balancing Process with Delay	One of the Senge system archetypes. A single balancing loop with delay.
Black Swan	A concept proposed by Nassim Nicholas Taleb in his book of the same name. According to his back cover, "an event, positive or negative, that is deemed improbable yet causes massive consequences." See Chapter 2.
Diachronics	Considering the dynamic nature of structural change.
Echo Chamber (in a network)	A closely connected group of nodes. Information (or whatever traverses the network in study) will bounce around in the chamber.
Emergence	An interaction among objects at one level that generates new types of objects at another level. The emergent characteristic requires a new descriptive category at that next level.
Endogenous	Something with its origin inside the system. A system internal variable (or an output).
Eroding goals	One of the Senge system archetypes. Two linked balancing loops where one loop has more delay than the other.
Escalation	One of the Senge system archetypes. Two linked

	balancing loops with different balancing rates.
Exogenous	Something with its origin outside of the system. A system input.
Feedback Loop	A process where information from the past has influence on that same phenomena in the present.
Fixes that Fail	One of the Senge system archetypes. Linked balancing and reinforcing loops with a delay in the reinforcing loop (representing unintended consequences).
Flow	A construct used in system dynamic simulations. It represents a channel for the items in the flow to move through. One could think of water flowing through the drain pipe in the bottom of the bathtub as a flow. The flows are measured in units of the stock item per unit of time.
Generative Science	This argument, originally proposed by Epstein and Axtell (1996), states that being able to generate a phenomenon with a model adds support for the assertions of the model.
Genetic Algorithm	An optimization algorithm designed to mimic the processes of natural evolution.
Growth and Underinvestment	One of the Senge system archetypes. Somewhat related to limits to growth, this structure has three interdependent feedback loops (two balancing and one reinforcing).
Information Brokers (in a network)	Nodes in a network that connect echo chambers. Brokers are critical to efficient flow of information (or whatever traverses the network in study) across a network.
Information Cascade (or Information Mirage)	A situation (it could be considered a game in game theory) where participants make incorrect decisions due to observations of other's actions (observational learning).
Inquiry System	Essentially a modeling methodology. See Chapter 8.
Limits to growth	One of the Senge system archetypes. Linked reinforcing and balancing loops.
Metcalfe's Law	Actually, it's not a law, just a heuristic. It argues

	that the value of something grows as the square of the number of people using it.
Narrative Fallacy	Taking a sequence of facts and binding them together in a story. The idea is from Taleb's book *The Black Swan*. See Chapter 2.
NetLogo	An agent-based simulation (ABS) program. It can be downloaded free from the internet.
Networking Effect	A phrase coined by economists to describe the growth in value of a technology as its adoption increases. For example, as more and more people used Facebook for their social networking needs, its value grew nonlinearly.
Observational Learning	When individuals use observations of other's actions in their decision process.
Patches	The grid in an agent-based simulation. Patches can hold agents and state.
Prospect Theory	A descriptive theory of decision making by Kahneman and Tversky
Reinforcing Feedback Loop	A feedback loop where a perturbation through the system at the input will be increased as it travels around the loop.
Second Order Emergence	When emergent effects change due to the emergent effect itself.
Self-Organized Criticality	An idea explaining some sudden changes in systems by P. Bak and colleagues.
Shifting the Burden	One of the Senge system archetypes. The eroding goals structure (two linked balancing loops where one loop has more delay than the other) with a third reinforcing loop.
Stock	A construct used in system dynamic simulations. One can think of it as a container for something. For example, a bathtub is a container for water. The value of a stock variable is measured in units (for the bathtub it would be gallons of water).
Success to the Successful	One of the Senge system archetypes. Two linked reinforcing loops. It is particularly important for business.
Sugarscape	An agent-based simulation model created by Joshua Epstein and Robert Axtell (1996) and

	described in their book *Growing Artificial Societies*.
Synchronics	Considering dynamics when the structure is not changing.
System 1/System 2 mind	A construct of the mind discussed by Daniel Kahneman in *Thinking, Fast and Slow*.
System Archetype	A connection of feedback loops and delays that are frequently seen in complex human social systems.
TOP—Multiple Perspectives	An example of a Singerian inquiry system that uses three perspectives in the analysis. TOP is an acronym for Technical, Organizational, and Personal. See Chapter 8.
Tragedy of the Commons	One of the Senge system archetypes. The most structurally complex archetype includes four linked feedback loops.
Vensim	A system dynamic simulation software package. A free version is available for download.
WYSIATI	An acronym from Kahneman's *Thinking, Fast and Slow* to describe a characteristic of the System 1 mind. It stands for: What You See Is All There Is

Index

Printed in Great Britain
by Amazon

21341976R00142